P9-CMS-667
Ex Libris
Kristin Lindahl

Fundamental Mathematics of Life Insurance

FLOYD S. HARPER Ph.D., M.A.A.A.

LEWIS C. WORKMAN B.S., F.S.A., M.A.A.A.
Actuarial Vice President
Central Life Assurance Company

Published for
LIFE OFFICE MANAGEMENT ASSOCIATION
100 Colony Square/Atlanta, Georgia 30361

Fundamental Mathematics of Life Insurance

'y
Richard D. Irwin, Inc., Homewood, Illinois 60430
'win-Dorsey International, Arundel, Sussex BN18 9AB
'win-Dorsey Limited, Georgetown, Ontario L7G 4B3

4 5 6 7 8 9 0 K 5 4 3 2 1 0 9

ISBN 0–256–00231–2
Library of Congress Catalog Card No. 70–124165
Printed in the United States of America

Dedicated to Our Children:

The seven J. Harpers

and

The three D. Workmans

Preface

This book has been prepared primarily to provide students of the Life Office Management Association Institute with a basic introduction to the fundamental concepts underlying the mathematics of life insurance, an area too often characterized by the uninitiated as being foreboding or mysterious. It replaces the text *Elementary Mathematics of Life Insurance* by Floyd S. Harper and the late George A. Parks, previously used in the LOMA Insurance Education Program. The book is also suitable as a text for a college course in the subject. There, its appeal would be particularly to insurance or business students who do not have extensive mathematical background.

Basic concepts of life insurance mathematics are introduced in an easily understood manner so that this text is not too technical for the beginning student. The aim is to provide an *understanding* of these concepts and problem-solving methods, rather than to emphasize memory work and arithmetical manipulation. The approach is one of leading the students through the material. Noncomplicated illustrations are given throughout the book, and the steps in the calculations are shown and explained. The use of special symbols, which could become complicated and confusing, has been kept to a minimum. Extensive use is made of the "line diagram" as a useful and valuable aid in solving problems. The manner of presentation will enable the student to proceed through the content on his own without classroom instruction, should none be available.

Chapters 1 and 2 are introductory. Their purpose is to acquaint the student with those areas of arithmetic (over and above elementary addition, subtraction, multiplication, and division) which will be used later. These areas are: fractions, decimals, factoring, equations, and exponents. Chapters 3 through 6 cover the subject of compound interest. Chapter 7 describes the subject of probability and its use in connection with mortality tables. Chapters 8 through 14 present the mathematics of annuity and insurance contracts. Chapter 15 discusses, briefly, an array of topics connected with the fundamental mathematics of life insurance.

The authors are indebted to a number of people who spent many hours in reviewing the drafts of this book and helping with the mechanical preparation. These include particularly James Streck and Lois Johnson of the Central Life staff, and Helen H. Wachsman of the LOMA staff. A special debt of gratitude is due the members of the Review Committee of the LOMA for their invaluable suggestions:

Chairman: James W. Spellman, FLMI
Vice President and Controller
State Farm Life Insurance Company

Warren A. Carter, ASA
Actuarial Officer
Teachers Insurance and Annuity Association

Randolph J. Edwards, FLMI
Director of Systems and Data Processing
Security Connecticut Life Insurance Company

Harold A. C. Johnson, FLMI
Assistant Computer Planning Officer
Great-West Life Assurance Company

Gene A. Morton
Manager, Administrative Services
LOMA Institute
Life Office Management Association

Des Moines, Iowa
October, 1970

Floyd S. Harper
Lewis C. Workman

Contents

10. Life Insurance, Annual Premiums 213

11. Net Level Premium Reserves 239

12. Modified Reserves 277

1. Some Fundamentals

1.1 INTRODUCTION

The life insurance business, of necessity, rests upon a *mathematical basis*, with the mathematical subjects of *compound interest* and *probability* as the chief foundation stones. This book will show how these two subjects are combined to make possible the operation of the life insurance business on a sound and scientific basis.

The student will discover early in his studies that, in the actual day-to-day operation of a life insurance company, calculations must be made constantly and in enormous volume. Formerly this required a great deal of handwork. Today, however, most calculations are performed by small electrically operated machines (called "desk calculators") and by large sophisticated electronic data processing machines (called "computers" or "EDP equipment").

In this book, the emphasis is placed upon making calculations by hand, because the student will understand insurance company operations better by actually doing many of these relatively simple computations.

1.2 ARITHMETICAL CALCULATION

This book will assume that the student is familiar with the four fundamental arithmetical operations: addition, subtraction, multiplication, and division. Certain other aspects of arithmetic will be reviewed.

SUBSTITUTION OF LETTERS. Letters of the alphabet are often written instead of numbers when arithmetical calculations are shown.

This indicates that the exact number is unknown, or that what is being written is *general* in nature. When letters are used, one letter stands for an entire number, *not* one letter for each digit of the number.

When two or more numbers are *multiplied* together and letters are being substituted for numbers, it is customary to write the two letters beside each other. For example,

ab means a times b, or $a \times b$
$4c$ means 4 times c, or $4 \times c$

ORDER OF OPERATIONS. When a series of arithmetical calculations involves more than one of the four fundamental operations, multiplications and divisions are performed before additions and subtractions. For example, to calculate

$$2 + 3 \times 5 - 1$$

the multiplication of 3×5 is performed first:

$$2 + 15 - 1$$

Then the addition of 2 and subtraction of 1 (either one first) are performed, to give

$$16$$

FACTORS. The factors of a number are those smaller whole numbers which, when multiplied together, equal that number. For example,

$$60 = 5 \times 12$$

$$60 = 6 \times 10$$

$$60 = 4 \times 15$$

$$60 = 3 \times 10 \times 2$$

The numbers 5 and 12 are factors of 60. The numbers 6 and 10 are also factors of 60, as are 4 and 15, etc.

When letters are used instead of numbers, the expression

$$C = DE$$

is a way of making a general statement of the fact that D and E are factors of C. The examples given above, such as $60 = 5 \times 12$, are specific instances of this general statement.

QUANTITIES. A quantity is all the numbers and letters which are included inside a pair of parentheses or brackets. For example, in the following expression

$$5 \times 4(A - 5) + 2B$$

$(A - 5)$ is a quantity. In performing arithmetical calculations, each quantity should be considered as if it were one number. Regardless of what is inside the parentheses, it should all be kept together.

Any number or letter written beside a quantity is to be *multiplied* by that quantity, such as 4 in the expression above. When a quantity is being multiplied by a number or letter, that quantity may instead be written showing each number inside the parentheses multiplied by that number or letter. For example, the above expression $5 \times 4(A - 5) + 2B$ may be written instead showing the A and the 5 each multiplied by the 4, as follows:

$$5 \times (4A - 20) + 2B$$

This does not change its value.

1.3 FRACTIONS

When an item is divided into four equal parts, each part is known as one fourth of the item and is represented by the symbol

$$\frac{1}{4}$$

The number below the line indicates division into "fourths." This number is known as the *denominator* and tells how many parts there are all together. The number above the line is known as the *numerator;* it tells how many of the parts are being considered. The entire symbol is known as a *fraction.*

Fractions are, in fact, a way of indicating division. For example, $\frac{1}{4}$ indicates the division of 1 by 4; $\frac{3}{4}$ indicates the division of 3 by 4.

When the numerator and denominator are equal to each other, the fraction has the value of 1. This is because any number divided by itself equals 1. For example,

$$\frac{6}{6} = 1$$

The value of a fraction is unchanged if the numerator and denominator are both multiplied or both divided by the same amount. For example, if both the numerator and denominator of the fraction $\frac{3}{4}$ are multiplied by 2, the fraction becomes

$$\frac{3 \times 2}{4 \times 2} = \frac{6}{8}$$

The value of the fraction is unchanged, that is,

$$\frac{3}{4} = \frac{6}{8}$$

As another example, if both the numerator and the denominator of the fraction $\frac{10}{15}$ are divided by 5, the fraction becomes

$$\frac{10 \div 5}{15 \div 5} = \frac{2}{3}$$

The value of the fraction is unchanged, that is,

$$\frac{10}{15} = \frac{2}{3}$$

REDUCING FRACTIONS. It is generally considered good form to "reduce" all fractions to their lowest terms, that is, to divide numerator and denominator by as large a number as possible so that the remaining numerator and denominator are as small as possible (with the value of the fraction being unchanged). This is exactly what is done above when the fraction $\frac{10}{15}$ is "reduced" to $\frac{2}{3}$. The *value is unchanged*, but the numbers are smaller.

To Illustrate—Reduce the fraction $\frac{6}{18}$ to its lowest terms.

Solution—Both the numerator and the denominator can be divided evenly by 2, and the fraction becomes

$$\frac{6 \div 2}{18 \div 2} = \frac{3}{9}$$

The fraction is now expressed in lower terms, but it can be reduced still more. Both the numerator and the denominator of the fraction $\frac{3}{9}$ can be divided evenly by 3, and the fraction becomes

$$\frac{3 \div 3}{9 \div 3} = \frac{1}{3}$$

The value is unchanged throughout, that is,

$$\frac{6}{18} = \frac{3}{9} = \frac{1}{3}$$

The original fraction, $\frac{6}{18}$, could have been reduced to $\frac{1}{3}$ without the intermediate step, by dividing both the numerator and the denominator by 6:

$$\frac{6 \div 6}{18 \div 6} = \frac{1}{3}$$

To Illustrate Again—Reduce the fraction $\dfrac{2A(2B + C)}{4(2B + C)}$ to its lowest terms.

Solution—The items included inside the parentheses represent a *quantity*, which is treated as if it were one number. The numerator is

$$2 \times A \times (2B + C)$$

The denominator is

$$4 \times (2B + C)$$

Since the quantity $(2B + C)$ appears in both the numerator and the denominator, the first step in reducing is to divide both the numerator and the denominator by this quantity:

$$\frac{2A(2B + C) \div (2B + C)}{4(2B + C) \div (2B + C)} = \frac{2A}{4}$$

The fraction may be reduced further by dividing both the numerator and the denominator by 2:

$$\frac{2A \div 2}{4 \div 2} = \frac{A}{2}$$

ADDITION AND SUBTRACTION OF FRACTIONS. Before two or more fractions can be added or subtracted, they must have a common denominator. Each of the fractions to be added or subtracted can be altered in form (but not in value) by multiplying its numerator and denominator by some number, until all the fractions have the same denominator. For example, the fractions

$$\frac{2}{3} \text{ and } \frac{1}{6}$$

may be expressed with a common denominator (6) by multiplying both the numerator and the denominator of the first fraction by 2, as follows:

$$\frac{2 \times 2}{3 \times 2} = \frac{4}{6}$$

The first fraction ($\frac{2}{3}$) may thus be expressed as

$$\frac{4}{6}$$

It now has the same denominator as the second fraction ($\frac{1}{6}$); that is, the two have a common denominator.

As another example, the fractions

$$\frac{2}{3} \text{ and } \frac{1}{4}$$

may be altered in form so that they have a common denominator (12) by multiplying both the numerator and the denominator of the first fraction by 4, and by multiplying both the numerator and the denominator of the second fraction by 3:

$$\frac{2 \times 4}{3 \times 4} = \frac{8}{12}$$

$$\frac{1 \times 3}{4 \times 3} = \frac{3}{12}$$

Only after the fractions have been expressed in terms which have a common denominator can they be added or subtracted.

When fractions are added or subtracted, the answer is a fraction which has a numerator equal to the numerators of the individual fractions added or subtracted together as the signs indicate, and which has a denominator equal to the common denominator.

For example,

$$\frac{9}{12} - \frac{6}{12} + \frac{2}{12} = \frac{9 - 6 + 2}{12}$$

$$= \frac{5}{12}$$

To Illustrate—Add the following fractions:

$$\frac{1}{6} + \frac{B}{2A}$$

Solution—

Multiplying numerator and denominator of first fraction by A; multiplying numerator and denominator of second fraction by 3 to get common denominator

$$\frac{1}{6} + \frac{B}{2A} = \frac{1 \times A}{6 \times A} + \frac{B \times 3}{2A \times 3}$$

Performing each of the multiplications (fractions have a common denominator)

$$= \frac{A}{6A} + \frac{3B}{6A}$$

Adding numerators of individual fractions; placing over common denominator

$$= \frac{A + 3B}{6A}$$

MULTIPLICATION OF FRACTIONS. *When fractions are multiplied, the answer is a fraction which has a numerator equal to the numer-*

ators of all the individual fractions multiplied together, and which has a denominator equal to the denominators of all the individual fractions multiplied together.

To Illustrate—Calculate $\frac{8}{3} \times \frac{3}{4}$, and express the answer in its lowest terms.

Solution—

Multiplying the numerators; multiplying the denominators

$$\frac{8}{3} \times \frac{3}{4} = \frac{8 \times 3}{3 \times 4} = \frac{24}{12}$$

Reducing the fraction by dividing both numerator and denominator by the same number

$$= \frac{24 \div 12}{12 \div 12}$$

$$= \frac{2}{1} = 2$$

DIVISION OF FRACTIONS. *When one fraction is divided by another, the numerator and denominator of the second fraction are inverted (switched) and the answer is then found by the multiplication procedure.*

To Illustrate—Calculate $\frac{5}{6} \div \frac{8}{3}$, and express the answer in its lowest terms.

Solution—

Inverting the second fraction and multiplying

$$\frac{5}{6} \div \frac{8}{3} = \frac{5}{6} \times \frac{3}{8}$$

Multiplying the numerators; multiplying the denominators

$$= \frac{5 \times 3}{6 \times 8}$$

$$= \frac{15}{48}$$

Reducing the fraction by dividing both numerator and denominator by the same number

$$= \frac{15 \div 3}{48 \div 3}$$

$$= \frac{5}{16}$$

To Illustrate Again – Calculate $\frac{5}{8} \div 7$.

Solution – The number 7 may be written as $\frac{7}{1}$.

Inverting the second fraction and multiplying

$$\frac{5}{8} \div \frac{7}{1} = \frac{5}{8} \times \frac{1}{7}$$

Multiplying the numerators; multiplying the denominators

$$= \frac{5 \times 1}{8 \times 7}$$

$$= \frac{5}{56}$$

EXERCISES

In each of the following exercises, find the answer to the indicated calculation:

1 $\frac{2}{3} + \frac{3}{4}$

2 $\frac{5}{6} + \frac{1}{8}$

3 $\frac{1}{2} + \frac{4}{5}$

4 $\frac{11}{12} - \frac{1}{4}$

5 $\frac{5}{6} - \frac{3}{4}$

6 $\frac{A}{5} + \frac{B}{3}$

7 $\frac{7}{8} + \frac{1}{2} + \frac{3}{4}$

8 $\frac{4}{5} \times \frac{3}{(A + B)}$

9 $\frac{2}{5} \times \frac{15}{32}$ (Hint. It is easier to reduce the answer if the student looks for factors common to both the numerator and denominator and divides by them before actually multiplying: $\frac{2 \times 15}{5 \times 32}$ may have numerator and denominator both divided by 2 and by 5 before actually multiplying.)

10 $\frac{3}{4} \times \frac{8}{15}$

11 $\frac{5}{6} \times \frac{2}{3} \times \frac{2}{5}$

12 $\frac{2}{3} \div \frac{8}{9}$

13 $\frac{21}{25} \div 3$

14 $\frac{A}{5} \div \frac{4A}{10(B + 10)}$

1.4 DECIMALS

Decimals occur with great frequency in the mathematics of life insurance, because our money system is a decimal system and because decimals are usually easier to handle in making calculations than are fractions.

A *decimal point* is a dot or period. Its appearance between two digits of a number means that all the digits to the right of the decimal point actually constitute a fraction. For example, the number

28.217

is actually the number 28 plus a fraction.

The fraction which is indicated by the digits to the right of the decimal point has a numerator equal to the number formed by those digits, and a denominator equal to 1 followed by as many zeros as there are digits in the numerator. For example, the number

$$28.217$$

may be written as

$$28 \text{ plus } \frac{217}{1{,}000}$$

The digits to the right of the decimal, namely 217, constitute the numerator. There are three such digits; hence the denominator is 1 followed by three zeros (1,000).

Any number without a decimal point (i.e., a "whole number") is assumed to have a decimal point at the end.

The value of a decimal number is not affected by adding any number of zeros *at the end.* This is because, if the decimal were to be expressed in fraction form, adding zeros would similarly increase both the numerator and denominator, leaving the value of the fraction unchanged.

When writing a fraction in decimal form, zeros may be placed *between* the decimal point and the digits which follow in order to achieve the total number of places needed to express the denominator. For example, it may be desired to express the fraction

$$\frac{23}{1{,}000{,}000}$$

in decimal form. Since there are six zeros in the denominator, there must be six digits following the decimal point. However, 23 has only two digits. The decimal form, then, would be

$$.000023$$

with the four zeros inserted in order to correctly position the decimal point.

ADDITION AND SUBTRACTION OF DECIMALS. Before adding or subtracting decimals, all the numbers should be given the same number of digits following the decimal point (known as the "number of decimal places"). This is done by adding the necessary number of zeros at the *ends* of the numbers. The numbers are then added or subtracted in the usual manner.

To Illustrate – Add the numbers 10.07, .047, 1800, and 176.4.

Solution – 10.07 has 2 decimal places; .047 has 3 decimal places; 1800 has no decimal places; and 176.4 has 1 decimal place. The greatest number of decimal places is 3, so zeros are added where necessary to produce 3 decimal places in each number. (.047 already has 3 decimal places.)

$$\begin{aligned} 10.07 &= 10.070 \\ .047 &= .047 \\ 1800 &= 1800.000 \\ 176.4 &= \underline{176.400} \\ & 1986.517 \text{ Total} \end{aligned}$$

The decimal point is placed in the answer so that there are 3 digits to the right or "3 decimal places." Note that numbers to be added are written with the decimal points directly over each other.

MULTIPLICATION OF DECIMALS. *To multiply two or more decimals, first multiply the numbers in the usual manner. Place the decimal point in the answer so that the number of decimal places is equal to the total of the number of decimal places in all the numbers being multiplied.*

To Illustrate—Multiply 14.231 by 1.04.

Solution—First multiply the numbers in the usual manner (ignoring the decimal points):

$$14231 \times 104 = 1480024$$

A decimal point must then be placed so that the answer will have 5 decimal places, because 14.231 has 3 decimal places and 1.04 has 2 decimal places:

$$14.231 \times 1.04 = 14.80024$$

When decimals are being multiplied by 10, or 100, or 1,000, etc., the answer is easily found by shifting the decimal point to the *right* by as many places as there are zeros in the multiplier.

To Illustrate—Calculate 12.4717 × 100.

Solution—The multiplier, 100, has 2 zeros. Hence the answer is found by shifting the decimal point in 12.4717 two places to the right:

$$12.4717 \times 100 = 1247.17$$

DIVISION OF DECIMALS. *To divide two decimals, first divide the numbers in the usual manner. Place the decimal point in the answer so that the number of decimal places is equal to the number of decimal places in the number that is being divided into, minus the number of decimal places in the number that it is being divided by.*

To Illustrate—Calculate 8.586 ÷ .3.

Solution—First divide the numbers in the usual manner (ignoring the decimal points):

$$8586 \div 3 = 2862$$

A decimal point must be placed so that the answer will have 2 decimal places, because 8.586 has 3 decimal places and .3 has 1 decimal place:

$$8.586 \div .3 = 28.62$$

It is often useful to add some zeros at the end of the number being divided into so that the answer will contain more decimal places.

To Illustrate—Calculate .3 ÷ 8.586, and show 4 decimal places in the answer.

Solution—If the division were performed in the usual way (ignoring the decimal points), the answer would be zero plus a remainder. This is because the number that is being divided into (.3) is smaller than the number it is being divided by (8.586). In this example, the number .3 may be written as

$$.3000000$$

This number contains 7 decimal places. Now divide in the usual manner:

$$3000000 \div 8586 = 349 \text{ (plus a small remainder)}$$

According to the rule for division of decimals, the answer will have 4 decimal places, because .3000000 has 7 decimal places and 8.586 has 3 decimal places:

$$.3 \div 8.586 = .0349$$

The number of zeros to be added is related to the number of decimal places desired in the answer. Usually the number of decimal places is specified in the problem.

When a number is divided by 10, or 100, or 1,000, etc., the answer is easily found by shifting the decimal point to the *left* by as many places as there are zeros in the number it is being divided by.

To Illustrate—Calculate 487.72 ÷ 100.

Solution—The number that 487.72 is being divided by (100) has 2 zeros. The answer is found by shifting the decimal point in 487.72 two places to the left:

$$487.72 \div 100 = 4.8772$$

CHANGING FROM FRACTIONS TO DECIMALS. Because fractions indicate that the numerator is divided by the denominator, fractions can be changed to decimals by actually performing this division. For example, the fraction $\frac{1}{8}$ can be changed into decimal form by dividing 1 by 8. The 1 can be expressed as

1.000

The division, according to the rule given above, would be performed by dividing 1,000 by 8, and placing the decimal point in the answer so there are three decimal places. The answer shows that

$$\frac{1}{8} = .125$$

Every fraction has its decimal equivalent. Because of their great usefulness, the following decimal equivalents of certain fractions should be memorized:

$\frac{1}{2} = .5$	$\frac{1}{8} = .125$	$\frac{1}{5} = .2$
$\frac{1}{4} = .25$	$\frac{3}{8} = .375$	$\frac{2}{5} = .4$
$\frac{3}{4} = .75$	$\frac{5}{8} = .625$	$\frac{3}{5} = .6$
	$\frac{7}{8} = .875$	$\frac{4}{5} = .8$

Some fractions produce a decimal equivalent which can never be expressed *exactly:* for example, the fraction $\frac{1}{3}$. When 1 is divided by 3, the result will be .33333 . . . , with no end to the 3's, regardless of how many decimal places the answer is made to have.

ROUNDING OFF DECIMALS. Decimals may be used to express exact or approximate values. The values are approximate if the decimal has been rounded off. The decimal .002, meaning $\frac{2}{1,000}$, is exact. The decimal .125, which is the equivalent of $\frac{1}{8}$, is also exact. However, if the decimal .08333 . . . , which is the equivalent of $\frac{1}{12}$, is rounded off to four decimal places and written .0833, then .0833 is called a decimal rounded off to four decimal places and it is approximate.

Consider the decimal .2168528, which is correct to seven decimal places. If six decimal places only are needed, it would not be correct just to drop the digit 8 in the seventh decimal place, and write the number as .216852. It would be more accurate to write .216853, because the latter is a closer approximation to the true value, .2168528. Similarly, if the given decimal were to be retained to only five decimal places, the correct result would be .21685.

The rule for rounding off is: If a decimal is to be rounded off to a fewer number of places, drop off the digits to be eliminated; then if the first digit dropped is 5 or more (i.e., 5, 6, 7, 8, or 9), add 1 to the last place digit of the number; if the first digit dropped is less than 5 (i.e., 0, 1, 2, 3, or 4), make no adjustment in the remaining number.

For example, if the decimal .42649 is to be rounded off to four decimal places, the last digit (9) is dropped. Since the digit dropped is 5 or more, 1 is added to the digit in last place of the number remaining:

.4265

If this same decimal .42649 is to be rounded off to three decimal places, the last two digits (49) are dropped. Since the first digit dropped is less than 5, the remaining number needs no adjustment:

.426

To Illustrate—Round off each of these decimals to 4 places; also to 3 places; also to 2 places: .24382, .52696, .84285, .77655, and .42852.

Solution—

Decimal	*Four Places*	*Three Places*	*Two Places*
.24382	.2438	.244	.24
.52696	.5270	.527	.53
.84285	.8429	.843	.84
.77655	.7766	.777	.78
.42852	.4285	.429	.43

It is important to observe that a decimal which has been rounded off to 3 decimal places, such as .429, may have originally been as small as .4285000, or as large as .4294999 . . . . Whenever calculations are performed using decimals which have been rounded off, the fact that they are not exact should be kept in mind.

For example, when adding 10.7 and 4.852, two zeros are added to 10.7 so that both numbers will have the same number of decimal places:

```
10.700
 4.852
------
15.552 Total
```

However, it is necessary to know whether 10.7 is exact or rounded off, in order to judge whether all of the decimal places in the answer are exact. If 10.7 has previously been rounded off from its original form, then the answer (15.552) is an inexact or approximate answer.

It is also important to observe that rounding in successive steps may result in a different answer (not so accurate) from rounding in one step. For example, if .42649 is to be rounded off to three decimal places, the answers would be as follows:

One step: .426
Two steps: .4265, .427

1.5 COMMON MULTIPLIER (FACTORING).

Consider the problem of finding the total wages to be paid to a man who works on three consecutive days for 7.6 hours, 9.2 hours, and 8.4 hours, respectively, at an hourly wage of \$2.25. His total wages may be represented by

$$\overbrace{7.6 \times \$2.25}^{\text{1st day}} + \overbrace{9.2 \times \$2.25}^{\text{2nd day}} + \overbrace{8.4 \times \$2.25}^{\text{3rd day}}$$
$$= \$17.10 + \$20.70 + \$18.90$$
$$= \$56.70$$

(Notice adherence to the rule that, in a series of arithmetical calculations, multiplications and divisions are performed before additions and subtractions.)

It is simpler to write the expression

$$7.6 \times \$2.25 + 9.2 \times \$2.25 + 8.4 \times \$2.25$$

in the following manner:

$$\$2.25(7.6 + 9.2 + 8.4)$$

The items inside the parentheses constitute a *quantity*. They are all treated the same (i.e., multiplied by \$2.25). The quantity itself is treated as a single number; in this case the quantity is $(7.6+9.2+8.4) = (25.2)$, the total number of hours worked. Therefore, the total wages are

$$\$2.25 \times 25.2 = \$56.70$$

Removing the factor \$2.25 from each of the three original terms and writing it as a common multiplier has reduced the number of multiplications from three to one. The number of additions has been left unchanged.

This operation of removing the common multiplier is called "factoring out a common multiplier," or simply "factoring."

To Illustrate—Calculate $573 \times 291 + 846 \times 291 - 755 \times 291$.

Solution—Factor out the common multiplier 291 to give the expression $291(573 + 846 - 755)$.

Adding and subtracting within the parentheses

$$291(573 + 846 - 755) = 291 \times 664$$

Multiplying

$$= 193{,}224$$

To Illustrate Again—Calculate $\frac{475}{1.03} - \frac{325}{1.03} + \frac{250}{1.03}$.

Solution—This expression may be written as

$$475\left(\frac{1}{1.03}\right) - 325\left(\frac{1}{1.03}\right) + 250\left(\frac{1}{1.03}\right)$$

showing that $\left(\frac{1}{1.03}\right)$ is the common multiplier.

Factoring out the common multiplier

$$475\left(\frac{1}{1.03}\right) - 325\left(\frac{1}{1.03}\right) + 250\left(\frac{1}{1.03}\right) = \frac{1}{1.03}(475 - 325 + 250)$$

Adding and subtracting within parentheses

$$= \frac{1}{1.03}(400)$$

Multiplying

$$= \frac{400}{1.03}$$

Dividing the numerator by the denominator; rounding to two decimal places

$$= 388.35$$

To Illustrate Again—Factor out the common multiplier from the expression $4ab - 2ac + 8abc$.

Solution—Each of the numbers has both 2 and a as factors. Therefore, factoring out the common multiplier, $2a$, shows

$$4ab - 2ac + 8abc = 2a(2b - c + 4bc)$$

EXERCISES

1 Add the following: 27, .032, 44.07, 5.55

2 Calculate $47.0001 \times .04$

3 Calculate the decimal equivalent of the fraction $\frac{1}{7}$, showing 5 decimal places in the answer.

4 Calculate each of the following:

a) 48.375×100	*e*) $728.42 \div 10$
b) $.0841 \times 10$	*f*) $3.8214 \div 100$
c) 327.49×1000	*g*) $4295.6 \div 1000$
d) $.000421 \times 100$	*h*) $.07148 \div 100$

5 Round off these decimals to 5 places; then round the same original decimals to 2 places: .482647; .953725; .384955; .718257

6 Calculate each of the following by first factoring out the common multiplier:

a) $37.50 \times \$1.15 + 32.75 \times \$1.15 + 20.00 \times \$1.15$

b) $\$500 \times 1.03 + \$350 \times 1.03 + \$150 \times 1.03$

c) $275 \times 27 - 1153 \times 27 + 2150 \times 27$

d) $\frac{\$100}{1.05} + \frac{\$415}{1.05} + \frac{\$750}{1.05}$

e) $3Y - 30YZ + 12Z$

1.6 ESTIMATING THE ANSWER

In order to avoid any gross error, it is advisable to estimate the magnitude and nature of an answer in advance. In addition, thought should be given to the reasonableness of an answer. This is especially important when multiplying or dividing decimals.

For example, suppose it is necessary to multiply 23.64×41.73. It can be estimated that the answer should be a little larger than 20×40, or 800. When the two numbers are multiplied together, the resulting digits are 9864972. The estimate indicates the answer must be 986.4972, not 98.64972 nor 9864.972.

A similar procedure is applicable in estimating for division. For example, suppose it is necessary to calculate $15{,}475.1 \div 288$. It can be estimated that the answer should be in the neighborhood of 15,000 divided by 300. Both 15,000 and 300 can be divided by 100 by shifting the decimal point in each number two places to the left, giving 150 divided by 3. Thus, the answer should be in the neighborhood of 50. After the actual calculation, when the digits 537 (plus a small remainder) are seen as the answer, the decimal point must be placed to show 53.7, which is in the neighborhood of 50.

Always remember: It pays to estimate the answer in advance and to assure oneself that the answer, when obtained, is reasonable.

EXERCISES

The multiplications and divisions in the following examples have been performed without the placing of decimal points in the answers. Determine, *by estimating*, the correct positions of the decimal points.

1 $145.261 \times 2.74 = 39802$

2 $21.4771 \times .531 = 1140434$

3 $1012.6 \times 1.0126 = 102535876$

4 $10{,}182{,}605 \times .01257 = 12799534$

5 $50.478998 \times 97.1687 = 49$

6 $1000 \div 97.61772 = 1024404$

7 $1.307 \div 2.14779 = 6085325$

8 $148{,}125.6 \div 147.14 = 10066984$

9 $146{,}227{,}899.3 \div 812{,}219.66 = 1800349$

10 $.04279 \div 97.422 = 4392$

2.

The Equation

2.1 CHANGING EQUATIONS

A statement that two things are equal to each other is known as an *equation*. For example, the following expression used in Chapter 1 is an *equation:*

$$\frac{2A \div 2}{4 \div 2} = \frac{A}{2}$$

Equations are useful in solving a variety of problems. For example, the selling price of an article is made up of its cost to the seller and his profit. If the selling price is represented by S, the cost to the seller by C, and the profit by P, their relationship may be expressed in symbols as the equation

$$C + P = S$$

that is, cost plus profit equals selling price.

The profit from selling an article is equal to the difference between the selling price and the cost to the seller. Using the same symbols as above, this relationship, which is also an equation, is represented by

$$P = S - C$$

that is, profit equals selling price less cost.

This simple illustration suggests that an equation can be changed from one useful form to another. The question naturally arises as to the kinds of changes which can properly be made on an equation without destroying the equality which exists between the amount or amounts on the right-hand side of the equal sign, and the amount or amounts on the left-hand side of the equal sign. The following rules apply:

I. The same amount can be added to both sides of an equation without destroying the equality.
II. The same amount can be subtracted from both sides of an equation without destroying the equality.
III. Both sides of an equation can be multiplied by the same amount without destroying the equality.
IV. Both sides of an equation can be divided by the same amount without destroying the equality.
V. The two sides of an equation can be interchanged (as a whole) without destroying the equality.

These five principles may be summarized in the single statement: *If both sides of an equation are increased, reduced, multiplied, or divided by the same amount, or if the sides are interchanged, the equality between the two sides of the equation is preserved.*

To Illustrate—If $S - C = P$, find the value of S. (This is known as "solving for S.")

Solution—As a working procedure in solving equations, first inspect the equation to decide what operations must be performed on the equation (i.e., addition, subtraction, multiplication, or division) so that the item being sought will stand alone on one side of the equation, and the answer on the other. Using rule I, add C to both sides of the equation:

$$S - C + C = P + C$$

Now, on the left-hand side of the equation, the "$-C$" offsets the "$+C$," and the equation becomes

$$S = P + C$$

To Illustrate Again—If $P + C = S$, solve for P.

Solution—Subtract C from both sides of the equation:

$$P + C - C = S - C$$

Again, on the left-hand side of the equation, the "$+C$" offsets the "$-C$," and the equation becomes

$$P = S - C$$

An alternate rule for dealing with equations is that *an amount may be moved from one side of the equal sign to the other side* (*transposed*) *by changing the sign of the amount.* Thus, in the first illustration where the equation $S - C = P$ was solved for S, the quantity C was moved from the left-hand side of the equal sign to the right-hand side. In so doing, the sign of C was changed from $-$ to $+$. The equation then became $S = P + C$. The result of transposing is the same as adding or subtracting the same amount to both sides of the equation.

To Illustrate Again—If the hourly wage rate, R, is equal to total income, T, divided by the number of hours worked, H, express this fact in equation form and solve the equation for T.

Solution—

Given relationship

$$\text{Hourly Rate} = \frac{\text{Total Income}}{\text{Hours Worked}}$$

Expressing the equation in symbols

$$R = \frac{T}{H}$$

Multiplying both sides by H

$$HR = H\left(\frac{T}{H}\right)$$

Expressing the right-hand side in an equivalent form

$$HR = \frac{HT}{H}$$

Reducing the fraction $\frac{HT}{H}$

$$HR = T$$

To Illustrate Again—Given the equation $HR = T$, solve for H.

Solution—

Given equation

$$HR = T$$

Dividing both sides by R

$$\frac{HR}{R} = \frac{T}{R}$$

Reducing the fraction $\frac{HR}{R}$

$$H = \frac{T}{R}$$

Note that the result in each illustration can be verified by commonsense reasoning. In every problem, the answer should be examined to test its reasonableness.

To Illustrate Again—If $\left(\frac{4R}{5} + 3\right) = R$, find R.

Solution—Note that R appears on both sides of the equation. To solve for R, it is necessary to make it stand alone on one side only. Also note that R is part of a fraction on the left-hand side, so that the fraction must be operated upon to express it in nonfractional form.

Given equation

$$\left(\frac{4R}{5} + 3\right) = R$$

Multiplying both sides by 5

$$5\left(\frac{4R}{5} + 3\right) = 5R$$

Multiplying each item in parentheses by 5

$$\frac{20R}{5} + 15 = 5R$$

Reducing the fraction $\frac{20R}{5}$

$$4R + 15 = 5R$$

Subtracting $4R$ from each side

$$4R - 4R + 15 = 5R - 4R$$

$$15 = R$$

This answer can be checked if, in the original equation, R is replaced by its value, 15. The equation then becomes

$$\frac{4 \times 15}{5} + 3 = 15$$

The arithmetical calculation on the left-hand side may be performed by multiplying 4×15 (which equals 60), then dividing by 5 (which gives 12), and then adding 3 (which gives 15). This proves that the value $R = 15$ is correct and that the equation was properly solved.

2.2 EXPONENTS

Multiplying two 10's together (i.e., 10×10) may be written as

$$10^2$$

Multiplying three 10's together (i.e., $10 \times 10 \times 10$) may be written as

$$10^3$$

Multiplying four 10's together (i.e., $10 \times 10 \times 10 \times 10$) may be written as

$$10^4$$

The small number appearing above and to the right of the 10 is called an *exponent*. (It is also sometimes called a power.) It tells how many 10's are multiplied together. The number being multiplied ("10" in this case) is called the *base*.

In more general terms (using letters):

$$A^B$$

means $A \times A \times A \times A \ldots$, until there are B of them altogether. In other words, it means A multiplied by itself B times. The *base* is A; the *exponent* is B.

Some illustrations of exponents are:

$7 \times 7 = 7^2$ (read as "7 to the second power" or "7 squared")
$2 \times 2 \times 2 \times 2 \times 2 \times 2 \times 2 = 2^7$ (read as "2 to the seventh power")
$(1.03)(1.03)(1.03) = 1.03^3$ (read as "1.03 to the third power" or "1.03 cubed")
$(1+i)(1+i)(1+i)(1+i) = (1+i)^4$ (read as "$(1+i)$ to the fourth power")
$\left(\frac{1}{1+i}\right)\left(\frac{1}{1+i}\right)\left(\frac{1}{1+i}\right) = \left(\frac{1}{1+i}\right)^3$ (read as "$\left(\frac{1}{1+i}\right)$ to the third power")

Note that everything inside the parentheses is kept together.

There is a convenient rule to use when multiplying or dividing numbers which have the same base: *If two or more numbers having the same base are multiplied together, the answer will be this base with an exponent equal to the total of the individual exponents. If two numbers having the same base are divided, the answer will be this base with an exponent equal to the difference between the two exponents.*

To Illustrate—Multiply 1.02^4 and 1.02^7.

Solution—The two numbers to be multiplied together have the same base, namely 1.02; therefore the answer will have this base. The exponent in the answer is found by adding the two exponents, 4 and 7:

Adding the exponents

$$1.02^4 \times 1.02^7 = 1.02^{(4+7)}$$
$$= 1.02^{11}$$

To Illustrate Again—Multiply $(R+3)^B(R+3)^J(R+3)^M$. Note that this means $(R+3)^B$ *times* $(R+3)^J$ *times* $(R+3)^M$.

Solution—The base, in each case, is in the form of a quantity which must be kept intact, namely $(R+3)$. The answer will have the *base* $(R+3)$; it will have its *exponent* equal to the sum of the 3 exponents:

$$(R+3)^B \times (R+3)^J \times (R+3)^M = (R+3)^{B+J+M}$$

To Illustrate Again—Divide M^9 by M^3.

Solution—To divide, it is necessary to subtract the exponents; hence the exponent in the answer is the difference between 9 and 3:

Subtracting the exponents

$$M^9 \div M^3 = M^{(9-3)}$$

$$= M^6$$

To Illustrate Again—Find the value of $\frac{(1+i)^5}{(1+i)^4}$.

Solution—Remember that a fraction indicates the division of two numbers:

Subtracting the exponents

$$\frac{(1+i)^5}{(1+i)^4} = (1+i)^{(5-4)}$$

$$= (1+i)^1$$

A number with the exponent 1 is that number itself

$$= (1+i)$$

The use of exponents becomes increasingly valuable when the base is a lengthy number or a complicated quantity, as in

$$\left(\frac{9a+8.17}{b+4ac} - m\right)\left(\frac{9a+8.17}{b+4ac} - m\right) = \left(\frac{9a+8.17}{b+4ac} - m\right)^2$$

2.3 FACTORING IN EQUATIONS

The process of factoring out a common multiplier, described in Section 1.5, is often useful in working with equations.

To Illustrate—Solve the following equation for X:

$$AX + BCX = D$$

Solution—

$$AX + BCX = D$$

Factoring out the common multiplier X

$$X(A + BC) = D$$

Dividing both sides by $(A + BC)$

$$\frac{X(A+BC)}{(A+BC)} = \frac{D}{(A+BC)}$$

$$X = \frac{D}{(A+BC)}$$

When factoring out a common multiplier, it is important to remember that any number, by itself, can be expressed as that number multiplied by 1. For example, in the equation

$$S = 10 + 10(1.03) + 10(1.03)^2 + 10(1.03)^3$$

each of the numbers on the right-hand side has the number 10 as a factor, since the 10 which stands by itself can be expressed as 10×1. After factoring out the common multiplier (10), this equation appears as follows:

$$S = 10[1 + 1.03 + 1.03^2 + 1.03^3]$$

Note that the first number inside the bracket is a 1.

The common factor may be a letter, such as the letter R in the equation

$$T = R + R(1.03) + R(1.03)^2 + R(1.03)^3$$

The R which is by itself can be expressed as $R \times 1$. Therefore, after factoring out the common multiplier, the equation appears as

$$T = R[1 + 1.03 + 1.03^2 + 1.03^3]$$

In some equations, there may be more than one multiplier which can be factored out. For example, in the equation

$$U = P(1+i) + P(1+i)^2 + P(1+i)^3$$

the three items on the right-hand side can be expressed as

$$P \times (1+i) \times 1$$

$$P \times (1+i) \times (1+i)$$

and $\quad P \times (1+i) \times (1+i)^2$

Thus, two common multipliers, P and $(1 + i)$, appear in every item. (Also note that the rule for multiplying and dividing with exponents has been used, since $(1+i)(1+i)^2$ has been used as being equivalent to $(1+i)^3$.) After factoring out the two common multipliers, the equation appears as follows:

$$U = P(1+i)[1 + (1+i) + (1+i)^2]$$

In some equations, the common multiplier may be a fraction, as in the final illustration in Section 1.5. Another example of a fractional common multiplier would be the equation

$$V = \frac{Q(1+i)}{(a+b)^2} + \frac{Q(1+i)^2}{(a+b)^3} + \frac{Q(1+i)^3}{(a+b)^4}$$

The three items on the right-hand side can be expressed as

$$\frac{Q(1+i)}{(a+b)^2} \times 1$$

$$\frac{Q(1+i)}{(a+b)^2} \times \frac{(1+i)}{(a+b)}$$

and $$\frac{Q(1+i)}{(a+b)^2} \times \frac{(1+i)^2}{(a+b)^2}$$

Thus, the common multiplier

$$\frac{Q(1+i)}{(a+b)^2}$$

appears in every item. After factoring out the common multiplier, the equation appears as follows:

$$V = \frac{Q(1+i)}{(a+b)^2}\left[1 + \frac{(1+i)}{(a+b)} + \frac{(1+i)^2}{(a+b)^2}\right]$$

EXERCISES

In Exercises 1 through 13, determine the value of the unknown quantity (i.e., the *letter*):

1 $B + 6 = 15$

2 $C + 9 = 2C + 6$

3 $3D + 5 = 17 - D$

4 $\frac{E}{3} - 2 = 2$

5 $\frac{2S}{3} + 10 = S$

6 $\frac{2}{3T} - \frac{1}{15} = 0$

7 $4 - R = \frac{R}{3}$

8 $3K - 15 = K + 5$

9 $16 - 2(L + 5) = 3 - L$

10 $3(13 - V) + 2 = 2(3 + V)$

11 $6 - R = 5(2R - 1)$

12 $\frac{M-2}{3} = 2(2 - M)$

13 $\frac{2u}{7} + 6 = \frac{4}{3}(u - 1)$

In Exercises 14 through 18, write each expression as the base 5 with a single exponent:

14 $5^2 \times 5^7$

15 $5^2 \times 5^5 \times 5^7$

16 $5^4 \times 5^2 \times 5^9 \times 5^{25}$

17 $5^7 \div 5^2$

18 $5^8 \div 5^7$

In Exercises 19 through 23, write each expression as the appropriate base with a single exponent:

19 $(1.04)^6(1.04)^5$

20 $R^3 \times R^8 \times R^{11} \times R^7$

21 $v^{10} \div v$

22 $\left(\frac{1}{1+i}\right)^9 \times \left(\frac{1}{1+i}\right)^5 \times \left(\frac{1}{1+i}\right)^4$

23 $\left(\frac{a+b}{c+d}\right)^5 \div \left(\frac{a+b}{c+d}\right)^2$

In Exercises 24 through 26, factor out all the common multipliers:

24 $25(1.03) + 25(1.03)^2 + 25(1.03)^3$

25 $7(1.02)^2 + 14(1.02)^4 + 21(1.02)^6$

26 $\frac{200}{1.04} + \frac{100}{(1.04)^2} + \frac{300}{(1.04)^3} + \frac{100}{(1.04)^4}$

3.

Interest and the Accumulated Value of Money

A life insurance company receives money from a number of sources, but the principal source is premiums paid by its policyowners. The company must invest much of this money and obtain the largest possible return consistent with the maximum degree of safety for the funds. To understand this phase of company activity, it is necessary to know how invested money accumulates with the passing of time.

3.1 SIMPLE ACCUMULATED VALUE

Money paid for the use of money is known as *interest.* Banks, for example, pay depositors interest on money in savings accounts because this money is largely available to the bank for its use. A person who borrows money pays interest to the person or institution who made the loan because he, the borrower, has the use of the money during the period of the loan.

Interest is calculated by multiplying the amount of money originally invested or borrowed by a number called the *interest rate,* or *rate of interest.* Whenever an interest rate is referred to without specification as to the period of time, it is assumed to be the rate used to calculate one year's interest. Interest rates are generally stated as being a certain "percent" (%). Percent means hundredths. For example, 3% means $\frac{3}{100}$, or .03. The amount of money originally invested, plus the total amount of interest earned on that investment, is known as the *accumulated value.*

To Illustrate—Find the accumulated value of $100 at the end of 1 year, if interest is earned at the rate of 3% per year.

Solution—The rate of interest, 3%, means that at the end of 1 year .03 times the sum invested will be due as interest. Consequently, the amount of interest earned is

$$.03(\$100) = \$3$$

and the accumulated value of $100 at the end of 1 year (the total of the original $100 investment plus the amount of interest earned) is

$$\$100 + \$3 = \$103$$

To Illustrate Again—Find the accumulated value of $750 at the end of 1 year, if money is assumed to accumulate at the annual rate of .025, or in other words, "if the annual interest rate is 2½%."

Solution—The amount of interest earned on $750 at the end of 1 year at 2½% is

$$\$750(.025) = \$18.75$$

The accumulated value of $750 at the end of 1 year ($750 plus the amount of interest earned) is

$$\$750 + \$18.75 = \$768.75$$

All such problems involve the same operation: that of adding the dollar amount of interest earned to the amount of money invested to obtain the accumulated value. If the letter I is used to represent the amount of interest, the letter A to represent the amount of money invested, and the letter S to represent the accumulated value, all such problems are represented by the equation

$$S = A + I$$

If the interest *rate* per year is i, the amount of interest earned in one year is equal to the amount of money invested multiplied by the interest rate. That is,

$$I = Ai$$

Since this equation says that I is equal to Ai, we can substitute Ai in place of I in the first equation above:

First equation above

$S = A + I$

Substituting Ai for I

$= A + Ai$

Factoring out common multiplier A

$= A(1 + i)$

This last equation states an important principle, namely: *to accumulate an amount of money for one year at a specified rate of interest, multiply the amount of money by the quantity (1 plus the rate of interest), which is called the accumulation factor.* Using this method, the solution of the last illustration above may be written:

Basic equation for accumulating

$S = A(1 + i)$

Substituting \$750 for A, .025 for i

$= \$750(1 + .025)$

Adding 1 plus .025 inside the parentheses

$= \$750(1.025)$

Multiplying

$= \$768.75$

The answer is the same as above.

A device which is helpful in clarifying many problems in finance is known as a *line diagram.* A line diagram makes it possible to see at a glance the essential elements of any problem, such as the amounts of money and the dates on which they are valued, the rate of interest, and the number of years involved. It also shows another essential element, the *evaluation date,* which means the date upon which the unknown, or sought-after, amount of money in the problem is to be determined.

The following line diagram for the last illustration exhibits all of the essential information of the problem:

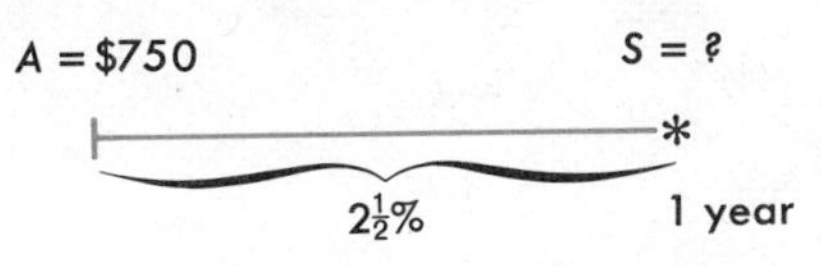

The amount of money A at the beginning of the year is \$750. The rate of interest i is placed under the line with the ⏟ indicating the period for which this rate applies (one year in this diagram). The value of S, indicated by a question mark, is to be determined as of the evaluation date. This is indicated by the symbol *.

3.2 ACCUMULATED VALUE AT COMPOUND INTEREST

The accumulated value of \$100 at the end of one year at 3% interest is \$100 multiplied by the accumulation factor $(1 + .03)$, that is, \$100(1.03). Now, suppose that the accumulated value of \$100 at the end of two years is desired.

To obtain the accumulated value of \$100 for two years, it is important to realize that the amount of money at the beginning of the second year is the same as the accumulated value at the end of the first year. Consider the following line diagram. This illustrates that \$100 accumulated for one year at 3% interest equals \$100(1.03). If this amount is accumulated for one more year, the accumulated value as of the evaluation date (the end of two years) is represented by S.

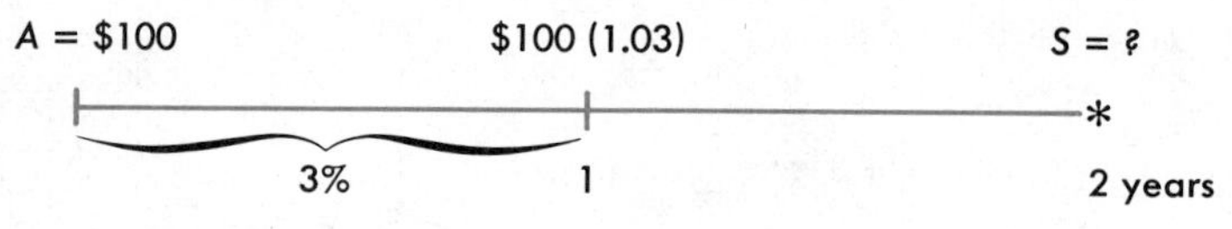

The amount of money at the end of the first year, or at the beginning of the second year, is \$100(1.03). This amount, accumulated for one more year at 3% is \$100(1.03)(1.03). Therefore, we may write

$$S = \$100(1.03)(1.03)$$
$$= \$100(1.03)^2$$

This is the accumulated value of \$100 at the end of two years at 3% interest.

Similarly, $\$100(1.03)^3$ is the accumulated value of \$100 at the end of three years; $\$100(1.03)^4$ is the accumulated value of \$100 at the end of four years; and $\$100(1.03)^n$ is the accumulated value of \$100 at the end of n years at 3% interest per year.

More generally, if A dollars are invested at interest rate i per year, the accumulated values at the end of two, three, and four years, respectively, are

$$A(1+i)^2$$
$$A(1+i)^3$$
and $$A(1+i)^4$$

It follows, therefore, that the accumulated value at the end of any number of years n is

$$S = A(1+i)^n$$

To Illustrate—What is the accumulated value of \$1,000 at the end of 2 years, if it earns interest at the rate of 4% per year?

Solution—The line diagram appears as follows:

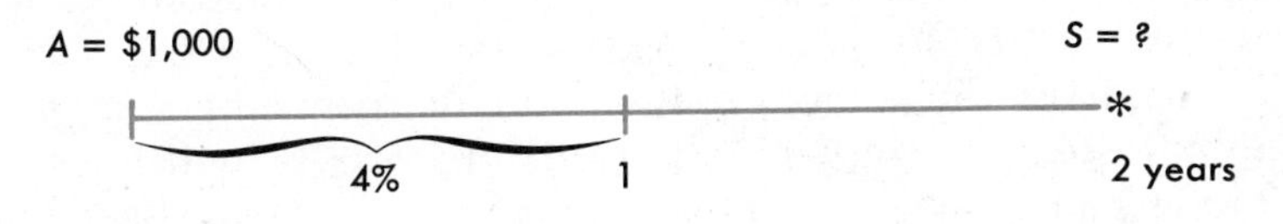

Using the equation just given:

Basic equation for accumulating

$S = A(1 + i)^n$

Substituting \$1,000 for A, .04 for i, and 2 for n

$= \$1{,}000(1 + .04)^2$

$= \$1{,}000(1.04)(1.04)$

Multiplying the first 2 numbers

$= \$1{,}040(1.04)$

Multiplying again; rounding to the nearest cent

$= \$1{,}081.60$

During the second year there is interest earned on the interest which was earned during the first year. It is this interest earned on interest which gives rise to the term *compound interest.* In this text, the term "interest" will always mean "compound interest," unless otherwise stated.

To Illustrate Again—If a man invests \$500 at 5% interest per year, how much will his investment amount to at the end of 4 years?

Solution—The line diagram appears as follows:

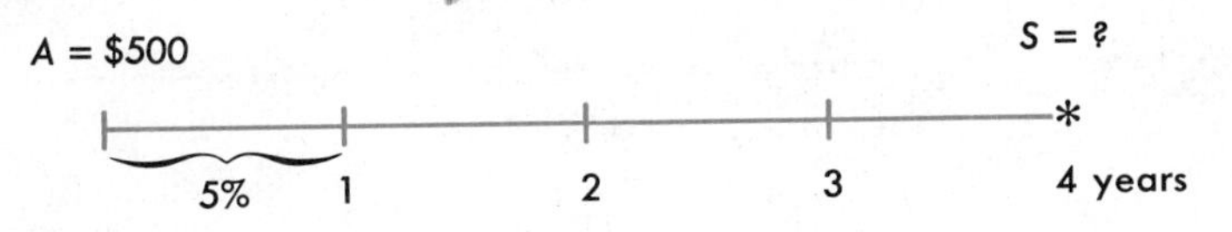

If \$500 accumulated at 5% for 4 years equals S, then using the equation for accumulating:

Basic equation for accumulating

$S = A(1 + i)^n$

Substituting \$500 for A, .05 for i, and 4 for n

$= \$500(1.05)^4$

In order to avoid having to recalculate values which are used frequently, such as the value of 1.05^4, every time the information is needed, tables of these values have been prepared. Such tables are generally prepared on the basis of a payment of $1 (or a series of payments of $1 each). The values shown in the tables may then be multiplied directly by the amount of the particular payment involved. For example, instead of obtaining the value of 1.05^4 by multiplication of the four factors, (1.05)(1.05)(1.05)(1.05), its value may be found in column (1) of Table I (5%) on page 372 in the appendix of this book. Table I, which runs for five pages, includes values of $(1+i)^n$ (the "Accumulated Value of 1") at various interest rates for all numbers of periods from 1 to 25 periods, inclusive. Each page of Table I shows values at a different interest rate.

If $i = .05$ (or 5%) and $n = 4$, column (1) of Table I (5%) shows the value of $(1+i)^n$ to be 1.215506. Therefore, the problem above can be solved as follows:

Basic equation for accumulating

$S = A(1+i)^n$

Substituting \$500 for A, .05 for i, and 4 for n

$= \$500(1.05)^4$

Substituting 1.215506 for 1.05^4

$= \$500(1.215506)$

Multiplying; rounding to nearest cent

$= \$607.75$

To Illustrate Again—To what sum will $500 accumulate in 20 years at 4% interest per year?

Solution—The line diagram appears as follows:

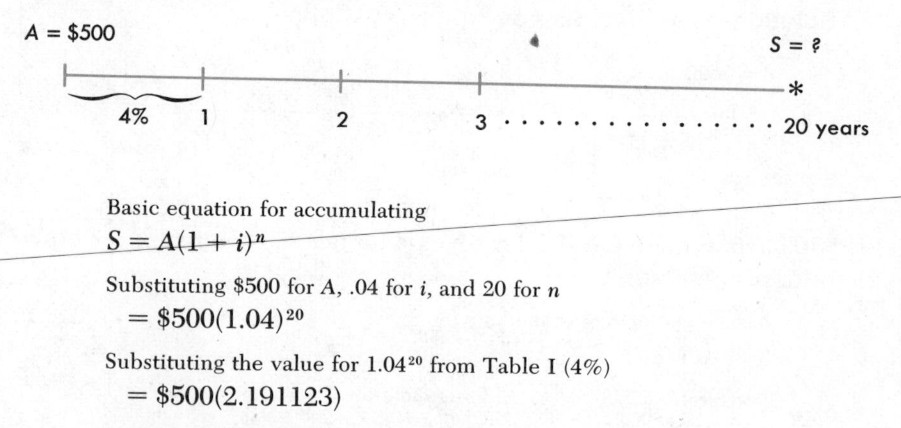

Basic equation for accumulating

$S = A(1+i)^n$

Substituting \$500 for A, .04 for i, and 20 for n

$= \$500(1.04)^{20}$

Substituting the value for 1.04^{20} from Table I (4%)

$= \$500(2.191123)$

Multiplying; rounding to nearest cent

$= \$1,095.56$

Having $(1 + i)^n$ tabulated becomes a very great advantage for problems in which the number of periods is large.

3.3 CONSTRUCTION OF INTEREST ACCUMULATION TABLES

Interest accumulation tables can be constructed by starting with the value of $(1 + i)$ and multiplying each successive value by $(1 + i)$, to progress down the table.

To Illustrate—Construct a table of values of 1.02^n, for the values of n from $n = 1$ to $n = 5$, inclusive, correct to 6 decimal places.

Solution—To construct a table correct to 6 decimal places, it is generally necessary to carry all calculations to at least 7 decimal places and then to round off each value to 6 decimal places. Remembering the rule that exponents are added when multiplying numbers with the same base, the calculation is as follows:

$$1.02^1 = 1.0200000$$

$$1.02^2 = (1.02)(1.02) = 1.0404000$$

$$1.02^3 = (1.02)^2(1.02) = (1.0404000)(1.02) = 1.0612080$$

$$1.02^4 = (1.02)^3(1.02) = (1.0612080)(1.02) = 1.0824321$$

$$1.02^5 = (1.02)^4(1.02) = (1.0824321)(1.02) = 1.1040807$$

and the table is

n	1.02^n
1	1.020000
2	1.040400
3	1.061208
4	1.082432
5	1.104081

These values check with the values in column (1) of Table I at 2% interest shown in the Appendix.

If a value from an interest accumulation table is known, the succeeding value may be determined by multiplying the known value by $(1 + i)$.

To Illustrate—Given $1.04^4 = 1.169859$, find the value of 1.04^5.

Solution—Applying the above rule, the value of 1.04^5, which is the value succeeding 1.04^4 in the 4% Table, may be found by multiplying:

Multiplying known value by $(1 + i)$

$$(1.04)^5 = (1.04)^4(1.04)$$

Substituting 1.169859 for 1.04^4 as given above

$$= 1.169859(1.04)$$

Multiplying; rounding to 6 decimal places

$$= 1.216653$$

If a value from an interest accumulation table is known, the preceding value may be determined by dividing the known value by $(1 + i)$.

To Illustrate—Given $1.04^5 = 1.216653$, find the value of 1.04^4.

Solution—Applying the above rule, the value of $(1.04)^4$, which is the value preceding 1.04^5, may be found by dividing:

Dividing known value by $(1 + i)$

$$1.04^4 = 1.04^5 \div 1.04$$

Substituting 1.216653 for 1.04^5 as given above

$$= 1.216653 \div 1.04$$

Dividing; rounding to 6 decimal places

$$= 1.169859$$

These two illustrations make use of the rules given in Section 2.2 regarding the use of exponents for multiplying or dividing numbers having the same base. These rules can be used further in constructing interest accumulation tables. A general method for finding values of $(1 + i)^n$ would be as follows:

$$(1 + i)^2 = (1 + i)(1 + i)$$

Adding exponents when multiplying

$$(1 + i)^4 = (1 + i)^2(1 + i)^2$$

Adding exponents when multiplying

$$(1 + i)^8 = (1 + i)^4(1 + i)^4$$

Adding exponents when multiplying

$$(1 + i)^{16} = (1 + i)^8(1 + i)^8$$

This process may be repeated as many times as necessary. With these results, intervening values may be found. For example,

$$(1+i)^9 = (1+i)^8(1+i)$$

$$(1+i)^{10} = (1+i)^8(1+i)^2$$

$$(1+i)^{11} = (1+i)^8(1+i)^2(1+i)$$

$$(1+i)^{12} = (1+i)^8(1+i)^4$$

$$(1+i)^{13} = (1+i)^8(1+i)^4(1+i)$$

Note that instead of performing 12 multiplications to obtain $(1+i)^{13}$, it was necessary to perform only five multiplications: three to obtain $(1+i)^8$, which incidentally yields $(1+i)^4$ in the process, and two to obtain the final result.

To Illustrate—Find the value of 1.035^7, assuming that tables of values of the accumulation factor at $3\frac{1}{2}\%$, i.e., 1.035^n, are not available.

Solution—

Multiplying to obtain 1.035^2

$$1.035^2 = (1.035)(1.035)$$
$$= 1.071225$$

Multiplying to obtain $(1.035)^4$

$$1.035^4 = (1.035)^2(1.035)^2$$
$$= (1.071225)(1.071225)$$
$$= 1.147523$$

Multiplying the values necessary for finding $(1.035)^7$

$$1.035^7 = (1.035)^4(1.035)^2(1.035)$$
$$= (1.147523)(1.071225)(1.035)$$
$$= 1.272279$$

EXERCISES

1 Verify the answers in the last column without reference to any table:

Amount Invested (A)	*Interest Rate per Year* (*i*)	*Years* (*n*)	*Accumulated Value* (S)
$ 500.00	.04	1	$ 520.00
125.00	.05	1	131.25
746.89	.03	1	769.30
1,283.56	.025	1	1,315.65
750.00	.02	2	780.30
300.00	.025	3	323.07

2 Verify the answers in the last column, making use of accumulation factors from Table I:

Amount Invested (A)	*Interest Rate per Year* (i)	*Years* (n)	*Accumulated Value* (S)
$2,500.00	.03	6	$2,985.13
1,250.00	.025	10	1,600.11
750.00	.02	8	878.74
276.43	.04	15	497.83
758.66	.03	20	1,370.22
1,426.54	.05	12	2,561.86
897.23	.025	9	1,120.52

3 A man borrows $3,000, giving in return a note promising to pay, at the end of 4 years, the principal with interest at $2\frac{1}{2}\%$ compounded annually. What will be the amount of his payment?

4 The recipient of a $7,500 legacy decides to invest the full sum in a fund at 4% interest compounded annually. To what sum will he be entitled at the end of 7 years?

5 According to Table I, the value of 1.05^{25} is 3.386355. Calculate the value of 1.05^{26}.

6 Using Table I, calculate the value of 1.03^{30}. (Hint: Any two values of 1.03^n the exponents of which add up to 30 can be multiplied together.)

3.4 ACCUMULATING MONEY FOR PERIODS OF TIME OF LESS THAN ONE YEAR

When finding the interest earned by a sum of money for a period of less than one year, it is customary to consider that the interest is proportional to the time. For example, the interest for one-half year is equal to one half of the interest for a whole year, and the interest for two thirds of a year is equal to two thirds of the interest for a whole year.

To Illustrate—Find the interest on, and the accumulated value of, $250 for 9 months, at 4% interest per year.

Solution—The interest for 9 months is $\frac{9}{12}$ or $\frac{3}{4}$ of the interest for a whole year. The amount of interest earned for a whole year is

$$.04(\$250) = \$10$$

Therefore, the amount of interest earned for $\frac{3}{4}$ of a year is

$$\frac{3}{4}(\$10.00) = \$7.50$$

The accumulated value at the end of 9 months is the original sum + interest:

Basic equation

$S = A + I$

Substituting $250 for A; $7.50 for I

$= \$250 + 7.50$

Adding

$= \$257.50$

If the period of time is expressed in terms of days instead of months, it is usually assumed that the number of days in one year is 360. If this assumption of 360 days is made, it is customary to assume that each of the 12 months contains 30 days.

To Illustrate – Find the interest on, and the accumulated value of, $500 for 60 days at 5% interest per year.

Solution – If one year is assumed to be 360 days, the interest for 60 days is $\frac{60}{360}$ or $\frac{1}{6}$ of the interest for a whole year. The amount of interest earned for a whole year is

$$.05(\$500) = \$25$$

Therefore, the amount of interest earned for $\frac{1}{6}$ of a year is

$$\frac{1}{6}(\$25) = \$4.17$$

The accumulated value at the end of 60 days is the original sum + interest:

Basic equation

$S = A + I$

Substituting $500 for A; $4.17 for I

$= \$500 + \$4.17$

Adding

$= \$504.17$

If the assumption were being made that a year contained 365 days, the year's interest would be multiplied by $\frac{60}{365}$ instead of $\frac{60}{360}$.

When counting the exact number of days between dates, it is customary to count either the beginning date or the ending date, but not both.

To Illustrate—Find the interest on $1,000 from February 3 to April 26 at 3% interest per year.

Solution—The first day, February 3, can be omitted and the last day, April 26, counted. If the assumption is made that a year consists of twelve 30-day months, then there are 27 more days in February after February 3; there are 30 days in March; and there are 26 days being counted in April. This is a total of

$$27 \text{ days} + 30 \text{ days} + 26 \text{ days} = 83 \text{ days}$$

The amount of interest earned for a whole year is

$$.03(\$1{,}000) = \$30$$

CHART 3–1

Table for Computing the Number of Days between Two Dates (on basis of 30 days each month)

Day of Month	*Jan.*	*Feb.*	*Mar.*	*Apr.*	*May*	*Jun.*	*Jul.*	*Aug.*	*Sep.*	*Oct.*	*Nov.*	*Dec.*
1	1	31	61	91	121	151	181	211	241	271	301	331
2	2	32	62	92	122	152	182	212	242	272	302	332
3	3	33	63	93	123	153	183	213	243	273	303	333
4	4	34	64	94	124	154	184	214	244	274	304	334
5	5	35	65	95	125	155	185	215	245	275	305	335
6	6	36	66	96	126	156	186	216	246	276	306	336
7	7	37	67	97	127	157	187	217	247	277	307	337
8	8	38	68	98	128	158	188	218	248	278	308	338
9	9	39	69	99	129	159	189	219	249	279	309	339
10	10	40	70	100	130	160	190	220	250	280	310	340
11	11	41	71	101	131	161	191	221	251	281	311	341
12	12	42	72	102	132	162	192	222	252	282	312	342
13	13	43	73	103	133	163	193	223	253	283	313	343
14	14	44	74	104	134	164	194	224	254	284	314	344
15	15	45	75	105	135	165	195	225	255	285	315	345
16	16	46	76	106	136	166	196	226	256	286	316	346
17	17	47	77	107	137	167	197	227	257	287	317	347
18	18	48	78	108	138	168	198	228	258	288	318	348
19	19	49	79	109	139	169	199	229	259	289	319	349
20	20	50	80	110	140	170	200	230	260	290	320	350
21	21	51	81	111	141	171	201	231	261	291	321	351
22	22	52	82	112	142	172	202	232	262	292	322	352
23	23	53	83	113	143	173	203	233	263	293	323	353
24	24	54	84	114	144	174	204	234	264	294	324	354
25	25	55	85	115	145	175	205	235	265	295	325	355
26	26	56	86	116	146	176	206	236	266	296	326	356
27	27	57	87	117	147	177	207	237	267	297	327	357
28	28	58	88	118	148	178	208	238	268	298	328	358
29	29	59	89	119	149	179	209	239	269	299	329	359
30	30	60	90	120	150	180	210	240	270	300	330	360

The amount of interest earned from February 3 to April 26 is therefore

$$\frac{83}{360}(\$30) = \$6.92$$

It is frequently necessary to calculate the time interval between two dates for which interest is earned, as in the last illustration. Determination of the number of days is made easier by the use of the special table (Chart 3–1) in which each day of the year is numbered, starting with January 1. (This chart is on a 360-day basis. A similar chart could be made based on the assumption of a 365-day year.)

In the last illustration, the two dates were February 3 and April 26. The chart shows

February 3 = 33rd day of the year
April 26 = 116th day of the year

By subtraction, the number of days between the two dates is

116th day − 33rd day = 83 days

This is the same period as was calculated above.

3.5 NOMINAL AND EFFECTIVE INTEREST RATES

NOMINAL INTEREST RATES. It is customary to quote interest rates on a yearly basis. In this text, the rate of interest quoted means an annual interest rate, unless otherwise stated. When annual interest earned is added to the principal at the end of each year, interest is said to be compounded annually.

However, interest is often compounded more frequently than once a year; for example, semiannually or quarterly. When an annual interest rate is quoted with the understanding that interest is to be compounded more than once a year, the given rate is referred to as a *nominal interest rate.* If the nominal interest rate is divided by the number of compounding periods per year, the result is the interest rate per compounding period. For example, a nominal 6% compounded semiannually means that interest at the rate of 3% is added to the principal each half-year. An investment of \$100 at such a rate would earn \$100(.03) = \$3 interest during the first half-year. The accumulated sum would then be \$100 + \$3 = \$103. During the second half-year, the interest earned would be \$103(.03) = \$3.09; and so on.

Up to this point, the i and n in the equation

$$S = A(1 + i)^n$$

have been interpreted as the interest rate per year and the number of years, respectively, during which A accumulates to S. Such a restriction is unnecessary, however; all that is necessary is that i and n refer to the same period of time. For example, if i is the interest rate per month then n must be measured in months. Similarly if i is the interest rate per quarter then n must be measured in quarters, and if i is quoted as the interest rate per half-year, then n must be measured in half-years.

To Illustrate—Find the accumulated value of \$250 at the end of 2 years at a nominal 8%, compounded quarterly.

Solution—Since there are 4 quarters in one year, the interest rate is $\frac{1}{4}$ of 8%, or 2% each quarter. The line diagram appears as follows:

A = \$250 S = ?

2% $\frac{1}{4}$	$\frac{1}{2}$	$\frac{3}{4}$	1	$1\frac{1}{4}$	$1\frac{1}{2}$	$1\frac{3}{4}$	2 years
1	2	3	4	5	6	7	8 periods

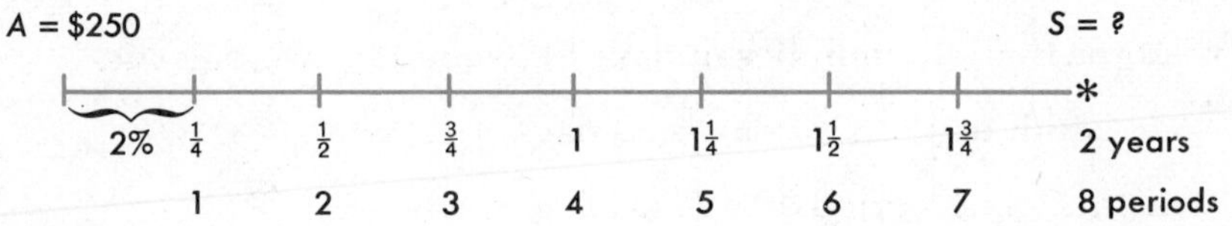

Since the interest rate is a rate per quarter, the time, 2 years, must be measured in quarters. Since there are 4 quarters in one year, then there are 4(2) = 8 quarters in 2 years. The problem therefore deals with eight periods, i.e., the interest will be compounded 8 times during the 2 years.

Basic equation for accumulating

$$S = A(1+i)^n$$

Substituting \$250 for A, .02 for i, 8 for n

$$= \$250(1.02)^8$$

Substituting the value for $(1.02)^8$ from Table I (2% for 8 periods)

$$= \$250(1.171659)$$

Multiplying; rounding to nearest cent

$$= \$292.91$$

To Illustrate Again—Find the accumulated value of \$2,000 at the end of $5\frac{1}{2}$ years, if the interest rate is 4% compounded annually during the first 2 years and a nominal 5% compounded semiannually during the last $3\frac{1}{2}$ years.

Solution—The line diagram appears as follows:

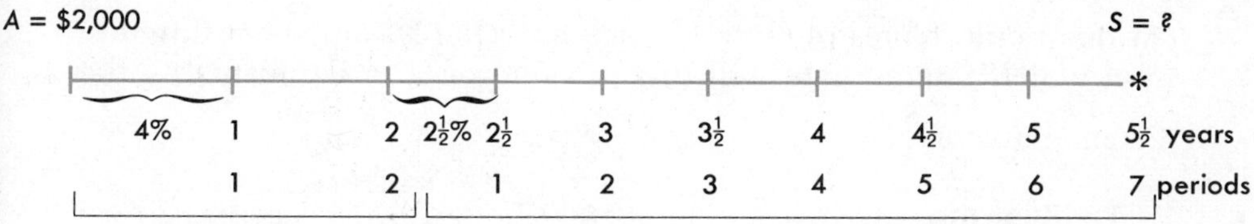

A = $2,000										S = ?
4%	1	2	$2\frac{1}{2}$%	$2\frac{1}{2}$	3	$3\frac{1}{2}$	4	$4\frac{1}{2}$	5	$5\frac{1}{2}$ years
	1	2		1	2	3	4	5	6	7 periods

The accumulated value must be found in 2 steps, since only one rate of interest is used at a time in applying the accumulation formula $S = A(1+i)^n$. The first step is to find the accumulated value at the end of the period during which the interest rate is 4% (i.e., 2 years):

Basic equation for accumulating

$$S(\text{end of 2 years}) = A(1+i)^n$$

Substituting \$2,000 for A, .04 for i, 2 for n

$$= \$2{,}000(1.04)^2$$

The second step is to accumulate this value to the end of the entire period, that is, for the $3\frac{1}{2}$ years during which the interest rate is a nominal 5% compounded semiannually. This means that $2\frac{1}{2}$% interest will be compounded for 7 periods. The beginning value, A, in this case will be the same as the ending value, S, found at the end of 2 years:

Basic equation for accumulating

$$S(\text{end of entire period}) = A(1+i)^n$$

Substituting \$2,000 (1.04)² for A, .025 for i, 7 for n

$$= \underbrace{\$2{,}000(1.04)^2}_{A}(1.025)^7$$

Substituting values from Table I for 1.04^2 and 1.025^7

$$= \$2{,}000(1.081600)(1.188686)$$

Multiplying; rounding to nearest cent

$$= \$2{,}571.37$$

Sometimes it is desired to find out what rate of interest has been earned when the beginning value, A, and the accumulated value, S, are known. A procedure for finding the *approximate* rate of interest is as follows:

Basic equation for accumulating

$$S = A(1+i)^n$$

Dividing both sides by A

$$\frac{S}{A} = (1+i)^n$$

At this point, tables of $(1 + i)^n$ (such as Table I) can be consulted to find which interest rate will give a value of $(1 + i)^n$ nearest to the actual value of $\frac{S}{A}$.

To Illustrate – An investment of $500 made 10 years ago has grown in value to $750. What interest rate per year was earned during that time?

Solution – The line diagram appears as follows:

A = $500 S = $750

?% 1 2 3 10

Equation derived above

$$\frac{S}{A} = (1 + i)^n$$

Substituting $750 for S, $500 for A, 10 for n

$$\frac{\$750}{\$500} = (1 + i)^{10}$$

Dividing $750 by $500

$$1.5 = (1 + i)^{10}$$

From Table I, the values of $(1 + i)^{10}$, for various values of i, are as follows:

i	$(1 + i)^{10}$
2%	1.218994
2½%	1.280084
3%	1.343916
4%	1.480244
5%	1.628895

The rate of interest being sought is the one which will yield a value of 1.5 for $(1 + i)^{10}$. An examination of the values of $(1 + i)^{10}$ above shows that 4% yields a value of 1.480244 (which is smaller than the 1.5), and 5% yields a value of 1.628895 (which is larger than the 1.5). Therefore, the exact interest rate being sought must lie between 4% and 5%.

Greater accuracy in determining the exact rate earned could be achieved either by the use of tables showing more intervening interest rates, or by some methods of higher mathematics.

EFFECTIVE INTEREST RATES. When interest is compounded more frequently than once a year, an annual interest rate can be found which will produce the same accumulated values as the given nominal rate. This annual interest rate is called the *effective interest rate,* and is actually the true interest rate earned.

For example, in the first paragraph of this section it was pointed out that $100 earning a nominal 6% compounded semiannually would earn $3 interest the first half-year, and the resultant $103 would earn $3.09 the second half-year. Therefore, the $100 would grow to $106.09 at the end of one year. If, instead, the interest rate were 6.09% compounded annually, the accumulated value at the end of one year would be

Basic equation for accumulating

$$S = A(1 + i)$$

Substituting $100 for A, .0609 for *i*

$$= \$100(1 + .0609)$$

Adding inside the parentheses

$$= \$100(1.0609)$$

Multiplying

$$= \$106.09$$

This is the same accumulated value as was produced by a nominal 6% compounded semiannually. Therefore, 6.09% may be said to be the *effective interest rate* which corresponds to a nominal 6% compounded semiannually.

Whenever two interest rates produce the same accumulated value in the same period of time, they are said to be *equivalent rates.* Therefore, in the example above, a nominal 6% compounded semiannually is equivalent to 6.09% compounded annually. The two rates were shown to be equivalent since they produced the same accumulated value at the end of one year; however, if this is true, the two rates will necessarily produce the same accumulated value at the end of any number of years.

The *effective* rate corresponding to any given *nominal* rate may be calculated by the equation

$$\text{Effective Rate (decimal)} = (1 + i)^n - 1$$

where n is the number of periods per year, and i is the interest rate per period. This answer will be expressed in decimal form. It must be multiplied by 100 if it is to be expressed in percentage form:

$$\text{Effective Rate (\%)} = [(1 + i)^n - 1]100$$

To Illustrate—Find the effective interest rate which is equivalent to a nominal 8% compounded quarterly.

Solution—In using the above equation, it must be recognized that there are 4 periods in 1 year (because interest is compounded quarterly), and the interest rate per quarter is 2% (because $\frac{1}{4}$ of 8% is 2%).

Equation given above

$$\text{Effective Rate (decimal)} = (1 + i)^n - 1$$

Substituting .02 for i, 4 for n

$$= 1.02^4 - 1$$

Substituting the value for 1.02^4 from Table I

$$= 1.082432 - 1$$

Subtracting

$$= .082432$$

This is the effective rate expressed in decimal form. If this answer is desired in percentage form, it must be multiplied by 100:

$$.082432(100) = 8.2432\%$$

Nominal interest rates compounded semiannually, quarterly, and monthly are very common in business. As the frequency of compounding increases, the corresponding effective rate increases because more interest is earned on interest. The following tabulation shows this specifically for a nominal interest rate of 6% compounded semiannually, quarterly, monthly, weekly, and daily:

6% Nominal Rate	*Effective Rate*
Compounded semiannually	6.090%
Compounded quarterly	6.136%
Compounded monthly	6.168%
Compounded weekly	6.180%
Compounded daily	6.183%

It is interesting to note that if the compoundings were to take place at increasingly short intervals of time, such as every hour, minute, second, etc., the corresponding effective interest rate in the above table would ultimately approach 6.184% (correct to three decimal places). This is said to be the effective rate when the money is compounded *continuously*.

It becomes increasingly impractical to compound money more and more frequently. However, this lengthy calculation can be avoided by computing the accumulation at the equivalent *effective* interest rate. This is what is actually done by banks and savings and loan associations which advertise that money deposited with them is compounded daily or continuously.

EXERCISES

1 Using the assumption of 360 days in 1 year, calculate the amount of interest which would be due at the end of 60 days on a $1,000 loan, if the interest rate were 6%.

2 Using the special table in Section 3.4, calculate the exact number of days between August 10 and the following April 2. (Hint: Before subtracting, add 360 to the number being used for April 2, because it is in the following year.)

3 Using the assumption of 360 days in 1 year, calculate the accumulated value on November 15 of $5,000 which was invested at 5% interest on February 7.

4 Using the assumption of 360 days in 1 year, calculate the accumulated value on December 2 of $2,000 which was invested at 5% interest on September 20.

5 Calculate the accumulated amount at the end of 5 years of $500 which earns interest at a nominal 4% compounded semiannually.

6 If $1,000 earns interest at 4% compounded annually from May 10, 1971, to May 10, 1985, and the accumulated amount is then withdrawn and invested elsewhere at a nominal 8% compounded quarterly, what will be the accumulated value on November 10, 1990?

7 What effective interest rate is equivalent to a nominal 5% compounded semiannually? (Hint: Use Table I and the appropriate equation.)

8 What effective interest rate is equivalent to a nominal 4% compounded quarterly? (Hint: Assume an investment of $100 and perform the 4 compoundings.)

9 Approximately what annual rate of interest has been earned on $1,000 if the accumulated value at the end of 12 years is $1,795.86?

10 Approximately what nominal rate of interest, compounded semiannually, has been earned on $2,000 if the accumulated value at the end of 5 years is $2,600?

4. The Present Value of Money

4.1 BASIC CONCEPT

In Chapter 3, it was demonstrated that the accumulated value, S, of an amount of money, A, at the end of n periods, at interest rate i per period, is given by the accumulation equation

$$S = A(1 + i)^n$$

The equally important converse problem is that of determining how much money, A, must be invested so that it will accumulate for n periods, at an interest rate of i per period, to a given amount, S.

Just as S was called the accumulated value of A, now A will be called the *present value* of S. For example, in the equation

$$\$103 = \$100(1.03)$$

$103 is the accumulated value of $100 for one year at 3%. Also, $100 is the present value at 3% of $103 due at the end of one year.

Finding the present value of an amount of money is finding its equivalent value at an earlier date. For example, the present value of $100 due in five years at 3% is that amount of money which will accumulate at 3% interest to $100 in five years.

Finding present values, sometimes called discounting, is of special importance to life insurance companies because they are continually concerned with the present value of benefits to be paid in the future.

4.2 PRESENT VALUES

In finding a present value, the original amount to be invested, A, is sought. The accumulation equation can be solved for A, as follows:

Basic equation for accumulating

$$S = A(1+i)^n$$

Dividing both sides by $(1+i)^n$

$$\frac{S}{(1+i)^n} = A\left[\frac{(1+i)^n}{(1+i)^n}\right]$$

Dropping $\frac{(1+i)^n}{(1+i)^n}$ because it equals 1

$$\frac{S}{(1+i)^n} = A$$

This equation, $\frac{S}{(1+i)^n} = A$, implies that the known accumulated value, S, is divided by $(1+i)^n$ to arrive at the desired present value, A. Since values of $(1+i)^n$ are shown in Table I, this procedure can be followed.

A simpler procedure is possible, however. The equation, $A = \frac{S}{(1+i)^n}$, may be written as

$$A = S\left[\frac{1}{(1+i)^n}\right]$$

This implies that the known accumulated value, S, is multiplied by $\frac{1}{(1+i)^n}$ to arrive at the desired present value, A. For convenience, the fraction $\frac{1}{1+i}$ is often written as v. Accordingly, the fraction $\frac{1}{(1+i)^n}$ is written as v^n. The equation for finding present values (i.e., discounting) thus becomes

$$A = Sv^n$$

The factor, v^n, is therefore the quantity by which an amount of money, S, should be multiplied in order to determine its value n periods earlier, at interest rate i per period. It is important to remember that multiplying by v^n is the same as dividing by $(1+i)^n$. Values of the factor, v^n, are tabulated in column (2) of Table I for periods of 1 to 25, inclusive, for various interest rates.

Note that the interest rate being used, i, does not appear directly in the factor for discounting, v^n, as it does in the factor for accumulating,

$(1 + i)^n$. Therefore, while an equation for accumulating might be written as

$$S = \$100(1.03)^{10}$$

an equation for discounting should be written as

$$A = \$134.39(v^{10} \text{ at } 3\%)$$

To Illustrate—How much money must be deposited in a bank paying 3% interest per year on deposits, so that \$100 will be available at the end of 1 year?

Solution—The line diagram for this illustration appears as follows with A as the unknown:

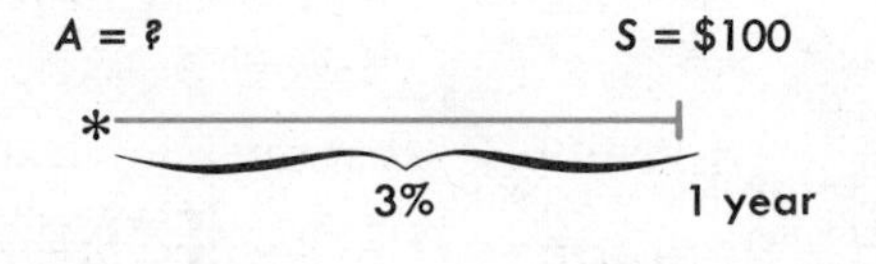

Using the basic equation for discounting:

$$A = Sv^n$$

Substituting \$100 for S, 1 for n; note interest rate is 3%

$$= \$100(v^1 \text{ at } 3\%)$$

Substituting value of v^1 at 3% from Table I

$$= \$100(.970874)$$

Multiplying; rounding to nearest cent

$$= \$97.09$$

This amount, \$97.09, is called the present value of \$100 due in 1 year at 3%.

Note that the expression "v^1" in the above solution could also have been written simply as "v."

To Illustrate Again—How much money must be deposited in a bank paying 3% interest per year on deposits, so that \$100 will be available at the end of 10 years?

Solution—The line diagram for this illustration appears as follows:

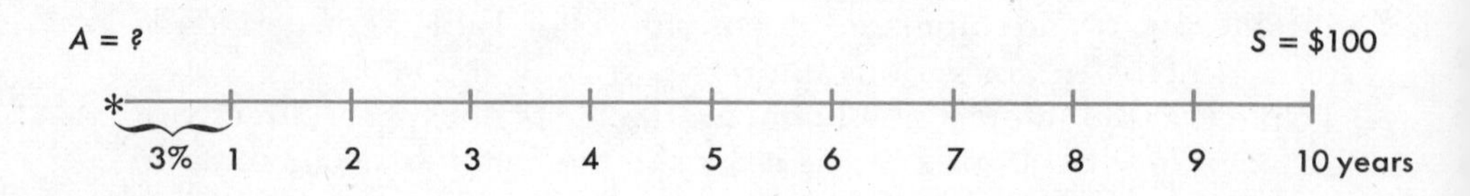

Basic equation for discounting

$A = Sv^n$

Substituting $100 for S, 10 for n (note interest rate is 3%)

$= \$100\ (v^{10} \text{ at } 3\%)$

Substituting value of v^{10} from Table I (3%)

$= \$100(.744094)$

Multiplying; rounding to nearest cent

$= \$74.41$

This amount, $74.41, is called the present value of $100 due in 10 years at 3%.

It is important to notice in these two illustrations that *when the number of periods is increased, the present value is decreased.* This is true because in a longer period of time more interest is earned; hence, a smaller amount of money is required at the beginning in order to accumulate to a fixed amount.

It is also important to understand that *when the interest rate is increased, the present value is decreased.* This is true because a higher interest rate will produce more interest over the period; hence, a smaller amount of money is required at the beginning in order to accumulate to a fixed amount.

To Illustrate—A father wishes to invest an amount of money for his son, age 10, which will provide a $5,000 educational fund when the son reaches age 18. Find the amount he should invest if the fund earns a nominal 4% compounded semiannually; also find the amount if the fund earns a nominal 5% compounded semiannually.

Solution—Since the son is now age 10, and the fund is needed when he reaches age 18, the total time is 8 years. However, interest is compounded every half-year, so there are 16 periods. The interest rate of a nominal 4% compounded semiannually means 2% every half-year; the interest rate of a nominal 5% compounded semiannually means $2\frac{1}{2}\%$ every half-year. The line diagram appears as follows:

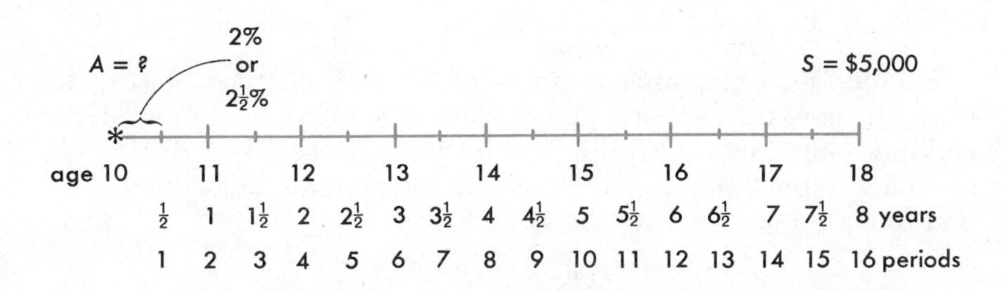

For a nominal 4% compounded semiannually:

Basic equation for discounting

$A = Sv^n$

Substituting \$5,000 for S, 16 for n (note interest rate is 2%)

$= \$5{,}000(v^{16} \text{ at } 2\%)$

Substituting value of v^{16} from Table I (2%)

$= \$5{,}000(.728446)$

Multiplying; rounding to nearest cent

$= \$3{,}642.23$

For a nominal 5% compounded semiannually:

Basic equation for discounting

$A = Sv^n$

Substituting \$5,000 for S, 16 for n (note interest rate is $2\frac{1}{2}\%$)

$= \$5{,}000(v^{16} \text{ at } 2\tfrac{1}{2}\%)$

Substituting value of v^{16} from Table I ($2\frac{1}{2}\%$)

$= \$5{,}000(.673625)$

Multiplying; rounding to nearest cent

$= \$3{,}368.13$

The answers show that the larger interest rate produces the lower present value.

4.3 CONSTRUCTION OF TABLES OF PRESENT VALUES

Present value tables may be constructed by starting with the value of v, which is found by dividing 1 by $(1 + i)$, and multiplying each successive value by v, to progress down the table.

To Illustrate – Construct a table of values of v^n at 2%, for values of n from $n = 1$ to $n = 3$, inclusive, correct to 6 decimal places.

Solution – To construct a table correct to 6 decimal places, it is generally necessary to carry all calculations to at least 7 decimal places and then round off each value to 6 decimal places. The calculation is as follows, remembering the rule that exponents are added when multiplying numbers with the same base:

$$v^1 \text{ at } 2\% = \frac{1}{(1.02)}$$
$$= .9803922$$
$$v^2 \text{ at } 2\% = v(v)$$
$$= (.9803922)(.9803922)$$
$$= .9611689$$
$$v^3 \text{ at } 2\% = v^2(v)$$
$$= (.9611689)(.9803922)$$
$$= .9423225$$

and the table is:

n	v^n
1	.980392
2	.961169
3	.942323

These values check with the values in Table I at 2% interest, except for the last one. Table I shows the value of v^3 at 2% to be .942322. The reason for this difference in the sixth decimal place lies in the number of decimal places used in the calculation. It is not unusual in this type of calculation for two independent computations of the same problem to arrive at answers which differ in the last decimal place.

If a value from a present value table is known, the succeeding value may be determined either by multiplying the known value by v, *or by dividing the known value by* $(1 + i)$.

To Illustrate—Given v^4 at 4% = .854804, find the value of v^5 at 4%.

Solution—In applying the above rule in this case, it will be easier to divide by $(1 + i)$ than to multiply by v, because the value of v is not given. Therefore, the value of v^5 at 4%, which is the value succeeding v^4 at 4% in the table, may be found as follows:

Basic rule

$$v^5 \text{ at } 4\% = (v^4 \text{ at } 4\%) \div (1 + i)$$

Substituting .854804 for v^4, .04 for i

$$= .854804 \div 1.04$$

Dividing; rounding to 6 decimal places

$$= .821927$$

If a value from a present value table is known, the preceding value *may be determined either by dividing the known value by v or by multiplying the known value by $(1+i)$.*

To Illustrate – Given v^{10} at 5% = .613913, find the value of v^9 at 5%.

Solution – In applying the above rule to this case, it will be easier to multiply by $(1+i)$ than to divide by v, because the value of v is not given. Therefore, the value of v^9 at 5%, which is the value preceding v^{10} at 5% in the table, may be found as follows:

Basic rule

v^9 at 5% = (v^{10} at 5%) $(1+i)$

Substituting .613913 for v^{10}, .05 for i

= .613913(1.05)

Multiplying; rounding to 6 decimal places

= .644609

EXERCISES

1 Without using values from any table, verify the present values listed in the last column of the following schedule:

S	*Interest Rate per Period* (*i*)	*Periods* (*n*)	*Present Value* (A)
$ 800.00	.025	1	$ 780.49
1,200.00	.03	1	1,165.05
7,500.00	.04	1	7,211.54
427.50	.02	2	410.90
963.84	.05	2	874.23
1,250.00	.025	2	1,189.77

2 Using present value factors from Table I, verify the present values listed in the last column of the following schedule:

S	*Interest Rate per Period* (*i*)	*Periods* (*n*)	*Present Value* (A)
$1,500.00	.03	5	$1,293.91
5,000.00	.025	9	4,003.64
125.00	.04	15	69.41
750.00	.02	20	504.73
775.81	.025	14	549.06
1,465.96	.02	6	1,301.73
943.83	.05	18	392.18
67.56	.03	20	37.41

3 How much money must be deposited now in an account paying $2\frac{1}{2}\%$ interest per year in order to provide $1,500 at the end of 1 year?

4 How much money must be deposited now in an account paying $2\frac{1}{2}\%$ interest per year in order to provide $1,500 at the end of 10 years?

5 Calculate the present value of $1,000 due in 5 years, if the interest rate is a nominal 10% compounded quarterly.

6 To assist in financing the future college education of his newborn son, what amount of money should a father immediately deposit in a savings account earning 4% interest annually so that $20,000 will be available when his son is age 18?

7 How much money would the father in Exercise 6 have to deposit immediately so that his son would have available $5,000 each year for the 4 consecutive years starting when his son is age 18? (Hint: Find the present value of each of the 4 payments separately, and add.)

8 Given that v^{10} at 6% = .558395, calculate v^9 and v^{11} at 6%.

9 Using Table I, calculate the value of v^{30} at 3%. (Hint: Any two values of v^n at 3% the exponents of which add up to 30 can be multiplied together.)

5. The Accumulated Value of Annuities Certain

5.1 INTRODUCTION

Any series of payments made or received at regular intervals of time is known as an *annuity*. Some examples found in everyday life are payments on mortgages, salaries, pensions, rents, regular periodic deposits in savings accounts, social security checks, payments for installment purchases, and life insurance premiums.

Every instance of an annuity represents payments going out from the viewpoint of the payer and payments coming in from the viewpoint of the receiver. The accumulated values explained in this chapter are applicable from either viewpoint.

In general, annuities fall into two broad classifications:

1. Those which involve a fixed number of payments. These are known as *annuities certain*. An example would be the payment for a television set by regular monthly installments for two years.
2. Those in which the continuation of the payments depends upon the occurrence or nonoccurrence of some event. An example would be the premiums for a life insurance policy, which are terminated by death; that is, the payments depend upon the nonoccurrence of the event of death.

Attention will be limited in this and the next chapter to *annuities certain.* Chapter 8 will be devoted to a study of annuities wherein the continuation of payments depends upon the payer or the receiver being alive.

Within the broad classification of *annuities certain,* there are two other classifications, depending upon the time when each payment is made:

1. Those in which the payments are made at the *end* of each interval of time. These are known as *annuities immediate.* An example would be salaries which are paid in arrears (that is, after the related work period has ended).
2. Those in which the payments are made at the *beginning* of each interval of time. These are known as *annuities due.* An example would be rents which are paid in advance (that is, before the start of the tenancy period).

In this text, the word "annuity" by itself refers to an annuity in which payments are made at the end of each interval of time.

5.2 THE ACCUMULATED VALUE OF AN ANNUITY IMMEDIATE

The accumulated value, at the time of the last payment, of a series of payments of 1 each, made at the *end* of each period for n periods, at interest rate i per period, is represented by the symbol

$$s_{\overline{n}|i}$$

The symbol is read as: "s angle n at rate i." The n and the i are written slightly lower than the s, and are called subscripts. This means that they are part of the whole symbol, not something which is being multiplied by s.

For example, consider a series of five payments of $1 each, made at the end of each year, accumulating at an interest rate of 4% per year. The line diagram appears as follows:

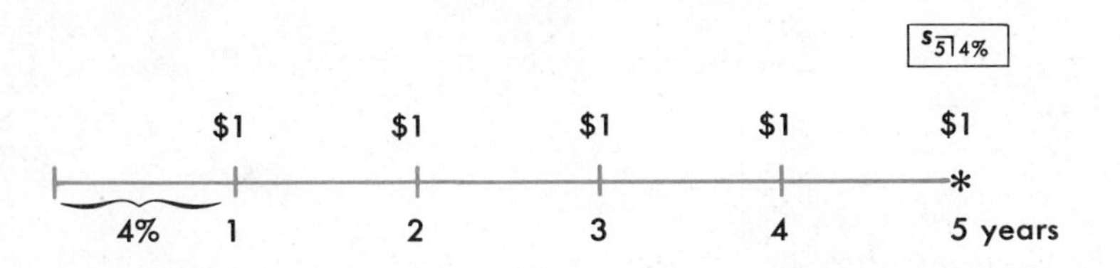

Since the number of payments is 5 and the interest rate is 4%, the accumulated value (at the end of five years) of the annuity is

$$s_{\overline{5}|4\%}$$

This symbol is read as: "s angle 5 at 4%." The number under the "angle" is the number of payments. The number beside the angle is the rate of interest.

If each payment had been \$10, then the accumulated value of the above annuity would have been \$10 multiplied by the above value, that is,

$$\$10 s_{\overline{5}|4\%}$$

The line diagram, then, would appear as follows:

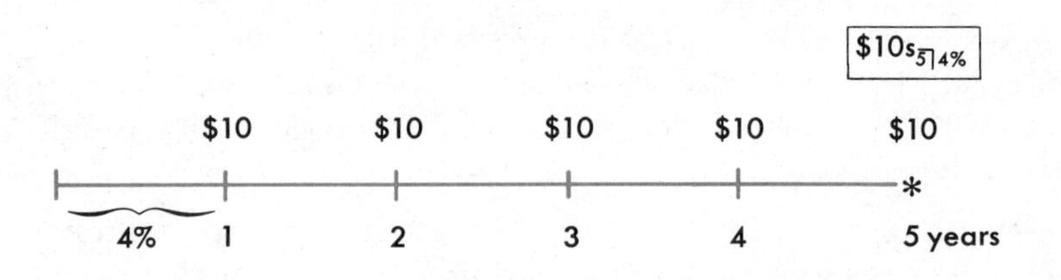

The accumulated value of this annuity at the end of the five years can be calculated as follows: Ten dollars is deposited at the end of the first year. This deposit will grow to \$10(1.04) at the end of the second year, at which time the second deposit of \$10 will increase the balance to

$$\$10(1.04) + \$10 = \$20.40$$

In one more year, this amount will have grown to \$20.40(1.04), and will be increased by a third deposit of \$10, giving

$$\$20.40(1.04) + \$10 = \$31.22$$

In the fourth year, this amount will have grown to \$31.22(1.04), and will be increased by a fourth deposit of \$10, giving

$$\$31.22(1.04) + \$10 = \$42.47$$

Similarly, at the end of the fifth year, the amount will have accumulated to

$$\$42.47(1.04) + \$10 = \$54.17$$

The same accumulated value can be calculated by a second method, namely, by accumulating each deposit of \$10 to the evaluation date and then finding the total of these five accumulations. The following line diagram illustrates this second method:

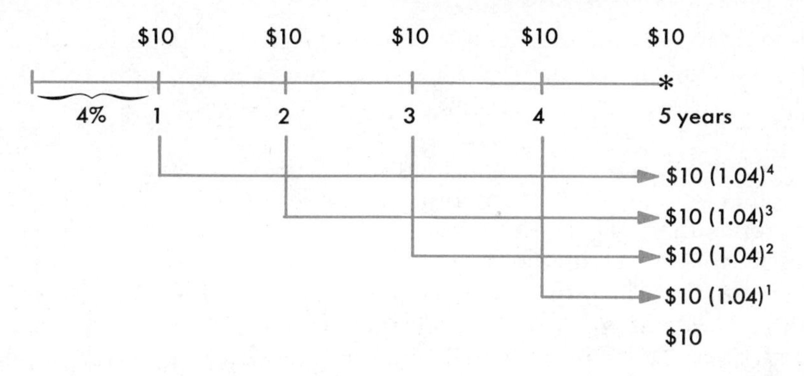

The first $10 deposit, made at the end of the first year, accumulates for four years; the second $10 deposit accumulates for three years; the third $10 deposit accumulates for two years; and the fourth $10 deposit accumulates for one year, all at 4% interest. The fifth $10 deposit, made upon the evaluation date, earns no interest. Using the equation for accumulating, $S = A(1+i)^n$, separately for each deposit, the total accumulated value is

$$\$10s_{\overline{5}|4\%} = \$10(1.04)^4 + \$10(1.04)^3 + \$10(1.04)^2 + \$10(1.04)^1 + \$10$$

The final $10 is not multiplied by any accumulation factor, since that deposit is made upon the evaluation date. In the above expression, the common multiplier, $10, can be factored out (noting that the final $10 can be expressed as $10 × 1):

$$\$10s_{\overline{5}|4\%} = \$10[1.04^4 + 1.04^3 + 1.04^2 + 1.04^1 + 1]$$

Each expression inside the brackets can be looked up in Table I (4%) and a substitution made:

$$\begin{aligned}\$10s_{\overline{5}|4\%} &= \$10[1.169859 + 1.124864 + 1.081600 + 1.040000 + 1]\\ &= \$10(5.416323)\\ &= \$54.16\end{aligned}$$

This answer is 1 cent different from that obtained above by the first method. This small difference is the result of rounding off at various stages of the calculations.

To use general terms: if the accumulated value at the end of n periods of a series of payments of 1, made at the end of each period for n periods, at interest rate i, is desired, the first term of the series will be $(1+i)^{n-1}$, because there will be only $(n-1)$ periods for the first payment to accumulate. The succeeding terms will be $(1 + i)$ with exponents diminishing by one each period, as follows:

$$s_{\overline{n}|i} = (1+i)^{n-1} + (1+i)^{n-2} + \cdots + (1+i)^2 + (1+i)^1 + 1$$

(The group of dots in the right-hand side of the equation indicates that a number of items are left out, but that the series continues in the same manner as the previous items.)

Note that 1.04^1 in the above example could have been written simply as 1.04; also that $(1 + i)^1$ could have been written simply as $(1 + i)$. This text will usually omit the exponent "1."

Values of $s_{\overline{n}|i}$ for periods of 1 to 25, inclusive, are given in column (3) of Table I at the various interest rates.

To Illustrate—Calculate the accumulated value of the annuity of \$10 per year for 5 years at 4%, which was discussed above, by using values of $s_{\overline{n}|i}$ from Table I (4%).

Solution—

$$\text{Accumulated Value} = \$10 s_{\overline{5}|4\%}$$

Substituting the value of $s_{\overline{5}|4\%}$ from Table I

$$= \$10(5.416323)$$

Multiplying; rounding to nearest cent

$$= \$54.16$$

The answer is the same as was derived above. Using values of $s_{\overline{n}|i}$ from Table I saves a great deal of calculation, especially as the number of periods increases.

To Illustrate Again—Calculate the accumulated value which will be in a savings account at the end of 12 years if deposits of \$150 are made at the end of each half-year, and interest is credited to the account at a nominal 5% compounded semiannually.

Solution—Since deposits are received every half-year (twice per year) for 12 years, there are 24 deposits all together. The rate of interest is equal to $2\frac{1}{2}\%$ ($\frac{1}{2}$ of 5%) compounded every half-year. The line diagram appears as follows:

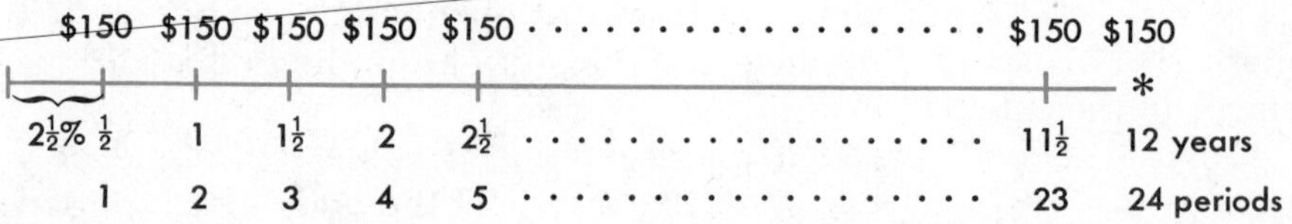

	\$150	\$150	\$150	\$150	\$150	· · · · · · · · ·	\$150	\$150
								*
$2\frac{1}{2}\%$	$\frac{1}{2}$	1	$1\frac{1}{2}$	2	$2\frac{1}{2}$	· · · · · · · · ·	$11\frac{1}{2}$	12 years
	1	2	3	4	5	· · · · · · · · ·	23	24 periods

This series of deposits constitutes an annuity of 24 payments, with interest at $2\frac{1}{2}\%$ *per period.*

Accumulated Value $= \$150s_{\overline{24}|2\frac{1}{2}\%}$

Substituting the value of $s_{\overline{24}|2\frac{1}{2}\%}$ from Table I

$= \$150(32.349038)$

Multiplying; rounding to nearest cent

$= \$4{,}852.36$

5.3 CONSTRUCTION OF TABLES OF $s_{\overline{n}|i}$

The equation given above, namely

$$s_{\overline{n}|i} = (1+i)^{n-1} + (1+i)^{n-2} + \cdots + (1+i)^2 + (1+i) + 1$$

can be used to construct a table of accumulated values of an annuity ($s_{\overline{n}|i}$). The right-hand side of the equation represents the addition of terms, each of which can be found in a table of values of $(1+i)^n$, such as Table I, column (1).

To Illustrate—Construct a table of $s_{\overline{n}|2\%}$ to 6 decimal places for values of n from $n = 1$ to $n = 4$, inclusive.

Solution—The first value, namely $s_{\overline{1}|2\%}$, will be equal to 1.000000, because in an annuity of just one payment, the payment will be made upon the evaluation date and hence earns no interest. This is always true, regardless of the interest rate.

$$s_{\overline{1}|i} = 1$$

The other values of $s_{\overline{n}|2\%}$ may be derived by use of the above equation, remembering that the exponent of the first term of the series is $(n-1)$, and the exponents of the succeeding terms diminish by 1 each period:

Basic equation

$$s_{\overline{n}|i} = (1+i)^{n-1} + 1$$

Substituting 2 for n

$$s_{\overline{2}|i} = (1+i)^1 + 1$$

Substituting .02 for i

$$s_{\overline{2}|2\%} = 1.02^1 + 1$$

Substituting the value for $(1.02)^1$ from Table I

$$= 1.020000 + 1$$

Adding

$$= 2.020000$$

Substituting 3 for n

$$s_{\overline{3}|i} = (1+i)^2 + (1+i) + 1$$

Substituting .02 for i

$$s_{\overline{3}|2\%} = 1.02^2 + 1.02 + 1$$

Substituting values from Table I

$$= 1.040400 + 1.020000 + 1$$

Adding

$$= 3.060400$$

Substituting 4 for n

$$s_{\overline{4}|i} = (1 + i)^3 + (1 + i)^2 + (1 + i) + 1$$

Substituting .02 for i

$$s_{\overline{4}|2\%} = 1.02^3 + 1.02^2 + 1.02 + 1$$

Substituting values from Table I

$$= 1.061208 + 1.040400 + 1.020000 + 1$$

Adding

$$= 4.121608$$

The table is:

n	$s_{\overline{n}|2\%}$
1	1.000000
2	2.020000
3	3.060400
4	4.121608

These values check with the values found in Table I, column (3).

In the above calculations, each value of $s_{\overline{n}|i}$ is determined independently; that is, no calculation makes use of a previously calculated value of $s_{\overline{n}|i}$. However, tables of accumulated values may also be constructed by a method in which each value of $s_{\overline{n}|i}$ is obtained from the preceding value.

In computing accumulated values of an annuity ($s_{\overline{n}|i}$), any value may be obtained by adding $(1 + i)^n$ to the preceding value.

This principle is summarized in the following equation:

$$s_{\overline{n+1}|i} = s_{\overline{n}|i} + (1 + i)^n$$

A line diagram of a specific example of an annuity of five payments of $1 each helps to visualize this relationship between successive values of $s_{\overline{n}|i}$:

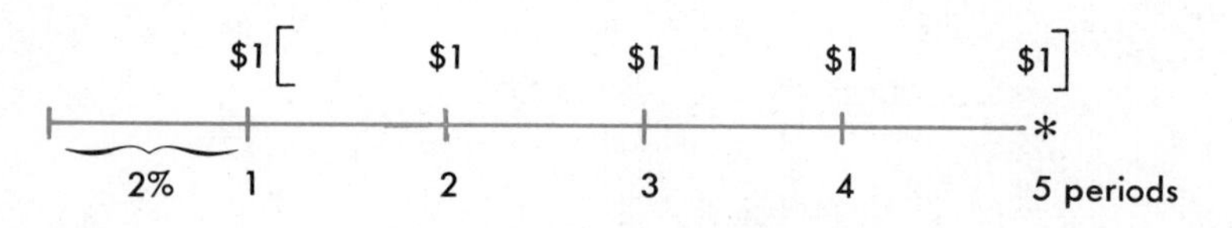

The accumulated value of the last four payments of $1 (those enclosed in the bracket) can be expressed as $s_{\overline{4}|2\%}$. The accumulated value of the first payment, accumulated to the same date as the other four payments, is 1.02^4. The accumulated value of all five payments is the total and is expressed by the equation

$$s_{\overline{5}|2\%} = s_{\overline{4}|2\%} + 1.02^4$$

To Illustrate—Given $s_{\overline{10}|5\%} = 12.577892$, calculate the value of $s_{\overline{11}|5\%}$, assuming that tables of $(1 + i)^n$ are available:

Solution—

Basic equation

$$s_{\overline{n+1}|i} = s_{\overline{n}|i} + (1 + i)^n$$

Substituting 10 for n, .05 for i

$$s_{\overline{11}|5\%} = s_{\overline{10}|5\%} + 1.05^{10}$$

Substituting given value of $s_{\overline{10}|5\%}$ and 1.05^{10} from Table I

$$= 12.577892 + 1.628895$$

Adding

$$= 14.206787$$

Caution: Where each value in a series of calculations depends on the preceding value, great care should be exercised to see that errors do not creep into the calculation, because all succeeding values will be in error after the first error is made.

5.4 OTHER RELATIONSHIPS BETWEEN SUCCESSIVE VALUES OF $s_{\overline{n}|i}$

To construct a table of values of $s_{\overline{n}|i}$ using the methods explained in Section 5.3, it is necessary to have values of $(1+i)^n$ available. There is, however, a method for computing successive values of $s_{\overline{n}|i}$ which does not require values of $(1 + i)^n$. In fact, it is not even necessary, under this method, to know the value of n.

To obtain the next higher value, $s_{\overline{n+1}|i}$, accumulate the known value of $s_{\overline{n}|i}$ for one period and add one payment. This may be expressed in equation form as follows:

$$s_{\overline{n+1}|i} = (1 + i)s_{\overline{n}|i} + 1$$

A line diagram of a specific example showing an annuity of five payments of $1 each helps to visualize this relationship between successive values of $s_{\overline{n}|i}$:

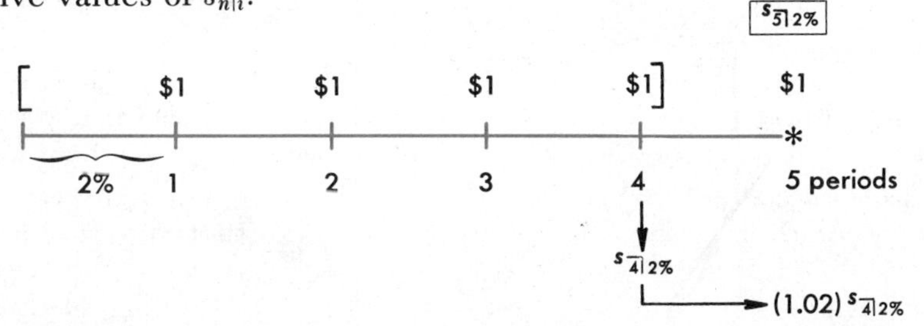

The accumulated value, at the end of four years, of the first four payments of $1 (shown in brackets) is $s_{\overline{4}|2\%}$. This value ($s_{\overline{4}|2\%}$) accumulated at 2% interest for one year amounts to $(1.02)s_{\overline{4}|2\%}$. To this is added the payment of $1 made at the end of the fifth year. The total value is expressed by the equation

$$s_{\overline{5}|2\%} = (1.02)s_{\overline{4}|2\%} + 1$$

To Illustrate—One entry in a table of $s_{\overline{n}|3\%}$ is 5.309. What is the *succeeding* value?

Solution—The succeeding value, $s_{\overline{n+1}|3\%}$, may be found by using the above equation:

Basic equation

$$s_{\overline{n+1}|i} = (1 + i)s_{\overline{n}|i} + 1$$

Substituting .03 for i, and the given value for $s_{\overline{n}|3\%}$

$$s_{\overline{n+1}|3\%} = (1.03)(5.309) + 1$$

Multiplying; rounding to 3 decimal places

$$= 5.468 + 1$$

Adding

$$= 6.468$$

The same equation may be used to find the value of $s_{\overline{n}|i}$ *preceding* a known value. This is done by using $s_{\overline{n+1}|i}$ as the known value and $s_{\overline{n}|i}$ as the unknown value.

To Illustrate—One entry in a table of $s_{\overline{n}|3\%}$ is 10.159. What is the *preceding* value?

Solution—In the basic equation, the known value, 10.159, will be substituted for $s_{\overline{n+1}|i}$. The $s_{\overline{n}|i}$ in the equation (the value preceding $s_{\overline{n+1}|i}$) will be solved for:

Basic equation

$$s_{\overline{n+1}|i} = (1 + i)s_{\overline{n}|i} + 1$$

Substituting 10.159 for $s_{\overline{n+1}|i}$, .03 for i

$$10.159 = (1.03)s_{\overline{n}|i} + 1$$

Subtracting 1 from both sides

$$9.159 = (1.03)s_{\overline{n}|i}$$

Dividing both sides by 1.03; rounding to 3 decimal places

$$8.892 = s_{\overline{n}|i}$$

This method for computing successive values of $s_{\overline{n}|i}$ is ideally suited for the actual construction of tables of $s_{\overline{n}|i}$, remembering the caution that great care should be exercised to see that errors do not creep into such calculation. It should also be remembered that rounding errors can creep in, due to failure to use a sufficient number of decimal places before doing the final rounding off.

To Illustrate—Without using values from any table, calculate to 6 decimal places the value of $s_{\overline{n}|2\%}$, for $n = 1$ to $n = 4$, inclusive.

Solution—The first value, namely $s_{\overline{1}|2\%}$, will be equal to 1.000000. This is because, in an annuity of just 1 payment, the payment will be made upon the evaluation date; hence, it earns no interest. This is true regardless of the interest rate.

$$s_{\overline{1}|i} = 1.000000$$

$$s_{\overline{1}|2\%} = 1.000000$$

The succeeding values of $s_{\overline{n}|2\%}$ can be derived as follows:

Basic equation

$$s_{\overline{n+1}|i} = (1 + i)s_{\overline{n}|i} + 1$$

Substituting 1 for n, .02 for i

$$s_{\overline{2}|2\%} = (1.02)s_{\overline{1}|2\%} + 1$$

Substituting value of $s_{\overline{1}|2\%}$

$$= (1.02)(1.000000) + 1$$

Multiplying; rounding to 6 decimal places

$$= 1.020000 + 1$$

Adding

$$= 2.020000$$

Substituting 2 for n

$$s_{\overline{3}|2\%} = (1.02)s_{\overline{2}|2\%} + 1$$

Substituting value of $s_{\overline{2}|2\%}$ from above

$$= (1.02)(2.020000) + 1$$

Multiplying; rounding to 6 decimal places

$$= (2.060400) + 1$$

Adding

$$= 3.060400$$

Substituting 3 for n

$$s_{\overline{4}|2\%} = (1.02)s_{\overline{3}|2\%} + 1$$

Substituting value of $s_{\overline{3}|2\%}$ from above

$$= (1.02)(3.060400) + 1$$

Multiplying; rounding to 6 decimal places

$$= 3.121608 + 1$$

Adding

$$= 4.121608$$

These values check with the values found in Table I (2%), as well as with those found in the illustration in Section 5.3.

It is sometimes necessary to find the value of $s_{\overline{n}|i}$ when the number of payments, n, is greater than the number shown in an available table. For example, Table I shows such values for any number of periods up to and including 25. The equation for calculating such a value *when* n *is larger than* 25 is

$$s_{\overline{n}|i} = s_{\overline{25}|i} + s_{\overline{n-25}|i}(1+i)^{25}$$

A line diagram of a specific example showing accumulation of payments for 30 years helps to visualize this relationship:

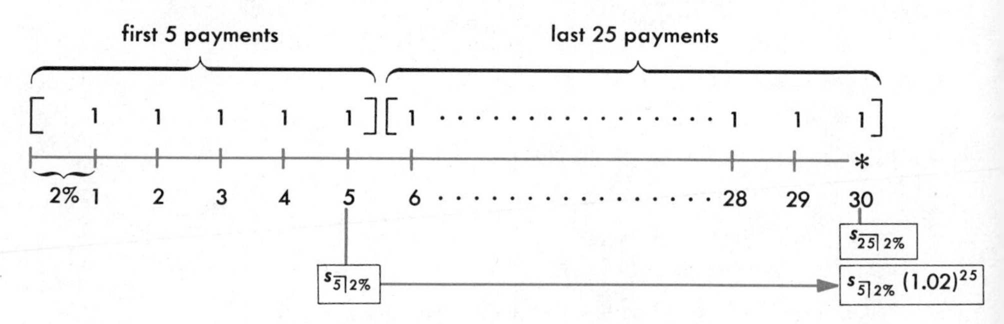

The accumulated value of the *last* 25 payments of 1 is $s_{\overline{25}|2\%}$. The accumulated value of the *first* 5 payments, accumulated to the date when the 5th payment is due, is $s_{\overline{5}|2\%}$. This latter value, accumulated to the true evaluation date, is

$$s_{\overline{5}|2\%}(1.02)^{25}$$

Therefore, the accumulated value of the 30 payments is

$$s_{\overline{30}|2\%} = s_{\overline{25}|2\%} + s_{\overline{5}|2\%}(1.02)^{25}$$

To Illustrate—Calculate the value of $s_{\overline{35}|4\%}$, using Table I.

Solution—Using the above equation:

Basic equation

$$s_{\overline{n}|i} = s_{\overline{25}|i} + s_{\overline{n-25}|i}(1+i)^{25}$$

Substituting 35 for n, .04 for i

$$s_{\overline{35}|4\%} = s_{\overline{25}|4\%} + s_{\overline{10}|4\%}(1.04)^{25}$$

Substituting the values from Table I for $s_{\overline{25}|4\%}$, $s_{\overline{10}|4\%}$, and 1.04^{25}

$$= 41.645908 + 12.006107(2.665836)$$

Multiplying the last 2 numbers; rounding to 6 decimal places

$$= 41.645908 + 32.006312$$

Adding

$$= 73.652220$$

Where n exceeds 50, values of $s_{\overline{n}|i}$ can be found by repeated use of the equation given above. For example, to find the value of $s_{\overline{58}|i}$:

Basic equation

$$s_{\overline{n}|i} = s_{\overline{25}|i} + s_{\overline{n-25}|i}(1+i)^{25}$$

Substituting 58 for n

$$s_{\overline{58}|i} = s_{\overline{25}|i} + s_{\overline{33}|i}(1+i)^{25}$$

The value of $s_{\overline{33}|i}$ is needed in the above equation, so it should be calculated first:

Basic equation

$$s_{\overline{n}|i} = s_{\overline{25}|i} + s_{\overline{n-25}|i}(1+i)^{25}$$

Substituting 33 for n

$$s_{\overline{33}|i} = s_{\overline{25}|i} + s_{\overline{8}|i}(1+i)^{25}$$

This expression for $s_{\overline{33}|i}$ can be substituted for $s_{\overline{33}|i}$ in the earlier equation, giving

$$s_{\overline{58}|i} = s_{\overline{25}|i} + [s_{\overline{25}|i} + s_{\overline{8}|i}(1+i)^{25}](1+i)^{25}$$

Values from the table can then be used to calculate $s_{\overline{58}|i}$.

EXERCISES

(Draw line diagrams for all exercises where appropriate)

1 Calculate the value of $s_{\overline{3}|5\%}$ by accumulating the value year by year of the payments to date, as was done in the first method in Section 5.2. Check the answer with Table I.

2 Calculate the value of $s_{\overline{3}|5\%}$ by accumulating each payment individually to the evaluation date and totaling them, as was done in the second method in Section 5.2. Check the answer with Table I.

3 Calculate the value of $\$625s_{\overline{12}|2\frac{1}{2}\%}$.

4 If a person deposits $250 at the end of each year into a savings account earning 3% interest per year, how much will he have to his credit at the end of 4 years?

5 If a bank is receiving deposits of $100 at the end of every 3 months from one of its depositors, how much will the bank owe the depositor at the end of 5 years if it allows interest at a nominal 8% compounded quarterly?

6 Calculate the value of $s_{\overline{50}|3\%}$.

7 One entry in a table of $s_{\overline{n}|6\%}$ is 6.975; calculate the succeeding and preceding values.

8 A loan of $500 is to be repaid at the end of 5 years with interest at 3%. In order to repay this loan, the borrower deposits $100 at the end of each year for 5 years in a savings account which earns interest at the rate of $2\frac{1}{2}\%$. At the end of 5 years, what additional amount will be needed to pay the obligation? (Hint: The borrower's obligation is found from the equation $S = A(1+i)^n$; the borrower's savings account is found from $s_{\overline{n}|i}$ tables.)

9 At the end of a certain number of years, the accumulated value of deposits of $250 each, made at the end of each year into a savings account paying 3% interest, is $1,617.10. Assuming such deposits continue, what is the accumulated value 1 year later?

10 At the end of a certain number of years, the accumulated value of deposits of $100 each, made at the end of every quarter into a savings account paying a nominal 4% compounded quarterly, is $1,268.25. What was the accumulated value 1 quarter earlier?

5.5 ACCUMULATED VALUE OF AN ANNUITY DUE

In Section 5.1, an *annuity due* was described as a series of payments made or received at the *beginning* of each regular interval of time.

Since payments in an annuity due are made at the *beginning* of each period, this means that the accumulated value is calculated as of one time period after the last payment.

The accumulated value, at the end of the period of the last payment, of a series of payments made at the *beginning* of each period for n periods, at interest rate i per period, is represented by the symbol

$$\ddot{s}_{\overline{n}|i}$$

The two dots over the s indicate that payments are made at the beginning of each period.

For example, consider a series of four payments of $1 each, made at the beginning of each year, accumulating at an interest rate of 3% per year. The line diagram appears as follows:

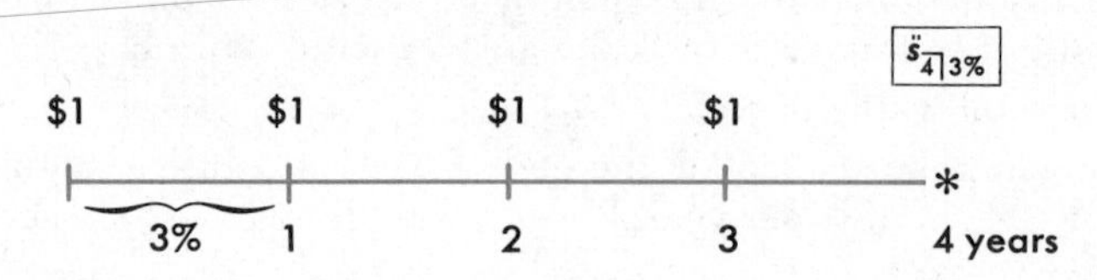

Since the number of payments is 4, and the interest rate is 3%, the accumulated value (at the end of the four years, one year after the time of the last payment) is

$$\ddot{s}_{\overline{4}|3\%}$$

If each payment had been $50, then the accumulated value of the above annuity due would have been $50 multiplied by the above value:

$$\$50\ddot{s}_{\overline{4}|3\%}$$

This value can be calculated by accumulating each deposit of $50 to the evaluation date and then finding the total of these four accumulations. The following line diagram illustrates this procedure:

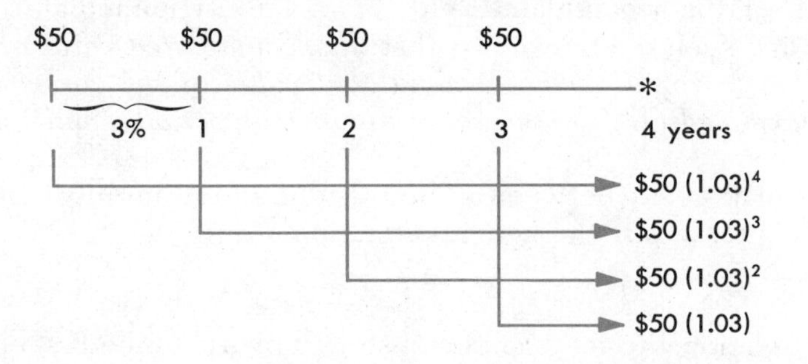

The first $50 deposit, made at the beginning of the first year, accumulates for four years; the second $50 deposit accumulates for three years; the third $50 deposit accumulates for two years; and the last $50 deposit accumulates for one year. Using the equation for accumulating, $S = A(1+i)^n$, separately for each deposit, the total accumulated value is

$$\$50\ddot{s}_{\overline{4}|3\%} = \$50(1.03)^4 + \$50(1.03)^3 + \$50(1.03)^2 + \$50(1.03)$$

The common multiplier, $50, can be factored out, as follows:

$$\$50\ddot{s}_{\overline{4}|3\%} = \$50[1.03^4 + 1.03^3 + 1.03^2 + 1.03]$$

Each expression inside the brackets can be looked up in Table I (3%) and the values substituted:

$$\begin{aligned}\$50\ddot{s}_{\overline{4}|3\%} &= \$50[1.125509 + 1.092727 + 1.060900 + 1.030000]\\ &= \$50(4.309136)\\ &= \$215.46\end{aligned}$$

To use general terms: if the accumulated value at the end of n periods of a series of payments of 1, made at the *beginning* of each period for n periods, at an interest rate of i per period, is desired, the first term of the series will be $(1+i)^n$. The succeeding terms will be $(1+i)$ with exponents diminishing by one each period, as follows:

$$\ddot{s}_{\overline{n}|i} = (1+i)^n + (1+i)^{n-1} + \cdots + (1+i)^2 + (1+i)$$

Assuming that a table of values of $(1+i)^n$ is available, this equation can be used to construct a table of accumulated values of an annuity due ($\ddot{s}_{\overline{n}|i}$). The procedure would be similar to that shown in the first illustration in Section 5.3.

Tables of $\ddot{s}_{\overline{n}|i}$ are not shown in this text and are not frequently found in practice. This is because there are two different relationships by which any desired value of $\ddot{s}_{\overline{n}|i}$ can be readily calculated by using a table of $s_{\overline{n}|i}$ (the accumulated value of an annuity immediate).

The first such relationship is that *the accumulated value of an annuity due is equal to the accumulated value of the corresponding annuity immediate, for the same number of periods, multiplied by* $(1 + i)$.

This relationship between an annuity due and an annuity immediate can be expressed by the general equation:

$$\ddot{s}_{\overline{n}|i} = (1 + i)s_{\overline{n}|i}$$

This relationship may be demonstrated by use of the first equation given above, namely,

$$\ddot{s}_{\overline{n}|i} = (1 + i)^n + (1 + i)^{n-1} + \cdots + (1 + i)^2 + (1 + i)$$

Using as an example a six-payment annuity due, this equation would be

$$\ddot{s}_{\overline{6}|4\%} = 1.04^6 + 1.04^5 + 1.04^4 + 1.04^3 + 1.04^2 + 1.04$$

Factoring out the common multiplier 1.04

$$\ddot{s}_{\overline{6}|4\%} = 1.04[1.04^5 + 1.04^4 + 1.04^3 + 1.04^2 + 1.04 + 1]$$

The expression inside the brackets is exactly the same as the expression for $s_{\overline{6}|4\%}$, using the equation given in Section 5.2. Therefore, substituting $s_{\overline{6}|4\%}$ for the expression inside the brackets, the relationship becomes

$$\ddot{s}_{\overline{6}|4\%} = (1.04)s_{\overline{6}|4\%}$$

To Illustrate—Find the accumulated value at the end of 4 years of an annuity due of \$50 per year at interest rate 3%.

Solution—The line diagram appears as follows:

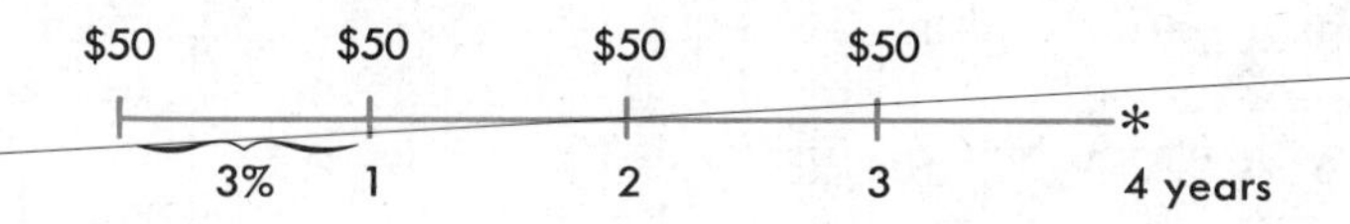

This is the same annuity due which was calculated above. The accumulated value was given as $\$50\ddot{s}_{\overline{4}|3\%}$. Now this value can be calculated more readily by use of the relationship:

$$\ddot{s}_{\overline{n}|i} = (1 + i)s_{\overline{n}|i}$$

as follows:

Basic equation

$$\$50\ddot{s}_{\overline{n}|i} = \$50(1+i)s_{\overline{n}|i}$$

Substituting 4 for n, .03 for i

$$\$50\ddot{s}_{\overline{4}|3\%} = \$50(1.03)s_{\overline{4}|3\%}$$

Substituting the value from Table I for $s_{\overline{4}|3\%}$

$$= \$50(1.03)(4.183627)$$

Multiplying; rounding to 6 decimal places

$$= \$50(4.309136)$$

Multiplying; rounding to nearest cent

$$= \$215.46$$

This answer agrees with that previously calculated.

A second relationship is that *the accumulated value of an annuity due is equal to the accumulated value of the corresponding annuity immediate for one more period, minus the amount of one payment.*

This relationship can be expressed in general terms by the equation:

$$\ddot{s}_{\overline{n}|i} = s_{\overline{n+1}|i} - 1$$

This relationship may be demonstrated by use of the equation:

$$\ddot{s}_{\overline{n}|i} = (1+i)^n + (1+i)^{n-1} + \cdot\cdot\cdot + (1+i)^2 + (1+i)$$

Using as an example a six-payment annuity due, this equation would be

$$\ddot{s}_{\overline{6}|4\%} = 1.04^6 + 1.04^5 + 1.04^4 + 1.04^3 + 1.04^2 + 1.04$$

Adding 1 to both sides

$$\ddot{s}_{\overline{6}|4\%} + 1 = 1.04^6 + 1.04^5 + 1.04^4 + 1.04^3 + 1.04^2 + 1.04 + 1$$

The right-hand side is exactly the expression for $s_{\overline{7}|4\%}$, with the exponent of the first term one less than the number of payments. Therefore, substituting $s_{\overline{7}|4\%}$ for the right-hand side, the above equation becomes

$$\ddot{s}_{\overline{6}|4\%} + 1 = s_{\overline{7}|4\%}$$

Subtracting 1 from both sides

$$\ddot{s}_{\overline{6}|4\%} = s_{\overline{7}|4\%} - 1$$

To Illustrate—Find the accumulated value at the end of 4 years of an annuity due of \$50 at interest rate 3% (the same annuity due as in the last illustration), this time using $\ddot{s}_{\overline{n}|i} = s_{\overline{n+1}|i} - 1$.

Solution—

Basic equation

$$\$50\ddot{s}_{\overline{n}|i} = \$50(s_{\overline{n+1}|i} - 1)$$

Substituting 4 for n, 3% for i

$$\$50\ddot{s}_{\overline{4}|3\%} = \$50(s_{\overline{5}|3\%} - 1)$$

Substituting the value from Table I for $s_{\overline{5}|3\%}$

$$= \$50(5.309136 - 1)$$

Subtracting inside the parentheses

$$= \$50(4.309136)$$

Multiplying; rounding to nearest cent

$$= \$215.46$$

This answer agrees with that calculated above.

Both equations give the same result. In deciding which one to use, the student must be governed by the information given in a particular problem. For example, in order to use the equation $\ddot{s}_{\overline{n}|i} = (1 + i)s_{\overline{n}|i}$, it is necessary to know the interest rate. In order to use the equation $\ddot{s}_{\overline{n}|i} = s_{\overline{n+1}|i} - 1$, the value of $s_{\overline{n+1}|i}$ must be known. Where both items of information are known, it is generally easier to subtract 1 from the known value than to multiply by $(1 + i)$.

To Illustrate Again—Calculate the accumulated value at the end of 10 years of a series of deposits of \$20 each made at the beginning of each half-year. Interest is credited at a nominal 5% compounded semiannually.

Solution—Since deposits are made each half-year for 10 years, there are 20 deposits in all. The rate of interest is $2\frac{1}{2}\%$ (one half of 5%) compounded every half-year. The line diagram appears as follows:

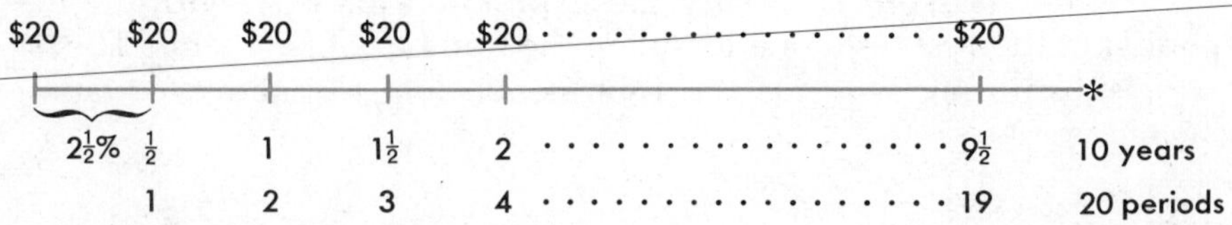

\$20	\$20	\$20	\$20	\$20	\$20	
						*
$2\frac{1}{2}\%$	$\frac{1}{2}$	1	$1\frac{1}{2}$	2	$9\frac{1}{2}$	10 years
	1	2	3	4	19	20 periods

This series of deposits constitutes an annuity due, since deposits are made at the beginning of each period, and the evaluation date is as of one time period after the last payment. Hence, the accumulated value is $\$20\ddot{s}_{\overline{20}|2\frac{1}{2}\%}$.

Basic equation

$$\$20\ddot{s}_{\overline{n}|i} = \$20(s_{\overline{n+1}|i} - 1)$$

Substituting 20 for n, $2\frac{1}{2}\%$ for i

$$\$20\ddot{s}_{\overline{20}|2\frac{1}{2}\%} = \$20(s_{\overline{21}|2\frac{1}{2}\%} - 1)$$

Substituting the value from Table I for $s_{\overline{21}|2\frac{1}{2}\%}$

$$= \$20(27.183274 - 1)$$

Subtracting inside the parentheses

$$= \$20(26.183274)$$

Multiplying; rounding to nearest cent

$$= \$523.67$$

5.6 SINKING FUND PAYMENTS

A regular periodic payment into a fund, made for the purpose of accumulating a certain amount on a certain date, is known as a *sinking fund payment*. The fund which is being accumulated is known as a *sinking fund*.

Up to this point, the amount of the regular periodic or sinking fund payment has been known and the accumulated value of the fund had to be calculated. Now, the converse problem will be considered: the accumulated value of the payments is known, and the amount of each payment will be calculated.

Suppose that sinking fund payments are being made for n years, and are being credited with interest at the rate i per year. If each sinking fund payment is made at the *end* of the year, then these payments constitute an annuity immediate. The equation for the accumulated value at the time of the last payment is

$$\begin{pmatrix}\text{Sinking Fund}\\ \text{Payment}\end{pmatrix} s_{\overline{n}|i} = \text{Accumulated Value}$$

The line diagram is as follows:

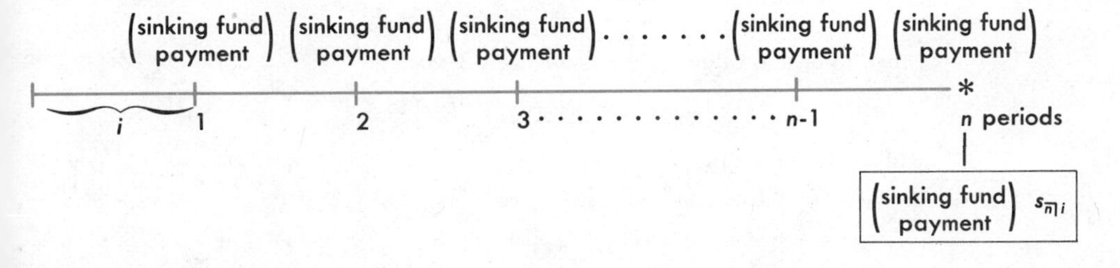

Since it is the sinking fund payment which is wanted, both sides of the equation can be divided by $s_{\overline{n}|i}$, to give an equation for the sinking fund payment:

$$\begin{pmatrix}\text{Sinking Fund}\\ \text{Payment}\end{pmatrix} = \frac{\text{Accumulated Value}}{s_{\overline{n}|i}}$$

This equation states that the known accumulated value is divided by $s_{\overline{n}|i}$ to arrive at the desired sinking fund payment.

This equation can also be written as

$$\begin{pmatrix}\text{Sinking Fund}\\ \text{Payment}\end{pmatrix} = (\text{Accumulated Value})\left(\frac{1}{s_{\overline{n}|i}}\right)$$

Values of this factor $\frac{1}{s_{\overline{n}|i}}$ are tabulated in column (5) of Table I for for various interest rates, and for periods of 1 to 25, inclusive.

To Illustrate—How large a sinking fund payment must be made at the end of each year for 4 years to yield an accumulated value of $600 at the end of 4 years? Assume the interest rate being credited to the fund is 3%.

Solution—The line diagram appears as follows:

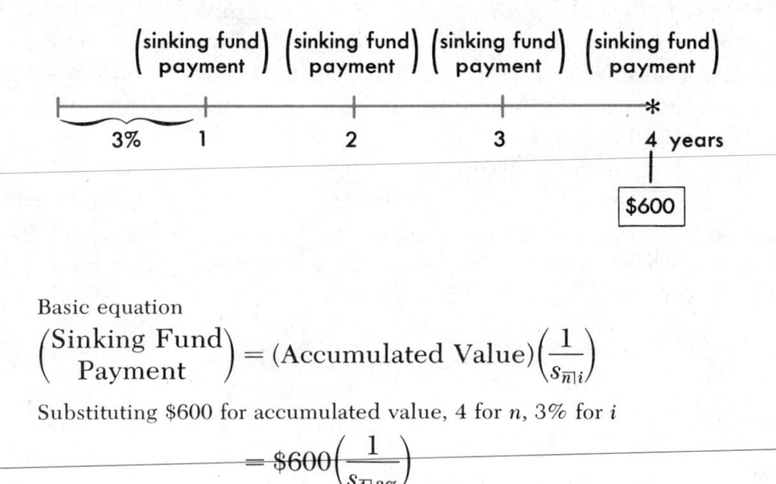

Basic equation

$$\begin{pmatrix}\text{Sinking Fund}\\ \text{Payment}\end{pmatrix} = (\text{Accumulated Value})\left(\frac{1}{s_{\overline{n}|i}}\right)$$

Substituting $600 for accumulated value, 4 for n, 3% for i

$$= \$600\left(\frac{1}{s_{\overline{4}|3\%}}\right)$$

Substituting the value of $\frac{1}{s_{\overline{4}|3\%}}$ from Table I

$$= \$600(.239027)$$

Multiplying; rounding to nearest cent

$$= \$143.42$$

It can be shown that the annual sinking fund payment of \$143.42 in the above illustration will actually accumulate to the desired \$600 in four years. The following schedule shows the progress of the sinking fund year by year:

(1) Year	(2) *Total in Fund Beginning of Year (Col. 6 of Previous Year)*	(3) *Interest Earned during Year (Col. 2 × .03)*	(4) *Deposit End of Year*	(5) *Growth in Fund for One Year (Col. 3 + Col. 4)*	(6) *Total in Fund End of Year (Col. 2 + Col. 5)*
1	\$ 0	\$ 0	\$143.42	\$143.42	\$143.42
2	143.42	4.30	143.42	147.72	291.14
3	291.14	8.73	143.42	152.15	443.29
4	443.29	13.30	143.42	156.72	600.01

The excess of 1 cent is the result of rounding off all figures to the nearest cent.

Sinking fund payments may be made at the *beginning* of each period, instead of at the end. In this case, the payments constitute an annuity due. The equation for the accumulated value of sinking fund payments made at the beginning of each year for n years, at interest rate i per year, is

$$\begin{pmatrix}\text{Sinking Fund}\\ \text{Payment}\end{pmatrix} \ddot{s}_{\overline{n}|i} = \text{Accumulated Value}$$

An expression for the sinking fund payment can be derived as before by dividing both sides of the equation by $\ddot{s}_{\overline{n}|i}$, giving

$$\begin{pmatrix}\text{Sinking Fund}\\ \text{Payment}\end{pmatrix} = \frac{\text{Accumulated Value}}{\ddot{s}_{\overline{n}|i}}$$

This equation can also be written as

$$\begin{pmatrix}\text{Sinking Fund}\\ \text{Payment}\end{pmatrix} = (\text{Accumulated Value})\left(\frac{1}{\ddot{s}_{\overline{n}|i}}\right)$$

However, values of the factor $\frac{1}{\ddot{s}_{\overline{n}|i}}$ are not tabulated in this text and they are seldom found tabulated in practice. The usual procedure is to divide the known accumulated value by $\ddot{s}_{\overline{n}|i}$. However, if the value of

$\ddot{s}_{\overline{n}|i}$ is not tabulated, it must first be calculated by use of one of the two equations:

$$\ddot{s}_{\overline{n}|i} = (1 + i)s_{\overline{n}|i}$$

or

$$\ddot{s}_{\overline{n}|i} = s_{\overline{n+1}|i} - 1$$

To Illustrate—How large a sinking fund payment must be made at the *beginning* of each year for 4 years to yield an accumulated value of $600 at the end of that time? Assume the interest rate being credited to the fund is 3%.

Solution—This is identical to the last illustration, except that the payments now constitute an annuity due. The line diagram appears as follows:

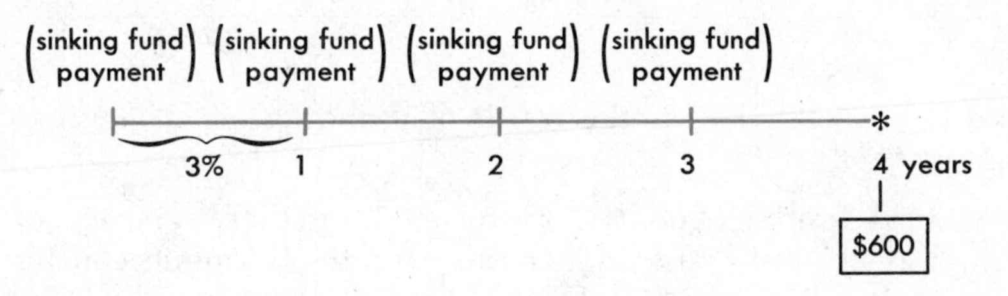

Using the equation for finding sinking fund payments which are made at the beginning of each period:

Basic equation

$$\binom{\text{Sinking Fund}}{\text{Payment}} = \frac{\text{Accumulated Value}}{\ddot{s}_{\overline{n}|i}}$$

Substituting $s_{\overline{n+1}|i} - 1$ for $\ddot{s}_{\overline{n}|i}$, since values of $\ddot{s}_{\overline{n}|i}$ are not tabulated

$$= \frac{\text{Accumulated Value}}{s_{\overline{n+1}|i} - 1}$$

Substituting $600 for accumulated value, 4 for n, 3% for i

$$= \frac{\$600}{s_{\overline{5}|3\%} - 1}$$

Substituting the value of $s_{\overline{5}|3\%}$ from Table I

$$= \frac{\$600}{5.309136 - 1}$$

Subtracting in the denominator

$$= \frac{\$600}{4.309136}$$

Dividing; rounding to nearest cent

$$= \$139.24$$

The following schedule shows, as before, that this annual sinking fund payment of $139.24 will actually accumulate to the desired $600 in four years:

(1) Year	(2) *Fund at Beginning of Year (Col. 6 of Previous Year)*	(3) *Deposit, Beginning of Year*	(4) *Total Fund, Beginning of Year (Col. 2 + Col. 3)*	(5) *Interest Earned during Year (Col. 4 × .03)*	(6) *Total Fund, End of Year (Col. 4 + Col. 5)*
1	$ 0	$139.24	$139.24	$ 4.18	$143.42
2	143.42	139.24	282.66	8.48	291.14
3	291.14	139.24	430.38	12.91	443.29
4	443.29	139.24	582.53	17.48	600.01

The excess of 1 cent is, as before, the result of rounding off all figures to the nearest cent.

In comparing the last two illustrations, it will be observed that the deposit of $139.24, needed at the beginning of each year, is smaller than the corresponding deposit of $143.42, needed at the end of each year. This is logical because the deposit made at the beginning of each year has one more year in which to earn interest. In fact, this is the exact relationship between the two payments:

$$\$139.24(1.03) = \$143.42$$

As another example, if it is known that $100 deposited at the *beginning* of each year will accumulate to a desired amount on a certain date, then it is true that the same amount can be accumulated on the same date by making payments at the *end* of each year of $\$100(1 + i)$.

The reverse relationship should also be noted. If it is known that a given payment deposited at the *end* of each year will accumulate to a desired amount on a certain date, the same amount can be accumulated on the same date by making payments at the *beginning* of each year which are equal to the payment at the end of the year divided by $(1 + i)$.

EXERCISES

(Draw line diagrams for all exercises where appropriate)

1 Calculate the value of $\ddot{s}_{\overline{12}|2\frac{1}{2}\%}$ by using both of the usual equations. Compare the two answers as a check.

2 Calculate the value of $\ddot{s}_{\overline{3}|5\%}$ by accumulating the value year by year of the

payments to date. Check the answer by accumulating each payment individually to the evaluation date and totaling them.

3 Calculate the value of $100 $\ddot{s}_{\overline{10}|2\%}$.

4 If a person deposits $400 at the beginning of each year into a savings account earning 4% interest per year, how much will he have to his credit at the end of 6 years?

5 On the day of his son's birth, a father deposits $75 into a bank paying interest at the rate of a nominal 5% compounded semiannually. If he makes a like deposit at the beginning of each half-year thereafter, what is the total amount credited to his account on his son's 10th birthday? Assume he makes no deposit on that day.

6 If $25 is deposited at the beginning of each year at 3% interest, what is the accumulated value at the end of 5 years, including a deposit then being made for the 6th year?

7 By what amount will the accumulated value of an annuity due of $300 for 5 years at 2½% interest exceed the accumulated value of an annuity immediate of the same amount, duration, and rate of interest?

8 What amount must be deposited at the end of each year for 7 years at 2½% interest to yield an accumulated value of $750 at the end of the 7th year?

9 In order to accumulate a sinking fund having $10,000 at the end of 5 years, at a nominal 8% compounded quarterly, what payment must be made into the fund at the beginning of each quarter?

10 It is known that $24 deposited at the beginning of each month, earning a nominal 6% compounded monthly, will accumulate to $1,682.85 at the end of 5 years. What monthly deposit made at the end of each month will yield this same $1,682.85 in 5 years?

6.

The Present Value of Annuities Certain

6.1 INTRODUCTION

Chapter 5 was devoted to a study of the accumulated value of a series of payments. An example of such a problem was that of finding the total amount on deposit in a savings account at the end of a certain time. This total represents the accumulated value of a series of deposits.

The equally important converse problem is that of finding the present value of a series of payments. A common example of such a problem is that of a debt which is to be repaid by periodic payments. The amount of the debt, plus interest thereon, must be exactly paid by the series of payments. This is the same as saying that the present value of the payments must be equal to the original debt.

A savings account from which periodic withdrawals will be made provides another example involving present value of a series of payments. The original amount in the account, plus interest thereon, must be exactly sufficient to provide for the series of withdrawals. This is the same as saying that the present value of the future withdrawals must equal the amount originally in the account.

6.2 THE PRESENT VALUE OF AN ANNUITY IMMEDIATE

The present value, at the beginning of the first period, of a series of payments of 1 each, made at the end of each period for n periods, at interest rate i per period, is represented by the symbol

$$a_{\overline{n}|i}$$

The symbol is read as: "a angle n at rate i." The number under the "angle" is the number of payments. The number beside the "angle" is the rate of interest.

For example, consider a series of four withdrawals of $1 each, made at the end of each year, from a savings account earning 5% interest per year. The line diagram appears as follows:

$a_{\overline{4}|5\%}$ $1 $1 $1 $1

* 5% 1 2 3 4 years

Since the number of payments is four, and the interest rate is 5%, the present value (at the beginning of the four years) of these payments is

$$a_{\overline{4}|5\%}$$

This symbol is read as: "a angle 4 at 5%."

If each withdrawal had been $20, then the present value of the above annuity would have been $20 multiplied by the above value, that is,

$$\$20a_{\overline{4}|5\%}$$

The line diagram, then, would appear as follows:

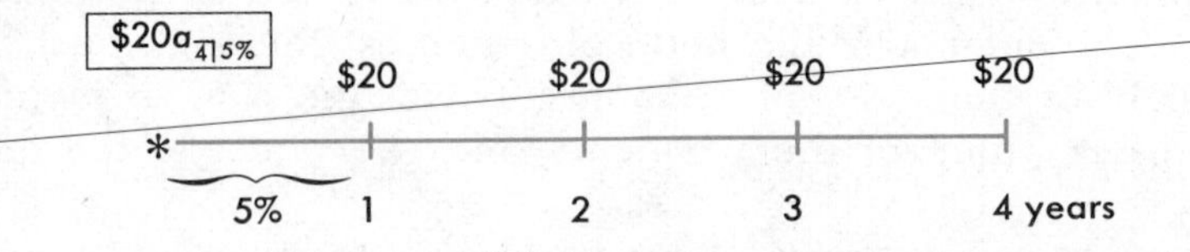

The present value can be calculated by discounting (i.e., finding the present value of) each withdrawal of $20 separately, and then finding the total of these four present values. The following diagram illustrates this procedure:

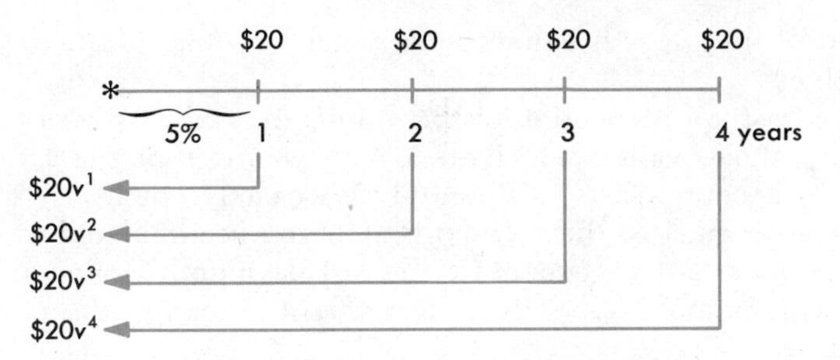

The first \$20 withdrawal, made at the end of the first year, is discounted for one year; the second \$20 withdrawal is discounted for two years; the third \$20 withdrawal is discounted for three years; and the fourth \$20 withdrawal is discounted for four years, all at 5% interest. Using the equation for finding present values, $A = Sv^n$, separately for each withdrawal, the total value is

$$\$20a_{\overline{4}|5\%} = \$20v^1 + \$20v^2 + \$20v^3 + \$20v^4, \text{ all } v\text{'s at } 5\%$$

In the above expression, the common multiplier, \$20, can be factored out:

$$\$20a_{\overline{4}|5\%} = \$20(v^1 + v^2 + v^3 + v^4), \text{ all } v\text{'s at } 5\%$$

A value for each expression inside the parentheses can be found in Table I (5%), column (2), and substituted in the equation

$$\begin{aligned} \$20a_{\overline{4}|5\%} &= \$20(.952381 + .907029 + .863838 + .822702) \\ &= \$20(3.545950) \\ &= \$70.92 \end{aligned}$$

Note that the expression "v^1" in the above example could also have been written simply as "v."

To use general terms: if the present value at the beginning of n periods of a series of payments of 1, made at the end of each period for n periods, is desired, the first term of the series will be v. The succeeding terms will have exponents increasing by one each period. The exponent of the final term will be n. The equation is

$$a_{\overline{n}|i} = v + v^2 + \cdot \cdot \cdot + v^{n-1} + v^n$$

Values of $a_{\overline{n}|i}$ for periods of 1 to 25, inclusive, at various interest rates are given in column (4) of Table I. An inspection of these values shows that $a_{\overline{n}|i}$ is always *less than* the value of n. For example, $a_{\overline{1}|i}$ is less than 1, $a_{\overline{2}|i}$ is less than 2, etc. This occurs because each of the payments is being evaluated at a date earlier than its due date. Hence, the total of the present values is less than the total of the payments themselves.

In contrast, an inspection of the values in a table of accumulated values $s_{\overline{n}|i}$ shows values which are always *greater than* the value of n. (The only exception is $s_{\overline{1}|i}$, which always exactly equals 1.) This occurs because each of the payments is being accumulated to a date later than its due date (except for the last payment). Hence, the total of the accumulated values is greater than the total of the payments themselves.

To Illustrate—Calculate the present value of the annuity of $20 per year for 4 years (the four withdrawals discussed above) by using values of $a_{\overline{n}|i}$ at 5% from Table I.

Solution—

Present Value $= \$20a_{\overline{4}|5\%}$

Substituting the value of $a_{\overline{4}|5\%}$ from Table I

$= \$20(3.545950)$

Multiplying; rounding to nearest cent

$= \$70.92$

The answer is the same as was derived above without the use of a table of values of $a_{\overline{n}|i}$. Using values of $a_{\overline{n}|i}$ from Table I saves a great deal of calculation, especially as the number of periods increases.

It can be demonstrated that the present value in the above illustration will actually provide the desired four withdrawals. The following schedule shows the condition of the savings account year by year:

(1) Year	(2) Amount in Account Beginning of Year	(3) Interest Earned during Year (Col. 2 × .05)	(4) Total in Account End of Year (Col. 2 + Col. 3)	(5) Payment End of Year	(6) Balance in Account End of Year (Col. 4 − Col. 5)
1	$70.92	$3.55	$74.47	$20.00	$54.47
2	54.47	2.72	57.19	20.00	37.19
3	37.19	1.86	39.05	20.00	19.05
4	19.05	.95	20.00	20.00	0

To Illustrate Again—If a debt is to be paid off by payments of $75 at the end of each quarter for 5 years, calculate the amount of the debt. Assume that interest is charged on the debt at a nominal 8% compounded quarterly.

Solution—The debt is equal to the present value of the periodic payments. Since payments are made quarterly (4 times per year), for 5 years, there are 20 payments altogether. The rate of interest is equal to 2% (one fourth of 8%) compounded every quarter. The line diagram appears as follows:

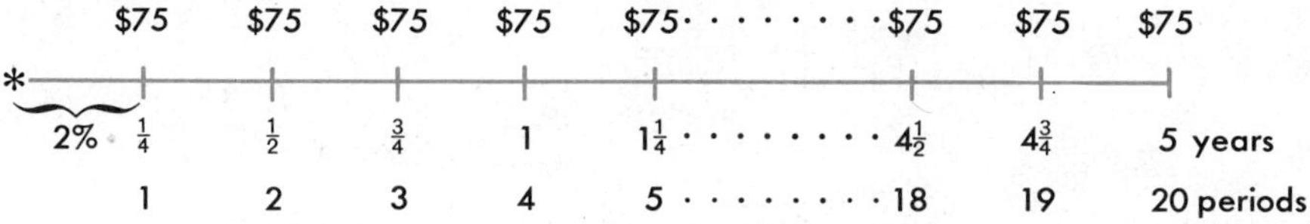

	\$75	\$75	\$75	\$75	\$75 · · · · · · · ·	\$75	\$75	\$75
* 2%	$\frac{1}{4}$	$\frac{1}{2}$	$\frac{3}{4}$	1	$1\frac{1}{4}$ · · · · · · · ·	$4\frac{1}{2}$	$4\frac{3}{4}$	5 years
	1	2	3	4	5 · · · · · · · ·	18	19	20 periods

This series of payments constitutes an annuity of 20 payments, with interest at 2% per period. Hence:

$$\text{Present Value} = \$75a_{\overline{20}|2\%}$$

Substituting the value of $a_{\overline{20}|2\%}$ from Table I

$$= \$75(16.351433)$$

Multiplying; rounding to nearest cent

$$= \$1{,}226.36$$

6.3 CONSTRUCTION OF TABLES OF $a_{\overline{n}|i}$

The equation given above, namely,

$$a_{\overline{n}|i} = v + v^2 + \cdots + v^{n-1} + v^n$$

suggests one method which can be used to construct a table of present values of an annuity ($a_{\overline{n}|i}$). The right-hand side represents the addition of terms, each of which can be found in a table of values of v^n, such as Table I, column (2).

To Illustrate—Construct a table of $a_{\overline{n}|3\%}$, to 6 decimal places, for values of n from $n = 1$ to $n = 4$, inclusive.

Solution—Each value may be derived by use of the above equation, remembering that the exponent of the first term is 1, and the exponents of the succeeding terms increase by 1 each period, with the exponent of the final term being n:

Substituting 1 for n

$$a_{\overline{1}|i} = v^1$$

Substituting 3% for i

$$a_{\overline{1}|3\%} = v \text{ at } 3\%$$

Substituting the value for v at 3% from Table I

$$= .970874$$

Substituting 2 for n

$$a_{\overline{2}|i} = v + v^2$$

Substituting 3% for i

$$a_{\overline{2}|3\%} = v + v^2, \text{ both at } 3\%$$

Substituting values from Table I

$$= .970874 + .942596$$

Adding

$$= 1.913470$$

Substituting 3 for n

$$a_{\overline{3}|i} = v + v^2 + v^3$$

Substituting 3% for i

$$a_{\overline{3}|3\%} = v + v^2 + v^3, \text{ all } v\text{'s at } 3\%$$

Substituting values from Table I

$$= .970874 + .942596 + .915142$$

Adding

$$= 2.828612$$

Substituting 4 for n

$$a_{\overline{4}|i} = v + v^2 + v^3 + v^4$$

Substituting 3% for i

$$a_{\overline{4}|3\%} = v + v^2 + v^3 + v^4, \text{ all } v\text{'s at } 3\%$$

Substituting values from Table I

$$= .970874 + .942596 + .915142 + .888487$$

Adding

$$= 3.717099$$

and the table is

n	$a_{\overline{n}|3\%}$
1	.970874
2	1.913470
3	2.828612
4	3.717099

These values check with the values found in Table I, except for the last two, each of which differ by 1 in sixth decimal place. These slight differences arise because the values of v^n used have been rounded off to 6 decimal places.

In the above calculations, each value of $a_{\overline{n}|i}$ is calculated independently; no calculation makes use of a previously calculated value of $a_{\overline{n}|i}$. However, another method of constructing such tables can be used in which each value of $a_{\overline{n}|i}$ is obtained from the preceding value.

Any value in a table of present values of an annuity ($a_{\overline{n}|i}$) may be obtained by adding v^n to the value for the previous period ($a_{\overline{n-1}|i}$), where the exponent n signifies the period being calculated.

The principle is summarized in the following equation:

$$a_{\overline{n}|i} = a_{\overline{n-1}|i} + v^n$$

Carrying this technique to the next period gives the equation:

$$a_{\overline{n+1}|i} = a_{\overline{n}|i} + v^{n+1}$$

A line diagram of a specific example of a series of five payments of $1 each helps to visualize this relationship between two successive values of $a_{\overline{n}|i}$:

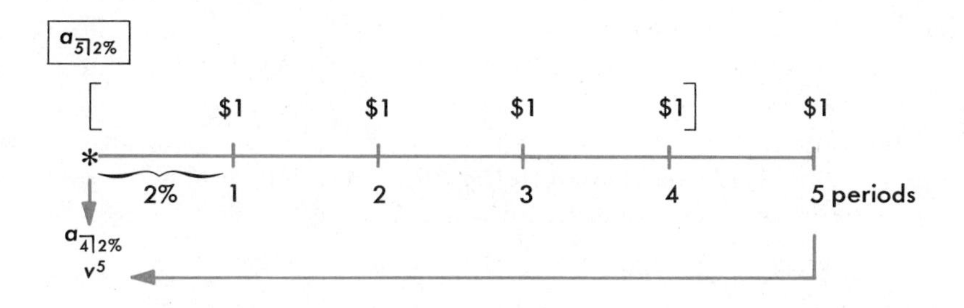

The present value of the first four payments of 1 (the payments enclosed in brackets) is $a_{\overline{4}|2\%}$. The present value of the last payment (i.e., one payment of 1 discounted to the same date upon which the other four payments are evaluated) is v^5. The total of these two expressions is the present value of five payments and is expressed as

$$a_{\overline{5}|2\%} = a_{\overline{4}|2\%} + v^5$$

To Illustrate—Given $a_{\overline{10}|5\%} = 7.721735$, calculate the value of $a_{\overline{11}|5\%}$, assuming that tables of v^n are available.

Solution—Using the above equation:

Basic equation

$$a_{\overline{n+1}|i} = a_{\overline{n}|i} + v^{n+1}$$

Substituting 10 for n, 5% for i

$$a_{\overline{11}|5\%} = a_{\overline{10}|5\%} + v^{11} \text{ at } 5\%$$

Substituting the given value of $a_{\overline{10}|5\%}$, and value of v^{11} at 5% from Table I

$$= 7.721735 + .584679$$

Adding

$$= 8.306414$$

To repeat the caution given in Chapter 5: where each value in a series of calculations depends on the preceding value, great care should be exercised to see that errors do not creep into the calculation, because all succeeding values will be in error after the first error is made. It should also be repeated that rounding errors can creep in, due to failure to use a sufficient number of decimal places before doing the final rounding off.

6.4 OTHER RELATIONSHIPS BETWEEN SUCCESSIVE VALUES OF $a_{\overline{n}|i}$

To construct a table of values of $a_{\overline{n}|i}$ using the methods explained in Section 6.3, it is necessary to have values of v^n available. There is, however, a method for computing successive values of $a_{\overline{n}|i}$ which does not require values of v^n:

To obtain the next higher value, $a_{\overline{n+1}|i}$, add one payment to the known value of $a_{\overline{n}|i}$, and discount the total for one period. This relationship is expressed in equation form as

$$a_{\overline{n+1}|i} = (a_{\overline{n}|i} + 1)v$$

It is important for the student to note that in this equation, the $a_{\overline{n}|i}$ and the 1 are enclosed in parentheses, which indicates they constitute a quantity and are to be treated as a unit when multiplying or dividing. Since multiplying by v is the same as dividing by $(1 + i)$, this equation can also be stated as

$$a_{\overline{n+1}|i} = (a_{\overline{n}|i} + 1) \div (1 + i)$$

or as

$$a_{\overline{n+1}|i} = \frac{(a_{\overline{n}|i} + 1)}{(1 + i)}$$

A line diagram of a specific example showing an annuity of five payments of $1 each helps to visualize this relationship between two consecutive values of $a_{\overline{n}|i}$:

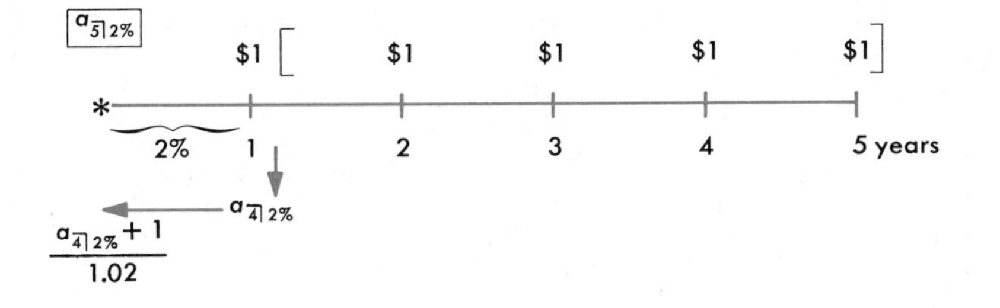

The present value, at the end of the first year, of the last four payments, excluding the one due on that date (the payments enclosed in brackets) is $a_{\overline{4}|2\%}$. The payment of 1 which is due on that date is added to this. The total, discounted for one year, amounts to $(a_{\overline{4}|2\%} + 1) \div (1.02)$. That is,

$$a_{\overline{5}|2\%} = (a_{\overline{4}|2\%} + 1) \div (1.02)$$

or

$$\frac{a_{\overline{4}|2\%} + 1}{1.02}$$

To Illustrate—One entry in a table of $a_{\overline{n}|3\%}$ is 5.417. What is the *succeeding* value?

Solution—The succeeding value, $a_{\overline{n+1}|3\%}$, may be found by applying the above equation:

Basic equation

$$a_{\overline{n+1}|i} = (a_{\overline{n}|i} + 1) \div (1 + i)$$

Substituting .03 for i, and given value for $a_{\overline{n}|3\%}$

$$a_{\overline{n+1}|3\%} = (5.417 + 1) \div (1.03)$$

Expressing the quantity (5.417 + 1) as one number

$$= (6.417) \div (1.03)$$

Dividing; rounding to 3 decimal places

$$= 6.230$$

The same equation may be used to find the value of $a_{\overline{n}|i}$ *preceding* a known value. This is done by using $a_{\overline{n+1}|i}$ as the known value and $a_{\overline{n}|i}$ as the unknown value.

To Illustrate—One entry in a table of $a_{\overline{n}|3\%}$ is 9.954. What is the *preceding* value?

Solution—In the basic equation, the known value, 9.954, will be substituted for $a_{\overline{n+1}|i}$. The $a_{\overline{n}|i}$ in the equation (the value preceding $a_{\overline{n+1}|i}$) will be solved for.

Basic equation

$$a_{\overline{n+1}|i} = (a_{\overline{n}|i} + 1) \div (1 + i)$$

Substituting 9.954 for $a_{\overline{n+1}|i}$, .03 for i

$$9.954 = (a_{\overline{n}|3\%} + 1) \div (1.03)$$

Multiplying both sides by 1.03

$$10.253 = a_{\overline{n}|3\%} + 1$$

Subtracting 1 from both sides

$$9.253 = a_{\overline{n}|3\%}$$

This method of computing successive values of $a_{\overline{n}|i}$ is ideally suited for the actual construction of tables of $a_{\overline{n}|i}$, remembering the caution that great care should be exercised to see that errors do not creep into such calculations.

To Illustrate—Without using values from any table, calculate to 6 decimal places the value of $a_{\overline{n}|2\%}$, for $n = 1$ to $n = 4$, inclusive.

Solution—The values may be derived successively by use of the equation

$$a_{\overline{n+1}|i} = (a_{\overline{n}|i} + 1) \div (1 + i)$$

Note that in calculating $a_{\overline{1}|2\%}$, the value of n in the above equation would be set at zero. Thus, on the right-hand side, the term $a_{\overline{0}|2\%}$ would appear. This term $a_{\overline{0}|2\%}$ would be equal to 0, since it symbolizes an annuity with no payments:

Substituting 0 for n, .02 for i

$$a_{\overline{1}|2\%} = (a_{\overline{0}|2\%} + 1) \div (1.02)$$

Substituting 0 for $a_{\overline{0}|2\%}$

$$= (0 + 1) \div (1.02)$$

Dividing; rounding to 6 decimal places

$$= .980392$$

Substituting 1 for n

$$a_{\overline{2}|2\%} = (a_{\overline{1}|2\%} + 1) \div (1.02)$$

Substituting value of $a_{\overline{1}|2\%}$ from above

$$= (.980392 + 1) \div (1.02)$$

Dividing; rounding to 6 decimal places

$$= 1.941561$$

Substituting 2 for n

$$a_{\overline{3}|2\%} = (a_{\overline{2}|2\%} + 1) \div (1.02)$$

Substituting value of $a_{\overline{2}|2\%}$ from above

$$= (1.941561 + 1) \div (1.02)$$

Dividing; rounding to 6 decimal places

$$= 2.883883$$

Substituting 3 for n

$$a_{\overline{4}|2\%} = (a_{\overline{3}|2\%} + 1) \div (1.02)$$

Substituting value of $a_{\overline{3}|2\%}$ from above

$$= (2.883883 + 1) \div (1.02)$$

Dividing, rounding to 6 decimal places

$$= 3.807728$$

These values check with the values of $a_{\overline{n}|i}$ found in Table I, except for the last value which differs by 1 in the sixth decimal place. The slight difference arises because of the rounding off to 6 decimal places which was used in each stage of the calculations.

It is sometimes necessary to find the value of $a_{\overline{n}|i}$ when the number of payments is greater than the number of periods shown in an available table. Table I, for example, shows such values for any number of periods up to and including 25. The equation for calculating such a value *when n is larger than* 25 is

$$a_{\overline{n}|i} = a_{\overline{25}|i} + a_{\overline{n-25}|i}v^{25}$$

A line diagram of a specific example showing present value of payments of $1 for 30 years helps visualize this relationship:

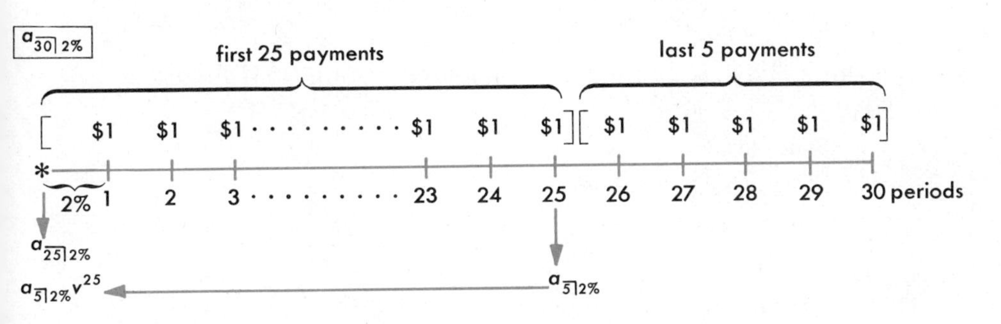

The present value of the *first* 25 payments of 1 is $a_{\overline{25}|2\%}$. The present value of the *last* five payments discounted to the beginning of the last five-year period, is $a_{\overline{5}|2\%}$. This latter value, discounted to the true evaluation date, is

$$a_{\overline{5}|2\%}v^{25}$$

Therefore, the present value of the 30 payments is

$$a_{\overline{30}|2\%} = a_{\overline{25}|2\%} + a_{\overline{5}|2\%}v^{25}$$

To Illustrate—Calculate the value of $a_{\overline{35}|4\%}$, using Table I.

Solution—

Basic equation

$$a_{\overline{n}|i} = a_{\overline{25}|i} + a_{\overline{n-25}|i}v^{25}$$

Substituting 35 for n, 4% for i

$$a_{\overline{35}|4\%} = a_{\overline{25}|4\%} + a_{\overline{10}|4\%}v^{25}$$

Substituting values from Table I

$$= 15.622080 + 8.110896(.375117)$$

Multiplying the last 2 numbers; rounding to 6 decimal places

$$= 15.622080 + 3.042535$$

Adding

$$= 18.664615$$

Values of $a_{\overline{n}|i}$ where n exceeds 50 can be found by repeated use of the equation given above.

For example, to find the value of $a_{\overline{64}|i}$:

Basic equation

$$a_{\overline{n}|i} = a_{\overline{25}|i} + a_{\overline{n-25}|i}v^{25}$$

Substituting 64 for n

$$a_{\overline{64}|i} = a_{\overline{25}|i} + a_{\overline{39}|i}v^{25}$$

The value of $a_{\overline{39}|i}$ is needed in the above equation, so it should be calculated first:

Basic equation

$$a_{\overline{n}|i} = a_{\overline{25}|i} + a_{\overline{n-25}|i}v^{25}$$

Substituting 39 for n

$$a_{\overline{39}|i} = a_{\overline{25}|i} + a_{\overline{14}|i}v^{25}$$

This expression for $a_{\overline{39}|i}$ can be substituted in the equation, as follows:

$$a_{\overline{64}|i} = a_{\overline{25}|i} + (a_{\overline{25}|i} + a_{\overline{14}|i}v^{25})v^{25}$$

Values from the table can then be substituted to calculate $a_{\overline{64}|i}$.

EXERCISES

(Draw line diagrams for all exercises where appropriate)

1 Calculate the value of $a_{\overline{3}|2\frac{1}{2}\%}$ by finding the present value of each payment individually at the evaluation date and totaling them. Check the answer with Table I.

2 Calculate the value of $\$50a_{\overline{14}|4\%}$.

3 The beneficiary of a life insurance policy is to receive $350 at the end of each year for 15 years. What is the present value of these payments, assuming the interest rate used is 3%?

4 How much must a man deposit now in a savings account, which credits interest at a nominal 6% compounded semiannually, in order to be able to withdraw $60 at the end of every half-year for 10 years?

5 Table I gives the value of $a_{\overline{24}|5\%}$ as 13.798642. Calculate the value of $a_{\overline{25}|5\%}$ by using the tables of v^n. Check the answer with Table I.

6 Table I gives the value of $a_{\overline{24}|5\%}$ as 13.798642. Calculate the value of $a_{\overline{25}|5\%}$ without using the tables of v^n. Check the answer with Table I.

7 One entry in a table of $a_{\overline{n}|7\%}$ is 5.389. Calculate the succeeding and preceding values.

8 The present value, at the beginning of the first year, of a certain number of payments of $75 each made at the end of each year, is $833.88. Assuming interest at 4% was used in calculating that value, calculate the present value of a like series having one more payment. (Hint: Use the equation whereby the next higher value of $a_{\overline{n}|i}$ is found by adding 1 payment and discounting this total for 1 period.)

9 What is the value on February 1, 1971, of a series of annual payments of $25 each, the first such payment being due on February 1, 1972, and the last such payment being due on February 1, 1990? Assume 2% interest.

10 A borrower is repaying a loan by means of payments of $100 at the end of every 3 months for 10 years. If interest on the loan is calculated at a nominal 8% compounded quarterly, calculate the amount of the original loan.

6.5 THE PRESENT VALUE OF AN ANNUITY DUE

In the study of the present value of a series of payments, it is just as important to know whether the payments are made at the beginning or at the end of each period as it was in the study of the accumulated value of such a series of payments.

The present value of an *annuity due* is calculated as of the beginning of the first interval of time. Since payments are made at the *beginning* of each period, this means that the present value is calculated at the time of the first payment.

The present value, at the time of the first payment of a series of payments of 1 each, made at the beginning of each period for n periods, at interest rate i per period, is represented by the symbol

$$\ddot{a}_{\overline{n}|i}$$

The two dots over the a indicate that payments are made at the *beginning* of each period, and that the series of payments constitutes an *annuity due.*

For example, consider a series of three payments of $1 each, made at the beginning of each year, at an interest rate of 2% per year. The line diagram appears as follows:

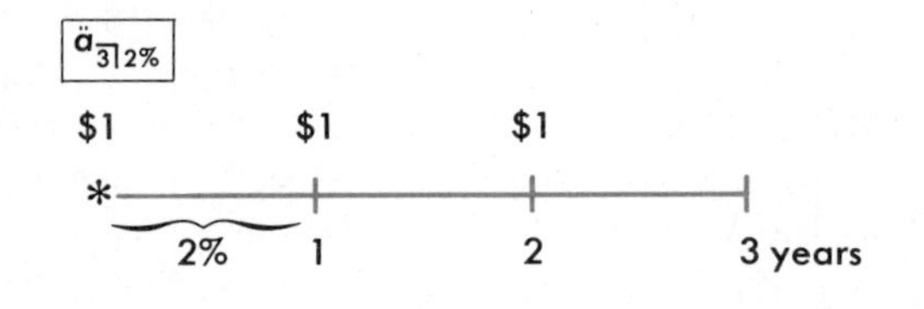

Since the number of payments is three and the interest rate is 2%, the present value (at the beginning of the first year) is

$$\ddot{a}_{\overline{3}|2\%}$$

If each payment had been $25, then the present value of the above annuity due would have been $25 multiplied by the above value, that is,

$$\$25\ddot{a}_{\overline{3}|2\%}$$

This present value can be calculated by finding separately the present value of each payment of $25 as of the evaluation date and then finding the total of these values. The following line diagram illustrates this procedure:

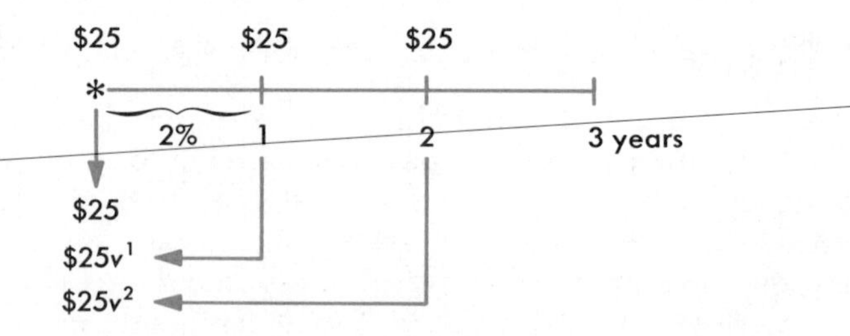

The first $25 payment, made upon the evaluation date, is not discounted at all, so its present value is $25. The second $25 payment, made at the beginning of the second year, is discounted for one year. The third $25 payment is discounted for two years. Using the equation for finding present values, $A = Sv^n$, separately for each payment after the first, the total present value is

$$\$25\ddot{a}_{\overline{3}|2\%} = \$25 + \$25v^1 + \$25v^2, \text{ all } v\text{'s at } 2\%$$

The common multiplier ($25) can be factored out, remembering that the first term, $25, can be expressed as $25(1):

$$\$25\ddot{a}_{\overline{3}|2\%} = \$25(1 + v^1 + v^2), \text{ all } v\text{'s at } 2\%$$

The numerical value for each expression inside the parentheses can be found in Table I (2%), column (2).

$$\begin{aligned}\$25\ddot{a}_{\overline{3}|2\%} &= \$25(1.000000 + .980392 + .961169)\\ &= \$25(2.941561)\\ &= \$73.54\end{aligned}$$

(The expression "v^1" in the equations could have been written as "v.")

To use general terms: if the present value at the beginning of n periods of a series of payments of 1, made at the *beginning* of each period for n periods, at interest rate i per period, is desired, the first term of the series will be 1. The second term will be v^1, and the succeeding terms will be v with the exponent increasing by one each year. The exponent of the final term will be $(n-1)$. The general equation is as follows:

$$\ddot{a}_{\overline{n}|i} = 1 + v + v^2 + \cdots + v^{n-2} + v^{n-1}$$

Assuming that a table of values of v^n is available, this equation can be used to construct a table of present values of an annuity due ($\ddot{a}_{\overline{n}|i}$). The procedure would be similar to that shown in the first illustration in Section 6.3.

Tables of the present value of annuities due ($\ddot{a}_{\overline{n}|i}$) are not shown in this text. They are not frequently found in practice. Any desired value of $\ddot{a}_{\overline{n}|i}$ can readily be calculated from a table of $a_{\overline{n}|i}$ (the present value of an annuity immediate), using one of two relationships.

The first such relationship is that *the present value of an annuity due is equal to the present value of the corresponding annuity immediate, for the same number of periods, multiplied by* $(1 + i)$.

This relationship can be expressed by the following equation:

$$\ddot{a}_{\overline{n}|i} = (1 + i)a_{\overline{n}|i}$$

To Illustrate—Find the present value, at the time of the first payment, of an annuity due of $25 per year for 3 years at interest rate 2%.

Solution—The line diagram is as follows:

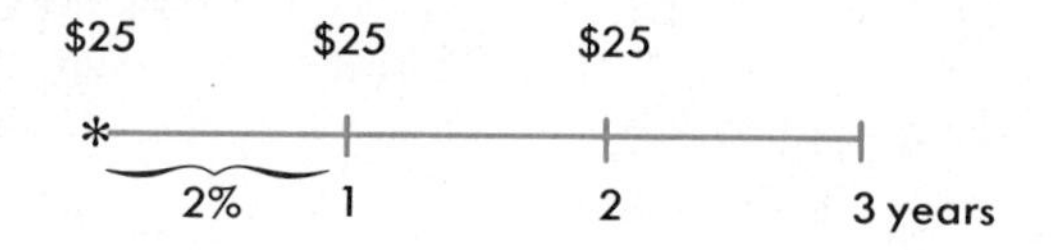

This is the same annuity due as above. The present value can be calculated more readily by use of the equation

$$\ddot{a}_{\overline{n}|i} = (1 + i)a_{\overline{n}|i}$$

as follows:

Basic equation

$$\$25\ddot{a}_{\overline{n}|i} = \$25(1 + i)a_{\overline{n}|i}$$

Substituting 3 for n, .02 for i

$$\$25\ddot{a}_{\overline{3}|2\%} = \$25(1.02)a_{\overline{3}|2\%}$$

Substituting the value from Table I for $a_{\overline{3}|2\%}$

$$= \$25(1.02)(2.883883)$$

Multiplying (1.02)(2.883883); rounding to 6 decimal places

$$= \$25(2.941561)$$

Multiplying; rounding to nearest cent

$$= \$73.54$$

This answer agrees with the present value calculated above by adding the separate present values of each payment.

A second relationship is that *the present value of an annuity due is equal to the present value of the corresponding annuity immediate for one fewer periods, plus the amount of one payment.*

This relationship can be expressed in general terms by the following equation:

$$\ddot{a}_{\overline{n}|i} = a_{\overline{n-1}|i} + 1$$

To Illustrate—Find the present value, at the time of the first payment, of an annuity due of $25 per year for 3 years at interest rate 2%.

Solution—This is the same annuity due as in the last illustration. Now the present value can be calculated by use of the equation

$$\ddot{a}_{\overline{n}|i} = a_{\overline{n-1}|i} + 1$$

as follows:

Basic equation

$$\$25\ddot{a}_{\overline{n}|i} = \$25(a_{\overline{n-1}|i} + 1)$$

Substituting 3 for n, 2% for i

$$\$25\ddot{a}_{\overline{3}|2\%} = \$25(a_{\overline{2}|2\%} + 1)$$

Substituting the value for $a_{\overline{2}|2\%}$ from Table I

$$= \$25(1.941561 + 1)$$

Adding within the parentheses

$$= \$25(2.941561)$$

Multiplying; rounding to nearest cent

$$= \$73.54$$

This answer agrees with the present value calculated above by the other two methods.

If the value of $a_{\overline{n-1}|i}$ is known, this last equation:

$$\ddot{a}_{\overline{n}|i} = a_{\overline{n-1}|i} + 1$$

is easier to use than the first equation:

$$\ddot{a}_{\overline{n}|i} = (1 + i)a_{\overline{n}|i}$$

because adding 1 is easier than multiplying by $(1 + i)$. It should also be noted that it is not necessary to know the interest rate involved in order to use the top equation.

To Illustrate—Calculate the present value, at the beginning of the first year, of a series of payments of \$8.50 each, payments being made at the beginning of each quarter for 5 years. Interest is calculated at a nominal 10% compounded quarterly.

Solution—Since payments are made each quarter for 5 years, there are 20 payments all together. The rate of interest is equal to $2\frac{1}{2}\%$ (one fourth of 10%). The line diagram appears as follows:

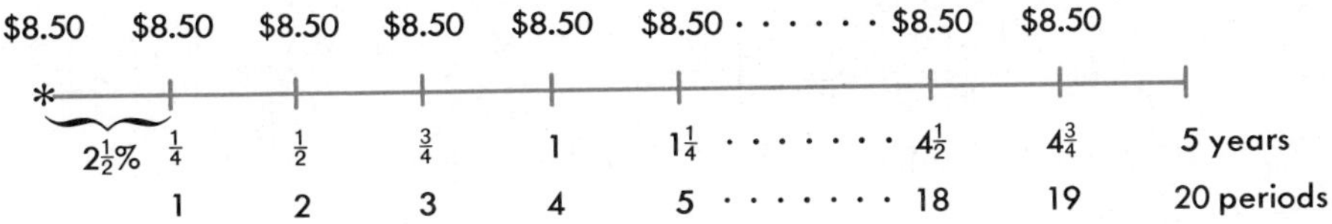

\$8.50	\$8.50	\$8.50	\$8.50	\$8.50	\$8.50 · · · · · ·	\$8.50	\$8.50	
*								
$2\frac{1}{2}\%$	$\frac{1}{4}$	$\frac{1}{2}$	$\frac{3}{4}$	1	$1\frac{1}{4}$ · · · · · · ·	$4\frac{1}{2}$	$4\frac{3}{4}$	5 years
	1	2	3	4	5 · · · · · · ·	18	19	20 periods

This series of payments constitutes an annuity due, since payments are made at the beginning of each period and the evaluation date is at the time of the first payment. Hence, the present value is $\$8.50\ddot{a}_{\overline{20}|2\frac{1}{2}\%}$.

Basic equation

$$\$8.50\ddot{a}_{\overline{n}|i} = \$8.50(a_{\overline{n-1}|i} + 1)$$

Substituting 20 for n, $2\frac{1}{2}\%$ for i

$$\$8.50\ddot{a}_{\overline{20}|2\frac{1}{2}\%} = \$8.50(a_{\overline{19}|2\frac{1}{2}\%} + 1)$$

Substituting the value for $a_{\overline{19}|2\frac{1}{2}\%}$ from Table I

$$= \$8.50(14.978891 + 1)$$

Adding within parentheses

$$= \$8.50(15.978891)$$

Multiplying; rounding to nearest cent

$$= \$135.82$$

6.6 PRESENT VALUE OF A DEFERRED ANNUITY

An annuity which has its first payment postponed for one period or more is known as a *deferred annuity.*

For example, consider an annuity of \$10 per year for five years, deferred three years, at 4%. The line diagram appears as follows:

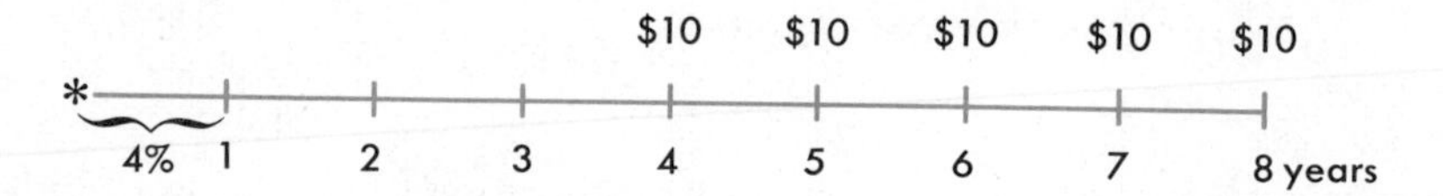

Instead of the first payment being made at the end of the first year, the first payment is made *three years later,* at the end of the fourth year. Each of the five payments falls three years later than it would if the annuity were not deferred.

The present value of the above deferred annuity can be calculated by finding the present value of each payment separately, and then finding the total of these five values. The first \$10 payment will be made four years after the evaluation date, hence its present value is

$$\$10v^4 \text{ at } 4\%$$

Similarly, the second payment will be made five years after the evaluation date; the third payment six years after the evaluation; etc. Hence the total of the five present values is

$$\text{Present Value} = \$10v^4 + \$10v^5 + \$10v^6 + \$10v^7 + \$10v^8, \text{ all } v\text{'s at } 4\%$$

Factoring out the common multiplier

$$= \$10(v^4 + v^5 + v^6 + v^7 + v^8), \text{ all } v\text{'s at } 4\%$$

Substituting values from Table I

$$= \$10(.854804 + .821927 + .790315 + .759918 + .730690)$$

Adding inside the parentheses

$$= \$10(3.957654)$$

Multiplying; rounding to nearest cent

$$= \$39.58$$

A second method is available which generally requires less calculating. Consider the following line diagram. It is similar to the preceding line diagram, but has additional payments at the end of one, two, and three years (enclosed in brackets):

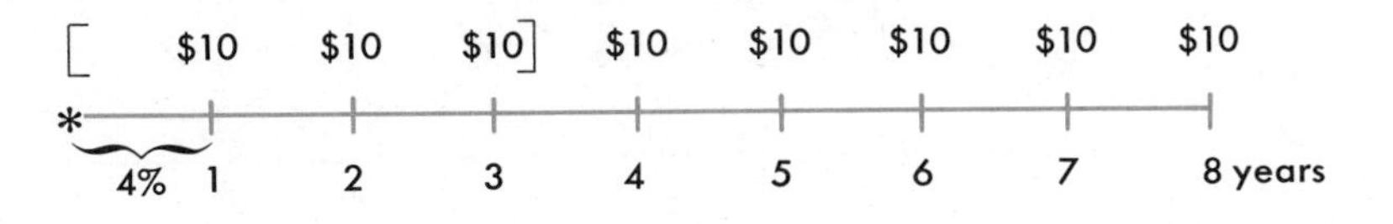

The addition of the three bracketed payments to the original five payments gives a total of eight payments. The entire eight payments constitute an annuity which has a present value of $\$10a_{\overline{8}|4\%}$.

If the present value of a three-year annuity (the three bracketed payments) is subtracted from the present value of the eight-year annuity described above, the answer is the present value of a five-year annuity deferred three years:

$$\text{Present Value} = \$10a_{\overline{8}|4\%} - \$10a_{\overline{3}|4\%}$$

Factoring out the common multiplier

$$= \$10(a_{\overline{8}|4\%} - a_{\overline{3}|4\%})$$

Substituting values from Table I

$$= \$10(6.732745 - 2.775091)$$

Subtracting inside the parentheses

$$= \$10(3.957654)$$

Multiplying; rounding to nearest cent

$$= \$39.58$$

This agrees with the answer calculated by the first method.

A third method is also available. Consider the following line diagram. It is the same as the first line diagram for this deferred annuity, except that the evaluation date is shown as three years later:

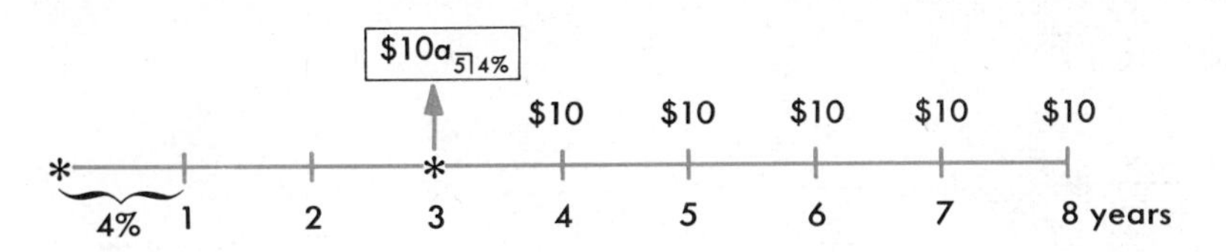

The present value of this annuity, *at a time one year before the first payment*, is

$$\$10a_{\overline{5}|4\%}$$

The true desired evaluation date is actually three years earlier than the evaluation date shown in the above line diagram. Hence, the present value $\$10a_{\overline{5}|4\%}$ can be discounted for those three years of the deferred period.

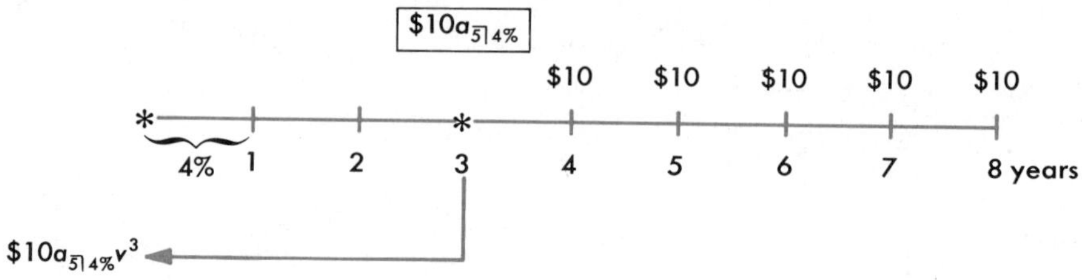

Basic equation for discounting

$A = Sv^n$

Substituting $\$10a_{\overline{5}|4\%}$ for S, 3 for n

$= \$10a_{\overline{5}|4\%}v^3$ at 4%

Substituting values from Table I

$= \$10(4.451822)(.888996)$

Multiplying (4.451822)(.888996); rounding to 6 decimal places

$= \$10(3.957652)$

Multiplying again; rounding to nearest cent

$= \$39.58$

This answer agrees with the answers calculated by the first two methods.

The second method above, in which the present value of an annuity for the deferred period is subtracted from the present value of an annuity for the entire period, usually requires the least work. The third method, however, is generally used in cases where the entire period exceeds the period shown in available tables of $a_{\overline{n}|i}$.

To Illustrate—Calculate the present value at 2% of a 3-year annuity of $35 per year, deferred 5 years.

Solution—The line diagram appears as follows:

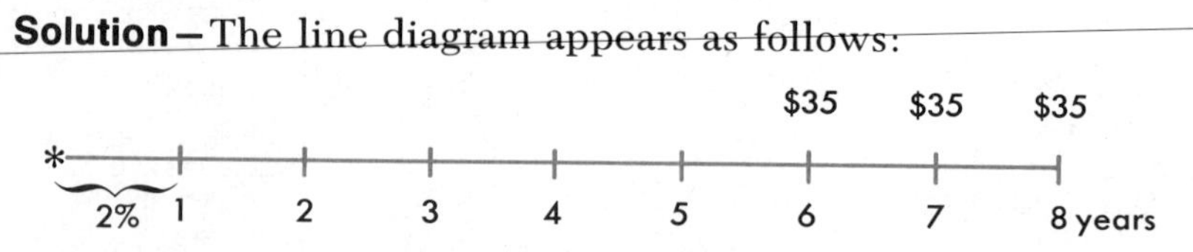

The first payment, instead of being made at the end of the first year, is deferred for 5 years to the end of the sixth year.

Using the first method:

Totaling the present values of individual payments

Present Value $= \$35v^6 + \$35v^7 + \$35v^8$, all v's at 2%

Factoring out the common multiplier

$= \$35(v^6 + v^7 + v^8)$, all v's at 2%

Substituting values from Table I

$= \$35(.887971 + .870560 + .853490)$

Adding inside the parentheses

$= \$35(2.612021)$

Multiplying; rounding to nearest cent

$= \$91.42$

Using the second method:

Subtracting annuity for deferred period from annuity for entire period

Present Value $= \$35a_{\overline{8}|2\%} - \$35a_{\overline{5}|2\%}$

Factoring out the common multiplier

$= \$35(a_{\overline{8}|2\%} - a_{\overline{5}|2\%})$

Substituting values from Table I

$= \$35(7.325481 - 4.713460)$

Subtracting inside the parentheses

$= \$35(2.612021)$

Multiplying; rounding to nearest cent

$= \$91.42$

Using the third method:

Discounting the present value of a 3-year annuity for the 5-year deferred period

Present Value $= \$35a_{\overline{3}|2\%}v^5$ at 2%

Substituting values from Table I

$= \$35(2.883883)(.905731)$

Multiplying (2.883883)(.905731); rounding to 6 decimal places

$= \$35(2.612022)$

Multiplying; rounding to nearest cent

$= \$91.42$

The answers are identical with each of the three methods.

These same three methods can also be used in calculating the present value of a *deferred annuity due.*

EXERCISES

(Draw line diagrams for all exercises where appropriate)

1 Calculate the value of $\ddot{a}_{\overline{4}|5\%}$ by finding the present value of each payment individually at the evaluation date and totaling them.

2 Calculate the value of $\ddot{a}_{\overline{12}|2\frac{1}{2}\%}$ by using both of the usual equations. Compare the two answers as a check.

3 Calculate the value of $\$40\ddot{a}_{\overline{17}|2\%}$.

4 If a person wishes to make a $150 withdrawal at the beginning of each year for 10 years from a savings account which credits 4% interest per year, how much must be in the account just prior to the first withdrawal?

5 If a debt is to be repaid by payments of $25 at the beginning of each quarter for 6 years, what is the amount of the debt? Assume interest is owed at a nominal 8% compounded quarterly.

6 Annual payments of $100 are due from May 1, 1974, to May 1, 1988, inclusive. Calculate the present value of the payments on May 1, 1974, and the accumulated value of the payments on May 1, 1988, assuming interest at 5% per year.

7 Calculate the present value of an annuity of $10 per year for 8 years, deferred 2 years, at 4% interest. Use 2 different methods.

8 Calculate the present value of an annuity *due* of $10 per year for 8 years, deferred 2 years, at 4% interest. Use 2 different methods.

9 Calculate the value on January 1, 1977, of a series of 4 annual payments of $200 each at 3%, if the first payment is made on January 1, 1983.

6.7 AMORTIZATION PAYMENTS

To repay a debt by means of regular periodic payments is known as *amortizing* the debt. The payments themselves are known as *amortization payments.* The present value of all the amortization payments must be equal to the debt.

In the illustrations presented up to this point, the amount of each periodic payment (amortization payment) has been known. The present value had to be calculated. Now the converse problem will be considered. The present value of the payments is known, and the amount of each payment will be calculated. This problem has frequent application in practice.

Suppose that amortization payments are being made for n years, and interest is being charged at the rate of i per year. If each amortization payment is made at the *end* of the year, these payments constitute an *annuity immediate.* The equation for the present value, at the beginning of the first year, is

$$(\text{Amortization Payment})a_{\overline{n}|i} = \text{Present Value}$$

The line diagram is as follows:

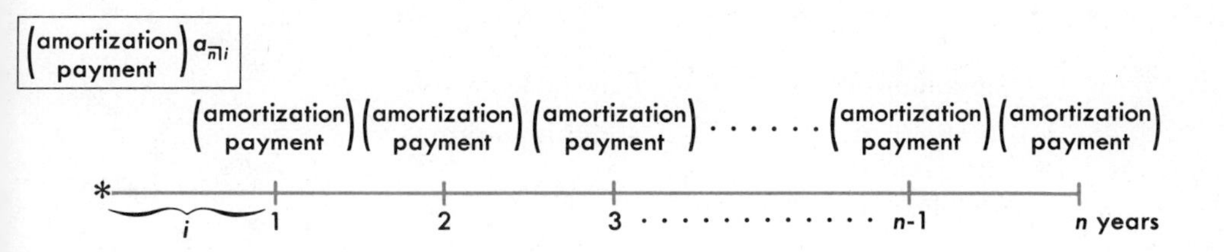

To find the amortization payment, both sides of the equation can be divided by $a_{\overline{n}|i}$, giving

$$(\text{Amortization Payment}) = \frac{\text{Present Value}}{a_{\overline{n}|i}}$$

This equation states that the known present value is divided by $a_{\overline{n}|i}$ to arrive at the desired amortization payment.

The equation can also be written as

$$(\text{Amortization Payment}) = (\text{Present Value}) \left(\frac{1}{a_{\overline{n}|i}}\right)$$

This shows that the known present value could, instead, be multiplied by $\left(\frac{1}{a_{\overline{n}|i}}\right)$ to arrive at the desired amortization payment.

Values of this factor $\left(\frac{1}{a_{\overline{n}|i}}\right)$ are tabulated for periods of 1 to 25, inclusive, in column (6) of Table I at various interest rates.

To Illustrate—How large an amortization payment must be made at the end of each year for 4 years to amortize a debt of $600? Assume 3% interest is charged on the debt.

Solution—The line diagram appears as follows:

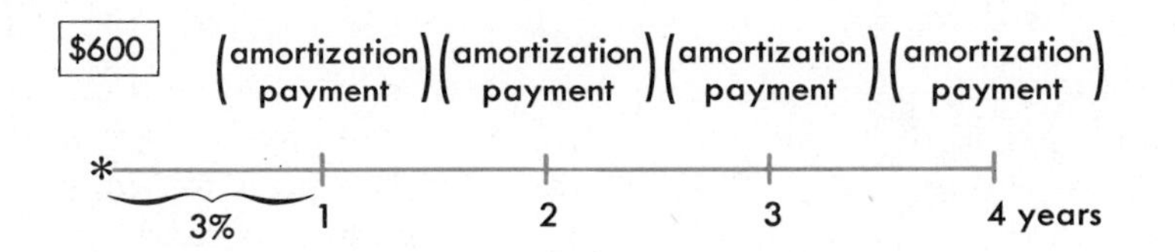

Using the equation for finding amortization payments:

$$(\text{Amortization Payment}) = (\text{Present Value})\left(\frac{1}{a_{\overline{n}|i}}\right)$$

Substituting \$600 for present value, 4 for n, 3% for i

$$= \$600\left(\frac{1}{a_{\overline{4}|3\%}}\right)$$

Substituting the value of $\frac{1}{a_{\overline{4}|3\%}}$ from Table I

$$= \$600(.269027)$$

Multiplying; rounding to nearest cent

$$= \$161.42$$

It can be demonstrated that the annual amortization payment of \$161.42 in the above illustration will exactly repay the \$600 loan plus 3% interest. The following schedule shows the progress of the amortization year by year:

(1) Year	(2) Debt Beginning of Year	(3) Interest for Year (Col. 2 × .03)	(4) Payment Made End of Year	(5) Amount Applied on Debt (Col. 4 − Col. 3)	(6) Debt after Annual Payment (Col. 2 − Col. 5)
1	\$600.00	\$18.00	\$161.42	\$143.42	\$456.58
2	456.58	13.70	161.42	147.72	308.86
3	308.86	9.27	161.42	152.15	156.71
4	156.71	4.70	161.42	156.72	(−.01)

The apparent overpayment of 1 cent is due to rounding off all figures to the nearest cent. In actual practice, a final payment of \$161.41 would extinguish the debt.

The schedule is arranged to show the portion of the yearly payment which is needed to pay the yearly interest, the balance of the payment being applied on the debt. As the amount of the outstanding debt decreases each year, the interest on the debt decreases and a greater portion of the yearly payment is applied to reduce the principal of the debt.

Amortization payments may be made at the *beginning* of each period, instead of at the end. In this case, the payments would constitute an *annuity due*. The equation for the present value, at the time of the first payment, of amortization payments made at the beginning of each year for n years, at interest rate i per year, is

$$(\text{Amortization Payment})\ddot{a}_{\overline{n}|i} = \text{Present Value}$$

The line diagram is as follows:

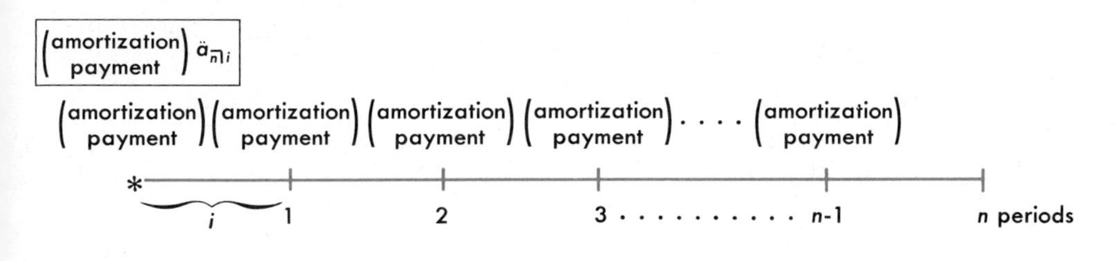

As before, to find the amortization payment, both sides of the equation can be divided by $\ddot{a}_{\overline{n}|i}$, giving

$$(\text{Amortization Payment}) = \frac{\text{Present Value}}{\ddot{a}_{\overline{n}|i}}$$

This equation states that the known present value is divided by $\ddot{a}_{\overline{n}|i}$ to arrive at the desired amortization payment.

The equation can also be written as

$$(\text{Amortization Payment}) = (\text{Present Value})\left(\frac{1}{\ddot{a}_{\overline{n}|i}}\right)$$

Values of the factor $\left(\frac{1}{\ddot{a}_{\overline{n}|i}}\right)$ are not tabulated in this text and they are seldom found tabulated in practice. The usual procedure is to *divide* the known present value by $\ddot{a}_{\overline{n}|i}$. However, if the value of $\ddot{a}_{\overline{n}|i}$ is not tabulated, it must first be calculated by use of one of the two equations:

$$\ddot{a}_{\overline{n}|i} = (1 + i)a_{\overline{n}|i}$$

or

$$\ddot{a}_{\overline{n}|i} = a_{\overline{n-1}|i} + 1$$

To Illustrate—A man has been granted a lump-sum compensation of $600 for an injury. Instead of the lump-sum payment, he requests 4 equal annual payments, the first to be paid now. What amount will he receive each year? Assume an interest rate of 3%.

Solution—The line diagram appears as follows:

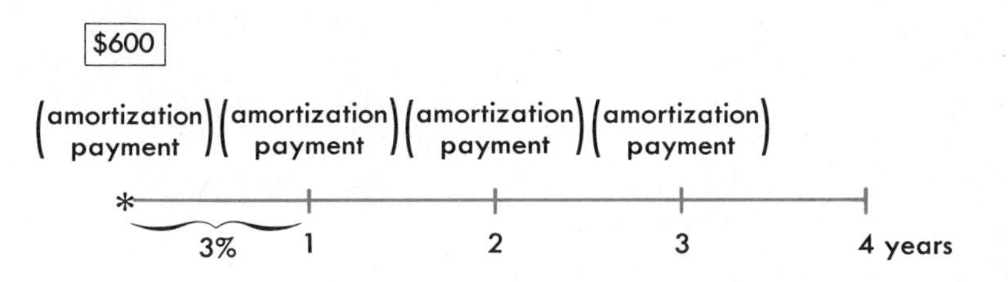

Since the first payment is due on the evaluation date, this series constitutes an *annuity due.* Using the equation for finding amortization payments which are made at the beginning of each period:

$$(\text{Amortization Payment}) = \frac{\text{Present Value}}{\ddot{a}_{\overline{n}|i}}$$

Substituting $a_{\overline{n-1}|i} + 1$ for $\ddot{a}_{\overline{n}|i}$

$$= \frac{\text{Present Value}}{a_{\overline{n-1}|i} + 1}$$

Substituting \$600 for present value, 4 for n, 3% for i

$$= \frac{\$600}{a_{\overline{3}|3\%} + 1}$$

Substituting the value of $a_{\overline{3}|3\%}$ from Table I

$$= \frac{\$600}{2.828611 + 1}$$

Adding in the denominator

$$= \frac{\$600}{3.828611}$$

Dividing; rounding to nearest cent

$$= \$156.71$$

Comparing the last two illustrations, it will be observed that the amortization payment of \$156.71, needed at the *beginning* of each year, is less than the corresponding payment of \$161.42, needed at the *end* of each year. This is true because the debt has one more year to accrue interest if payments are made at the end of each year. In fact, the exact relationship between the two payments is

$$\$156.71(1.03) = \$161.42$$

6.8 PURCHASE PRICE OF A COUPON BOND

Life insurance companies are continually investing large sums of money. One common type of investment is the purchase of coupon bonds. A bond is a certificate of indebtedness, issued by a corporation or governmental body, in which the issuer agrees to reimburse the purchaser for an amount of money known as the *face amount,* which is stated on the bond certificate. Interest is paid periodically on this face amount, at the rate specified (known as "bond rate" or "coupon rate"). On corporate bonds, the interest due is commonly represented in the form of *coupons* which are to be detached from the bond and presented for payment as they fall due. In addition to the periodic interest, the face amount of the bond is paid to the purchaser on the date the bond matures, that is, at the expiration of the term of the bond.

Usually, bonds are paid off at their stated maturity date at par (100% of the face amount). However, some bonds are issued which provide that the issuer may redeem, or call, the bonds at an earlier date at a different price, known as the redemption or call price. A bond might state, for example, that it may be redeemed by the issuer on a certain date at 102, which means at 102% of the face amount, or it might be redeemable on a certain date at 98, which would mean that 98% of the face amount would be paid.

The determination of what the purchase price of a coupon bond must be, in order to yield the purchaser a desired rate of interest, represents a practical application of the methods that have been described for calculating present values. This desired rate of interest is called the "yield rate."

When a bond is purchased for an amount less than its face, it is said to be purchased at a *discount*. In this case, the coupon rate is lower than the yield rate.

When a bond is purchased for an amount greater than its face, it is said to be purchased at a *premium*. In this case, the coupon rate is higher than the yield rate.

The calculation of the purchase price consists of the following steps:

1. Determine the actual dollar amount of each *coupon* which is attached to the bond. This involves multiplying the coupon rate by the face amount of the bond. For example, a $1,000 bond paying 5% annually would have annual coupons of $1,000(.05) = $50 each.
2. Calculate the *present value* (at time of purchase) of these coupons at the yield rate (i.e., the rate desired by the purchaser). Since bond coupons are payable at the *end* of each period, this involves multiplying by the annuity factor, $a_{\overline{n}|i}$, where n is the number of coupons and i is the yield rate. For example, if there are 20 yearly $50 coupons, and the purchaser is realizing $2\frac{1}{2}\%$ on his investment, the present value of the coupons would be $\$50a_{\overline{20}|2\frac{1}{2}\%} = \$779.46$.
3. Determine the actual amount at which the bond will be paid off. If no redemption or call price is stated, the bond is assumed to be payable at its maturity date at par, and the lump sum payment will be equal to the face amount. If the bond is to be redeemed at another price, the face amount of the bond must be multiplied by the stated percentage. For example, a $1,000 bond to be "redeemed at 103" would have a redemption price of 103% of $1,000 = $1,030.
4. Calculate the present value (at time of purchase) of this lump-sum payment, at the yield rate. This involves applying the equation for finding present values, $A = Sv^n$. For example, if a redemption price of $1,030 is to be paid 20 years from time of purchase, and the purchaser is realizing $2\frac{1}{2}\%$ on his investment, the present value of the redemption price would be $\$1{,}030v^{20}$ at $2\frac{1}{2}\% = \$628.58$.

5. Add the present value of the coupons (from Step 2) to the present value of the maturity or redemption price (from Step 4). Using the examples from above concerning a 5% bond redeemable in 20 years at 103, the purchase price would be \$779.46 + \$628.58 = \$1,408.04.

To Illustrate—Find the purchase price of a \$500 bond (a bond with a \$500 face amount) which matures in 5 years, if the bond rate is 3% payable annually, and the bond is bought to yield 4% annually to the purchaser.

Solution—The 5 steps given above may be followed to calculate the purchase price:

1. The actual amount of each coupon is the bond (coupon) rate multiplied by the face amount:

$$\$500(.03) = \$15$$

Hence, the line diagram for the coupons appears as follows:

\$15 \$15 \$15 \$15 \$15
*
1 2 3 4 5
4% yield rate

2. The present value of the coupons for 5 years, at the purchaser's yield rate, is

$$\begin{aligned} \$15a_{\overline{5|}4\%} &= \$15(4.451822) \\ &= \$66.78 \end{aligned}$$

3. No special redemption or call price is given. Therefore, at maturity the bond is to be paid off at par, which means 100% of the face amount. This is \$500. The line diagram for the entire bond, showing all payments which the investor will receive appears as follows:

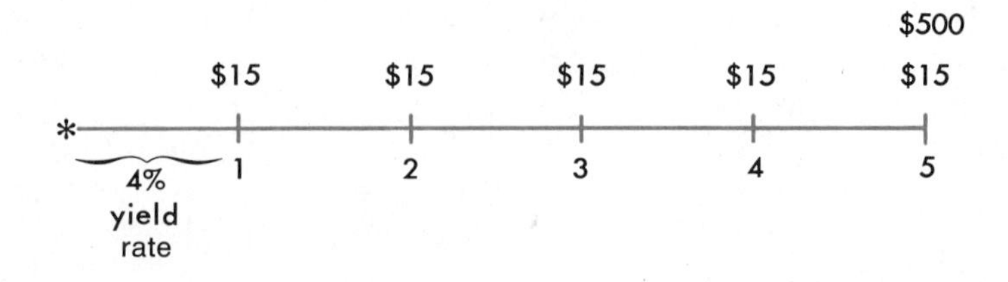

4. The present value of the \$500 maturity price, at the purchaser's yield rate, is

$$\$500v^5 \text{ at } 4\% = \$500(.821927)$$
$$= \$410.96$$

5. The total purchase price is the present value of the coupons plus the present value of the maturity price:

$$\$66.78 + \$410.96 = \$477.74$$

The purchase price (\$477.74) is thus less than the face (\$500), as is generally true when the coupon rate (3%) is lower than the yield rate (4%).

The purchaser in the above illustration paid \$477.74 for the bond. This price is calculated to yield him 4%. He would, therefore, have the right to expect interest at the end of the first year of

$$\$477.74(.04) = \$19.11$$

However, he will collect only \$15 by payment of the coupon. Hence, there is a deficiency in the interest actually received of

$$\$19.11 - \$15 = \$4.11$$

This deficiency will ultimately be made up by the excess of the maturity price over the purchase price. Therefore, at the end of the first year, the purchaser would be justified in assuming that the value of his bond has increased by this \$4.11.

A schedule showing how the bond value changes year by year (Chart 6–1), from \$477.74 at the date of purchase to \$500 at maturity is of considerable utility. If an investor uses this effective interest method, these bond values will be the *book values* for each year:

CHART 6–1

Schedule for \$500 5-Year 3% Bond with Annual Coupons, Bought to Yield 4%

(1) Year	(2) Book Value Beginning of Year	(3) Interest Earned during Year (Col. 2 × .04)	(4) Coupon Payments (3% of Face Value)	(5) Increase in Book Value (Col. 3 − Col. 4)	(6) Book Value End of Year (Col. 2 + Col. 5)
1	\$477.74	\$19.11	\$15.00	\$4.11	\$481.85
2	481.85	19.27	15.00	4.27	486.12
3	486.12	19.44	15.00	4.44	490.56
4	490.56	19.62	15.00	4.62	495.18
5	495.18	19.81	15.00	4.81	499.99

The shortage of 1 cent in the final book value is the result of rounding off calculations to two decimal places. Column (5) represents the amount each year by which the $15 coupon falls short of the amount of interest the investor has the right to expect (at 4%) on his bond's book value at the beginning of that year. This amount is added to the book value each year. At the end of the term, the book value equals the face value. This procedure is known as *accruing the discount.*

To Illustrate Again—Find the purchase price of a $1,000 bond which is redeemable in 4 years at 101, if the bond rate is a nominal 6% compounded semiannually, and the bond is bought to yield the purchaser a nominal 5% compounded semiannually.

Solution—The 5 steps given above may be followed to calculate the purchase price:

1. Since the coupon rate is compounded semiannually, coupons are payable every half-year and the coupon rate is equal to ½ of 6% = 3%. The amount of each coupon is the coupon rate multiplied by the face:

$$\$1{,}000(.03) = \$30$$

Hence, the line diagram for the coupons appears as follows:

*	$30	$30	$30	$30	$30	$30	$30	$30
2½%	½	1	1½	2	2½	3	3½	4 years
yield rate	1	2	3	4	5	6	7	8 periods

2. There are 8 coupons (one every half-year for 4 years). Their present value, at the purchaser's yield rate (½ of 5% = 2½% every half-year), is

$$\$30a_{\overline{8}|2\frac{1}{2}\%} = \$30(7.170137)$$
$$= \$215.10$$

3. The bond is to be redeemed at 101, which means 101% of the face. The redemption price is

$$101\% \text{ of } \$1{,}000 = \$1{,}010$$

Hence, the line diagram for the entire bond appears as follows:

*								$1,010
	$30	$30	$30	$30	$30	$30	$30	$30
2½%	½	1	1½	2	2½	3	3½	4 years
yield rate	1	2	3	4	5	6	7	8 periods

4. The present value of this $1,010 redemption price, at the yield rate, is

$$\$1{,}010v^8 \text{ at } 2\tfrac{1}{2}\% = \$1{,}010(.820746)$$
$$= \$828.95$$

5. The total purchase price is the present value of the coupons plus the present value of the redemption price:

$$\$215.10 + \$828.95 = \$1{,}044.05$$

The purchase price ($1,044.05) is thus greater than the face ($1,000), as is generally true when the coupon rate (3% every half-year) is greater than the yield rate ($2\frac{1}{2}$% every half-year).

Since the investor in the above illustration paid $1,044.05 for the bond, and this price is calculated to yield him $2\frac{1}{2}$% every half-year, he would have the right to expect interest at the end of the first half-year of

$$\$1{,}044.05(.025) = \$26.10$$

However, he will collect $30 by payment of the coupon. Hence, there is an overpayment in the interest actually received of

$$\$30 - \$26.10 = \$3.90$$

This overpayment may be considered a partial restoration of the premium paid at the date of purchase. Therefore, at the end of the first half-year, the purchaser should assume that the value of his bond has decreased by this $3.90.

The accompanying schedule (Chart 6–2) shows the change every

CHART 6–2

Schedule for $1000 4-Year 6% Bond with Semi-Annual Coupons, Bought to Yield 5%

(1) Period in Years	(2) Book Value Beginning of Half-Year Period	(3) Interest Earned during Half-Year Period (Col. 2 × .025)	(4) Coupon Payments End of Half-Year Period	(5) Decrease in Book Value (Col. 4 − Col. 3)	(6) Book Value End of Half-Year Period (Col. 2 − Col. 5)
$\frac{1}{2}$	$1044.05	$26.10	$30.00	$3.90	$1040.15
1	1040.15	26.00	30.00	4.00	1036.15
$1\frac{1}{2}$	1036.15	25.90	30.00	4.10	1032.05
2	1032.05	25.80	30.00	4.20	1027.85
$2\frac{1}{2}$	1027.85	25.70	30.00	4.30	1023.55
3	1023.55	25.59	30.00	4.41	1019.14
$3\frac{1}{2}$	1019.14	25.48	30.00	4.52	1014.62
4	1014.62	25.37	30.00	4.63	1009.99

half-year in the *bond value,* from $1,044.05 at the date of purchase to $1,010 at the date of redemption. If the investor uses this effective-interest method, these bond values will be the book values for each half-year. The shortage of 1 cent in the final book value is the result of rounding off calculations to two decimal places. Column (5) represents the amount each half-year by which the $30 coupon exceeds the amount of interest the investor has the right to expect (at $2\frac{1}{2}\%$ every half-year) on his bond's book value at the beginning of that period. This amount is deducted from the book value each half-year, and at the end of the term the book value equals the redemption price. This procedure is known as *amortizing the premium.*

In some situations, the purchase price of a bond may be known, and the rate of interest yielded to the investor must be calculated. An approximation of the yield rate can be obtained by calculating the present value of the coupons plus the present value of the maturity or redemption price at various interest rates, and finding which interest rate will give a purchase price nearest to the actual price. The exact yield rate can be calculated by some methods of higher mathematics.

EXERCISES

(Draw line diagrams for all exercises where appropriate)

1 The present value of 7 equal annual payments, due at the end of each year, at interest rate 2%, is $164.26. Find the amount of each payment.

2 The present value of 7 equal annual payments, due at the beginning of each year, at interest rate 2%, is $164.26. Find the amount of each payment.

3 A property purchased for $20,000 requires a down payment of $5,000 and the balance in equal payments at the end of each year for 10 years. Assuming an interest rate of 4%, calculate the amount of each annual payment.

4 Instead of a lump-sum payment of $1,200 for a new machine, the purchaser agrees to pay for it in 5 equal yearly payments, the first payment on date of purchase. If the interest rate is 5%, what is the amount of each payment?

5 A deposit of $1,000 is made into a fund with the understanding that it may be withdrawn in 5 equal annual payments, the first payment to be made at the end of 3 years. If the fund allows $2\frac{1}{2}\%$ interest, what will be the amount of each payment?

6 An injured workman who has been granted $15,000 as disability compensation requests that it be paid to him in 10 equal annual installments, the first installment payable immediately. Find the amount of the annual payment, if the rate of interest used is 3%.

7 What price should a purchaser pay for a 3% $1,000 bond (coupons pay-

able annually), maturing in 5 years, if the purchaser wishes to realize $2\frac{1}{2}\%$ per year on his investment?

8 A $5,000 bond with semiannual coupons of $100 is redeemable in 3 years at 102. What price should a purchaser pay for this bond in order to realize a nominal 6% compounded semiannually?

9 Calculate the book value at the end of each half-year for the bond in Exercise 8.

10 How much should a purchaser pay for a $400 bond with $8 coupons payable semiannually if it is to be redeemed in 6 years at 98 to yield the purchaser a nominal 5% compounded semiannually?

6.9 ANNUITIES PAYABLE MORE FREQUENTLY THAN THE INTEREST CONVERSION PERIOD

The annuities discussed up to this point have been payable with the same frequency as the interest compoundings. For example, where payments were quarterly, the interest was compounded quarterly. This period of time for the interest compoundings is known as the *interest conversion period.*

In actual practice, monthly payments are very common, while interest rates are frequently compounded annually or semiannually. Hence, many instances arise of annuities in which there are twelve or six payment periods in one interest conversion period.

PRESENT VALUES AND ACCUMULATED VALUES. In order to calculate the accumulated value or present value of such annuities, it is first necessary to replace all the payments occurring in each interest conversion period with a single equivalent payment due at the end of that period. This single payment equals the accumulated value as of the end of the period of the individual payments during the period. In practice, it is found by multiplying the total of the payments in each interest conversion period by a factor which is represented by the symbol

$$s^{(p)}_{\overline{1}|i}$$

The symbol is read as: "*s* angle 1 upper index *p* at rate *i*." The *p*, indicating the number of payments in one interest conversion period, is enclosed in parentheses to prevent possible confusion with exponents.

For example, in the case of an annuity having payments of $5 per quarter and an interest rate of 2% annually, the single equivalent payment due at the end of each year would be $20 (the total payments in one year) multiplied by the factor $s^{(4)}_{\overline{1}|2\%}$, or $\$20s^{(4)}_{\overline{1}|2\%}$.

Values of $s^{(p)}_{\overline{1}|i}$ are given at the bottom of each page of Table I for values of p equal to 2, 4, 6, 12, and infinity. "Infinity," which is represented by the symbol ∞, would indicate that an infinitely large number of payments are made in each interest conversion period, each such payment being infinitesimally small (since their total is 1). The values of $s^{(p)}_{\overline{1}|i}$ given were calculated by some methods of higher mathematics beyond the scope of this book.

After replacing all the payments within each interest conversion period with a single equivalent payment due at the end of each period, the problem is reduced to that of an ordinary annuity. If the above annuity of \$5 per quarter were payable for 10 years, the *present value* of the 40 quarterly payments would be the present value of the 10 annual payments of $\$20s^{(4)}_{\overline{1}|2\%}$ each:

$$\text{Present Value} = (\$20s^{(4)}_{\overline{1}|2\%})a_{\overline{10}|2\%}$$

Substituting values from Table I

$$= \$20(1.0074686)(8.982585)$$

Multiplying; rounding to nearest cent

$$= \$180.99$$

Similarly, the *accumulated value* of the annuity of 40 payments of \$5 per quarter would be the accumulated value of the 10 equivalent annual payments of $\$20s^{(4)}_{\overline{1}|2\%}$ each.

$$\text{Accumulated Value} = (\$20s^{(4)}_{\overline{1}|2\%})s_{\overline{10}|2\%}$$

Substituting values from Table I

$$= \$20(1.0074686)(10.949721)$$

Multiplying; rounding to nearest cent

$$= \$220.63$$

SINKING FUND AND AMORTIZATION PAYMENTS. If it is desired to find an unknown sinking fund payment or amortization payment, the above procedure can be followed, and the equations can be solved for the unknown value. For example, an unknown monthly payment may be represented by the letter m. If the present value of 12 such payments is \$1,000, and the interest rate is a nominal 6% compounded semiannually, then the total payments in one interest conversion period equals $6m$ (since the interest conversion period is a half-year). The present value equation is

$$\$1,000 = 6m(s^{(6)}_{\overline{1}|3\%})(a_{\overline{2}|3\%})$$

Values can be substituted from the tables and the equation can be solved for the unknown monthly payment, m.

CONTINUOUS PAYMENTS. Assuming interest is compounded yearly, there would be 52 payment periods in one interest conversion period when payments are weekly, 365 payment periods in one interest conversion period when payments are daily, etc. As the payments become more and more frequent (every hour, minute, second, etc.), they approach being made continuously. The concept of *continuous payments* mean that there is an infinitely large number of payments in one interest conversion period. This concept is only theoretical and could not exist in practice. However, there are places where this concept is used by life insurance companies in making calculations.

It will be noted in Table I that all the recorded values of the symbol $s^{(p)}_{\overline{1}|i}$ are just slightly larger than 1. This is because the added interest earned (during the time the individual payments are held) produces an equivalent single payment slightly exceeding the corresponding total of the payments. As one would expect, this excess increases as the frequency of the payment increases.

6.10 RELATIONSHIP BETWEEN PRESENT VALUE AND ACCUMULATED VALUE

Calculating the *present value* of an annuity has the effect of replacing the series of payments with a single amount. This single amount is evaluated as of the beginning of the first period of the series. Similarly, calculating the *accumulated value* of an annuity has the effect of replacing the series of payments with a single amount, evaluated as of the end of the last period of the series.

The following line diagram illustrates these situations for an n-year annuity of 1 per year:

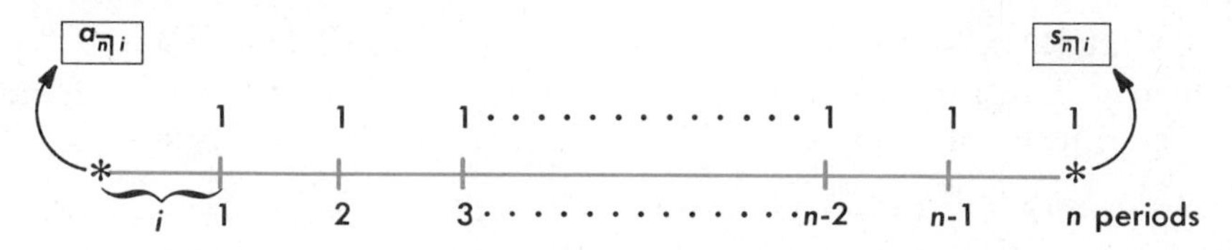

If $a_{\overline{n}|i}$ and $s_{\overline{n}|i}$ represent the present value and accumulated value, respectively, of the same annuity, then $a_{\overline{n}|i}$ is the present value of the single amount, $s_{\overline{n}|i}$. Similarly, $s_{\overline{n}|i}$ is the accumulated value of the single amount, $a_{\overline{n}|i}$.

In the equation for finding the *accumulated value* of a single amount:

$$S = A(1 + i)^n$$

the single amount, S, may be replaced by $s_{\overline{n}|i}$. The single amount evaluated at the beginning, A, may be replaced by $a_{\overline{n}|i}$:

Basic equation for accumulating

$$S = A(1 + i)^n$$

Substituting $s_{\overline{n}|i}$ for S, $a_{\overline{n}|i}$ for A

$$s_{\overline{n}|i} = a_{\overline{n}|i}(1+i)^n$$

An example of this relationship may be seen by checking a value shown in Table I. If $n = 5$ and $i = .04$:

Basic equation

$$s_{\overline{n}|i} = a_{\overline{n}|i}(1+i)^n$$

Substituting 5 for n, .04 for i

$$s_{\overline{5}|4\%} = a_{\overline{5}|4\%}(1.04)^5$$

Substituting values from Table I

$$= (4.451822)(1.216653)$$

Multiplying; rounding to 6 decimal places

$$= 5.416323$$

This answer agrees with the value given in Table I for $s_{\overline{5}|4\%}$.

In the basic equation for finding the *present value* of a single amount

$$A = Sv^n$$

S may be replaced by $s_{\overline{n}|i}$, and A may be replaced by $a_{\overline{n}|i}$.

$$A = Sv^n$$

$$a_{\overline{n}|i} = s_{\overline{n}|i}v^n$$

The relationships shown above are also applicable to annuities due.

To Illustrate—If the accumulated value, at the end of 15 years, of a yearly annuity due is $412.08, calculate the present value of the same annuity, at the time of the first payment. Use $2\frac{1}{2}\%$ interest.

Solution—The above equation implies that the *present* value of an annuity (or annuity due) can be found by multiplying the *accumulated* value by v^n. In this illustration, $412.08 would be multiplied by v^{15} at $2\frac{1}{2}\%$:

Basic equation

$$\text{Present Value} = Sv^n$$

Substituting 412.08 for S, 15 for n

$$= \$412.08(v^{15} \text{ at } 2\tfrac{1}{2}\%)$$

Substituting value of v^{15} at $2\frac{1}{2}\%$ from Table I

$$= \$412.08(.690466)$$

Multiplying; rounding to nearest cent

$$= \$284.53$$

REVIEW EXERCISES

1 What is the accumulated value of $500 at the end of 10 years at $2\frac{1}{2}\%$ interest?

2 What is the present value of $500 due at the end of 10 years at $2\frac{1}{2}\%$ interest?

3 A deposit of $50 is made at the end of each year into a savings account paying 2% interest. What is the value of the account at the end of 8 years?

4 What is the accumulated value of a 14-year annuity of $75, if the interest rate is 4%?

5 What is the present value of a 14-year annuity of $75, if the interest rate is 4%?

6 What is the accumulated value of an 8-year annuity due of $200 at $2\frac{1}{2}\%$?

7 What is the present value of an 8-year annuity due of $200 at $2\frac{1}{2}\%$?

8 If one entry in a 2% table of $s_{\overline{n}|i}$ is 22.840559, calculate the preceding and succeeding entries.

9 One entry in a table of $a_{\overline{n}|3\%}$ is 6.230283. Calculate the preceding and succeeding entries.

10 How much money must be deposited at the beginning of each year for 6 years, at 3%, in order to accumulate $1,000 at the end of that period?

11 Payments of $300 are to be made to a beneficiary at the end of each half-year for 10 years. If the interest rate is a nominal 4% compounded semi-annually, what is the present value of these payments?

12 Find the accumulated value of an annuity due of $75 per month for 2 years, assuming an interest rate of a nominal 24% compounded monthly.

13 What payment, made at the end of each year for 4 years into a fund earning 4%, will accumulate to $1,000 at the end of the fourth year?

14 Construct a schedule showing the accumulation of the annuity in Exercise 13, and thus verify the amount of the payment.

15 What effective interest rate is equivalent to a nominal 12% compounded every 2 months?

16 Calculate the present value of a 5-year annuity of $20 per quarter, deferred 5 years, at a nominal 10% compounded quarterly.

17 A father deposits $4,000 into an account which is to accumulate for 10 years, and the accumulated amount is then to be used to pay his son an equal amount at the beginning of each year for 4 years to cover college expenses. If interest is earned at $2\frac{1}{2}\%$, what amount will his son receive each year?

18 According to the terms of an agreement, a person is to receive $1,000, $750, $500, and $250 at the end of 1, 2, 3, and 4 years, respectively, from the date of the agreement. At the date of the agreement, what is the total present value at 4% of these payments?

19 A life insurance company uses an interest rate of 2% for calculating the present value of premiums paid in advance. On the due date of a gross

annual premium of $84.63, the insured wishes to pay the premium due, and four additional annual premiums in advance. What total amount must he pay?

20 A student borrows $1,000 on September 1 each year for 4 consecutive years. He agrees to repay the loan in 8 equal annual installments, the first payment to be made 2 years after the date of the last $1,000 loan. Assuming an interest rate of 5% for the entire transaction, what will be the amount of each annual payment?

21 Calculate the price one should pay for a $2,000, 5-year bond, with 4% interest payable annually, in order to earn 3% on the purchase price.

22 Find the accumulated value and the present value of an annuity of $5 per month for 2 years if the interest rate is a nominal 6% compounded semiannually.

23 A piece of machinery is purchased by making a down payment of $200 and quarterly payments of $50 thereafter for 3 years. What would be the equivalent cash price for the machinery if the interest rate is a nominal 8% compounded semiannually?

24 The accumulated value of a yearly annuity due is $1,208.15. Calculate the present value of the same annuity due, if the interest rate is 3% and there are 20 payments.

7.

Mortality Tables

7.1 PROBABILITY

In Chapter 1, it was stated that the subjects of *compound interest* and *probability* are the chief foundation stones of the mathematics of life insurance. Chapters 3 through 6 have dealt with compound interest.

In the life insurance business, the subject of *probability* has its application in calculating and using the *probabilities of living and dying*. The concern is with predicting future deaths, based on past experience. In so doing, it is usually expedient to use "mortality tables." This chapter deals with the subject of *probability* and its use in connection with "mortality tables." Succeeding chapters will show how *compound interest* and *probability* are combined in life insurance calculations.

In general, the probability, or likelihood, of some event occurring is expressed mathematically as a fraction or a decimal. This indicates how many times the event may be expected to occur out of a certain number of *opportunities* for it to occur. For example, the probability in one attempt of drawing an ace at random out of a deck of 52 playing cards (four of which are aces) is $\frac{4}{52}$, or simply $\frac{1}{13}$. This means that an ace can be expected to be drawn one time out of every 13 attempts.

If a very large number of such attempts were made, it would actually happen that very nearly $\frac{1}{13}$ of the attempts produce aces. This statement can be made with certainty, because of the statistical concept known as *the law of large numbers*. In this particular example, the probability given (namely $\frac{1}{13}$) could be derived either by

1. Exact mathematical calculation, since it is known that $\frac{1}{13}$ of the cards in the deck are aces; or
2. By observation of a large number of attempts, and calculation of the ratio of aces drawn to total draws.

A second example might be the probability of a person now age 75 dying within the next year. This probability might be .07337. This decimal may be expressed as the fraction $\frac{7,337}{100,000}$. This means that 7,337 persons now age 75 can be expected to die within the next year out of every 100,000 such persons now alive. In this particular example, the probability can be derived only by the observation of a large number of persons age 75. It cannot be calculated exactly by prior knowledge, as was the case with the aces in a deck of cards.

To Illustrate—A doctor has attended 5,000 births in his lifetime and observed that on 57 of these 5,000 occasions the birth was a multiple one (twins, triplets, etc.). Calculate the probability of a birth being a multiple one.

Solution—If the event occurs 57 times out of 5,000 opportunities for it to occur, the probability can be expressed as the fraction

$$\frac{57}{5,000}$$

If 57 is divided by 5,000, the above probability can be expressed as a decimal:

$$.0114$$

Note that $5,000 - 57 = 4,943$ of the observed births were not multiple. Hence, the probability that a birth will not be multiple can be calculated as

$$\frac{4,943}{5,000}$$

When an event is certain to occur, the probability of its occurrence is 1. This is evident because, if the event were to occur upon every opportunity, then the numerator of the fraction would always be the same as the denominator. Any number divided by itself is 1.

It is often necessary to consider probabilities involving the happening of more than one event. One of the two following rules will usually be applicable:

Rule 1. *If only one out of several events can occur, the probability that one such event will occur is the sum of the probabilities of each individual event happening.*

For example, if the "several events" are

1. Drawing an ace when one card is drawn from a deck, or
2. Drawing a king when the above drawing takes place,

it will be seen that only one can occur at any one time. Hence, the probability that one of the events will occur (that the draw will produce either an ace or a king) is the total of the probabilities of each event happening individually:

$$\text{Total Probability} = \begin{pmatrix}\text{Probability of}\\ \text{Drawing an Ace}\end{pmatrix} + \begin{pmatrix}\text{Probability of}\\ \text{Drawing a King}\end{pmatrix}$$

$$= \frac{1}{13} + \frac{1}{13}$$

$$= \frac{2}{13}$$

If the total of two probabilities equals 1, the probabilities are said to be *complementary.* In that instance, it is a certainty that either one or the other event will happen. The most common application of this situation in life insurance is the probabilities of either living or dying. In calculating the probability that a person will either live or die within a certain period, Rule 1 stated above is applicable (because only one of the two events can occur). When the two separate probabilities of living or dying are added, the total equals 1, because it is a certainty that one or the other of the events will occur.

To Illustrate— If the probability that a certain person will die within the next year is given as .0648, calculate the probability that the person will live at least to the end of the year.

Solution— Since only one of the two events can occur, Rule 1 is applicable. Therefore, the probabilities of the individual events are added.

$$\begin{pmatrix}\text{Probability}\\ \text{of Dying}\end{pmatrix} + \begin{pmatrix}\text{Probability}\\ \text{of Living}\end{pmatrix} = \begin{pmatrix}\text{Probability of}\\ \text{Either Living or Dying}\end{pmatrix}$$

In this illustration, the probability of dying is given. Also, it is known that the probability of either living or dying equals 1 because it is a certainty that either one or the other will happen. Hence, the above equation can be solved for the probability of living:

$$\begin{pmatrix}\text{Probability}\\ \text{of Dying}\end{pmatrix} + \begin{pmatrix}\text{Probability}\\ \text{of Living}\end{pmatrix} = \begin{pmatrix}\text{Probability of}\\ \text{Either Living or Dying}\end{pmatrix}$$

Substituting .0648 for probability of dying, 1 for probability of either living or dying

$$.0648 + \begin{pmatrix}\text{Probability}\\ \text{of Living}\end{pmatrix} = 1$$

Subtracting .0648 from each side

$$\begin{pmatrix}\text{Probability}\\ \text{of Living}\end{pmatrix} = .9352$$

Rule 2. *If several events are independent (i.e., the happening of any one has no effect on the happening of the others), the probability that all of the events will happen is the product of the probabilities of the individual events multiplied together.*

For example, if the "several events" are

1. Drawing an ace when one card is drawn from a yellow deck, and
2. Drawing a king when one card is drawn from a blue deck,

the happening of either one has no effect on the happening of the other. The probability that both of the events will occur is the product of the two individual probabilities multiplied together:

$$\begin{pmatrix}\text{Probability of}\\ \text{Drawing Both}\end{pmatrix} = \begin{pmatrix}\text{Probability of}\\ \text{Drawing an Ace}\\ \text{from Yellow Deck}\end{pmatrix}\begin{pmatrix}\text{Probability of}\\ \text{Drawing a King}\\ \text{from Blue Deck}\end{pmatrix}$$

$$= \left(\frac{1}{13}\right)\left(\frac{1}{13}\right)$$

$$= \frac{1}{169}$$

To Illustrate—Calculate the probability that a newly married couple will live to celebrate their 50th wedding anniversary, if the probability that the husband will live 50 years is .277033, and the probability that the wife will live 50 years is .521894.

Solution—Since the fact the one person stays alive has no effect upon another person's probability of living, Rule 2 is applicable.

$$\begin{pmatrix}\text{Probability of}\\ \text{Both Living}\\ \text{50 Years}\end{pmatrix} = \begin{pmatrix}\text{Probability of}\\ \text{Husband Living}\\ \text{50 Years}\end{pmatrix}\begin{pmatrix}\text{Probability of}\\ \text{Wife Living}\\ \text{50 Years}\end{pmatrix}$$

Substituting the given values for the probabilities

$$= (.277033)(.521894)$$

Multiplying; rounding to 6 decimal places

$$= .144582$$

7.2 DERIVING PROBABILITIES

The most important probability in life insurance mathematics is the probability that a particular person will die within one year. It has been found that many characteristics of the particular person affect that probability, but the most important such characteristic is the person's age. Therefore, a different probability exists for each age. Chart 7–1 shows examples of such probabilities.

CHART 7–1

Person's Age	*Probability That the Person Will Die within One Year*
20	.00179
21	.00183
22	.00186
.	.
.	.
.	.
85	.16114

It has been pointed out that probabilities of dying can be derived only by observing a large number of persons. In actual practice, insurance companies usually observe all of the persons they are currently insuring, but over a very limited period of time. By this means, persons of all ages are observed within this period, and probabilities of dying within one year are calculated for each age.

Basically, the probability of dying within one year at each age, called the *rate of mortality,* is equal to the ratio of the number dying at that age to the number who are exposed to the risk of dying at that age. (The number dying at a certain age includes those persons who die within the year starting at that exact age and before their next birthday.) The rate of mortality for a certain age is calculated by dividing the number dying at that age by the number so exposed. For example, if 910 persons are being observed who are all age 54, and 12 of them die during the year of observation, the probability that a person age 54 will die within a year (the rate of mortality at age 54) may be calculated as

$$\frac{12}{910}, \text{ or } .01319 \text{ (rounded off)}$$

To Illustrate—A certain group of insured persons all the same age has been observed over a period of years. The group contains 4,112 persons celebrating their 64th birthday. Calculate the rate of mortality at age 63, if it was observed that 87 out of this same age group had died the previous year.

Solution—Since 87 of the group died the year before, there were actually 4,112 + 87 = 4,199 persons attaining age 63 (one year previous). Hence, the rate of mortality at age 63 may be calculated as

$$\text{Rate of Mortality at Age 63} = \frac{\text{Number Age 63 Dying within the Year}}{\text{Number Exposed at Age 63}}$$

Substituting 87 for number dying, 4,199 for number exposed

$$= \frac{87}{4{,}199}$$

$$= .02072$$

Most of the practical problems faced by an insurance company in deriving these probabilities are associated with the calculation of the number so exposed. For example, while the period of time being observed may be a calender year (from January 1 to December 31), birth dates occur over the entire year. If a particular person attained the age of 45 on July 1 that year, he would be exposed to death as a person age 44 for half the year and as a person age 45 for half the year. Adjustments also have to be made for those persons who enter the group or terminate at some time during the observation period. It would be wrong to exclude them completely from the number exposed, because had they died while under observation, they would certainly have been included in the number dying.

The actual rates of mortality for each age experienced by a single insurance company will show considerable fluctuation from year to year. To produce valid and reliable estimates of the mortality rates and to minimize accidental fluctuations, it is usual to base the rates of mortality on the experience of a number of years, rather than on that of a single year. However, the number of years used is small enough to reflect current experience. In addition, it is common to combine the experience of a number of companies.

Even with a large volume of experience, the actual rates of mortality will not vary from age to age exactly in the manner that would be theoretically expected, because of accidental fluctuations in the experience. These rates of mortality are then adjusted slightly to correct for accidental fluctuations, in order to obtain the theoretically proper relationship between mortality rates for the various ages. The mathematical process of adjusting the experience rates to produce a theoretically consistent mortality table is called *graduation*.

In addition to age, there are other important characteristics which affect the probability of dying. For a life insurance company, the most important are

1. The person's sex;
2. The health status of the person at the time he became insured; and
3. The length of time since he became insured.

Therefore, separate probabilities of dying within one year (age by age) are often derived for each of these characteristics.

In practice, safety margins are usually added to the computed rates of mortality before the rates are used for certain insurance calculations, such as setting premiums. These provide for unpredicted increases in mortality or for temporary adverse mortality fluctuations.

EXERCISES

1 What is the probability of getting a 3 with a throw of 1 ordinary 6-faced dice?

2 If a red dice and a green dice are thrown, what is the probability that the red dice will show a 2 and the green dice will show a 5?

3 If the probability that an expectant woman will bear twins is .0114, triplets is .0017, quadruplets is .0003, and quintuplets is virtually 0, what is the probability that an expectant woman will have a multiple birth?

4 If the probability that a man age 35 will live to age 36 is .9994, and the probability that a man age 36 will die before reaching age 37 is .0008, what is the probability that a man age 35 will live to age 36 and then die before reaching age 37?

5 If the probability that a newborn baby will be a boy is .5039, what is the probability that a newborn baby will be a girl?

6 If a group of 1,000 persons age 25 is observed for 1 year and 2 of them die during that year, compute the rate of mortality at age 25.

7 If a group of 1,000 persons age 25 is observed for 1 year and 2 of them die during that year, compute the probability that a person age 25 will live at least 1 year.

8 If an observed group has 100 persons living 1 year after they all became age 88, and 22 persons were observed to have died out of that age group in the past year, compute the rate of mortality at age 88.

7.3 TYPES OF MORTALITY TABLES

A mortality table, as the name implies, is a tabulation of the probabilities of dying during the year at each age, i.e., the rates of mortality. Generally, it also includes related information which can be derived from these rates.

There are two principal types of mortality tables, depending on the origin of the data used in deriving the rates of mortality:

1. Tables derived from population statistics. These are generally prepared by the National Office of Vital Statistics, based upon data collected during a regular census and registered deaths. An example is the "1960 U.S. Life Tables."
2. Tables derived from data on insured lives. These generally repre-

sent the pooled experience of a number of life insurance companies. These tables are classified into two types:

a) Annuity mortality tables, for use with annuity contracts (benefits payable only if the contract-holder is alive). An example is the "Annuity Table for 1949" which is printed in the Appendix of this text in Table II.

b) Insurance mortality tables, for use with life insurance contracts (benefits payable when the contract-holder dies). An example is the "1958 C.S.O. Table" which is printed in the Appendix of this text in Table III.

Experience has shown that the rates of mortality for persons buying annuity contracts are lower, age by age, than for those buying life insurance contracts. This apparently results from the fact that some persons base their selection of one or the other type of contract upon the knowledge that their own probabilities of dying are better or worse than the average. Therefore, life insurance companies use different mortality tables for life insurance and for annuities.

In both annuity and insurance operations, it is important that the rates of mortality assumed be conservative. In life insurance, this requires that the table used should exhibit higher rates of mortality than will probably be experienced. This is needed so that the company will not be required to pay death benefits sooner than was anticipated. The converse is true in the selection of a conservative table to use for annuity contracts. Here the rates of mortality assumed should be lower than the expected rates, so that the company will not be required to pay annuity benefits for a longer period of time than was assumed in the calculations.

In general, there has been an observed trend over a period of many years toward lower mortality rates. This has been a result of our economic and medical advances. Therefore, conservative insurance mortality tables have tended to become more conservative. On the other hand, conservative annuity mortality tables have tended to become less conservative (because more people are living longer).

It was pointed out in Section 7.2 that separate probabilities of dying are often derived for each sex. Experience has shown that the rates of mortality for females are lower, age by age, than for males. At many ages this difference is very substantial. This accounts for the fact that the Annuity Table for 1949 is actually two separate tables: one for males and one for females. Only the male table is printed in Table II.

The 1958 Commissioners' Standard Ordinary Table, which is used in connection with life insurance, was developed from experience for both male and female lives. However, it is customary (and permitted by law) to assume that the rates of mortality contained in this table apply only to males. When using this table for females, the usual procedure is to subtract three years from the true age of the female. For example, a woman age 25 is considered to be subject to the rate of mortality applicable to a man age 22. This is known as "using a 3-year setback," or a "3-year rating down in age." In Table III, the label "male" is used, as a reminder that it is customary to make an adjustment where a female life is involved. At the very young and very old ages, a 3-year setback is not appropriate, however, and other types of adjustments are customary.

The Annuity Table for 1949 (Table II) and the 1958 C.S.O. Table (Table III) will be used for all calculations in this text. However, the principles discussed are general and can be applied to any mortality table.

7.4 STRUCTURE OF A MORTALITY TABLE

A mortality table is generally shown with four basic columns. The beginning and ending portions of the 1958 C.S.O. Table, which is printed in full in Table III, appear in Chart 7–2. This shows the columns to be described, and will be used later to explain the interrelationships among them.

CHART 7–2

Portions of the 1958 C.S.O. Table

Age x	*Number Living at Age x* l_x	*Number Dying Between Age x and Age (x + 1)* d_x	*Rate of Mortality* q_x
0	10,000,000	70,800	.00708
1	9,929,200	17,475	.00176
2	9,911,725	15,066	.00152
.	.	.	.
.	.	.	.
.	.	.	.
97	37,787	18,456	.48842
98	19,331	12,916	.66815
99	6,415	6,415	1.00000

COLUMNS FOR AGE AND RATE OF MORTALITY. The first column represents the age. Ages are very often shown starting with age zero (a person's first year of life).

Another column contains the rates of mortality. The rate of mortality shown opposite each age represents the assumed probability of dying within one year for a person who is that particular age. It is customary to assume that the probability of dying is a certainty (equals 1) at some very high age, such as 99. This age, then, is the highest age shown in the first column.

The rate of mortality, or the probability of dying, at age x is represented by the symbol

$$q_x$$

In this symbol, the letter x, shown to the right and slightly lower than the q, is a "subscript." Hence, it is a part of the whole symbol, and q_x does not mean "q multiplied by x." The symbol is read "q sub x" or simply "q x." An example would be

$$q_{27}$$

which is read "q sub 27" or "q 27." It means the rate of mortality at age 27, or the probability that a person age 27 will die within a year (before he reaches age 28).

This symbol q_x appears at the top of the rate of mortality column in a mortality table. Since the letter x is used therein as a general representation for age, the letter x appears at the top of the age column.

GRAPHIC PRESENTATION OF q_x. Relative values of q_x can be seen on the graph, Figure 7–1. The two curved lines represent values of q_x (for males) from the Annuity Table for 1949 and the 1958 C.S.O. Table. Ages from age 0 to age 70 are shown along the bottom of the graph. For each age, the distance up to one of the lines indicates the value of q_x at that age, as set forth in the particular mortality table. Space limitations make it impossible to show the graph to the highest age in the tables. The value of q_x is 1.000 at age 99 in the 1958 C.S.O. Table and at age 109 in the Annuity Table for 1949. This gives an indication of how rapidly the death rates increase after age 70. This graph would have to be 20 times as tall as it is to show values for all ages up through the highest age.

It is interesting to note that the rates of mortality actually decrease age by age from age 0 to approximately age 10. From this point, the rates increase very slowly until about age 40. It should also be noted that the graph clearly portrays that rates of mortality for those buying annuity contracts are lower, age by age, than for those buying life insurance contracts.

COLUMNS FOR NUMBER LIVING AND DYING. The other two basic columns of a mortality table are set up to show what happens each year to a large group of people all the same age, starting when they are all a certain low age, such as age zero. An arbitrary number of people, such as 10,000,000, are assumed to be alive at this time. During the first year a certain number will die, leaving the remaining persons to begin the second year. Then a certain number of these will die before reaching the end of the second year, etc.

FIGURE 7-1

Values of q_x

(black line is Annuity Table for 1949—colored line is 1958 C.S.O. Table)

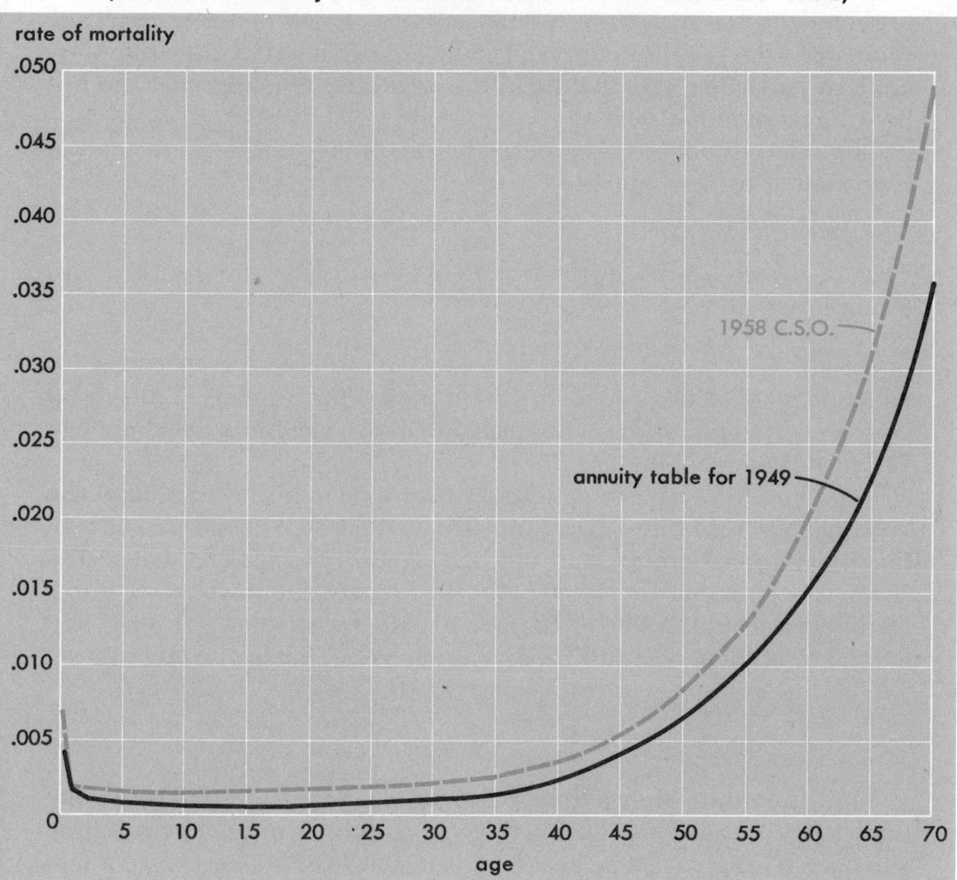

One column shows how many persons (out of the original group) are assumed to still be alive at each age. The number shown opposite each age represents the assumed number out of the original group who are still living at that particular age.

The number of this group who are still alive at age x is represented by the symbol

$$l_x$$

That is, l with a subscript x. It is read "l sub x" or simply "l x." An example would be

$$l_{20}$$

which is read "l sub 20" or "l 20." It means the assumed number out of the original group who are still living at age 20.

The other column shows how many persons out of this group are expected to die at each age. The number shown opposite each age represents the number of persons who are expected to die while they are that particular age, that is, in the year after reaching that age but before reaching the next age.

The number out of this group who die in the year they are age x is represented by the symbol

$$d_x$$

That is, d with a subscript x. It is read "d sub x" or simply "d x." An example would be

$$d_{74}$$

which is read "d sub 74" or "d 74." It means the number of the group who are expected to die while age 74 (in the year after reaching age 74 but before reaching age 75).

Referring to the basic columns shown above in the portion of the 1958 C.S.O. Table, the l_x column shows that 10,000,000 persons (in this hypothetical group) start out life together at age zero. This is the same as saying that $l_0 = 10{,}000{,}000$. The same column shows that it is assumed that 9,929,200 of them will still be alive at age one, and 9,911,725 of them will still be alive at age two. That is, the table shows

$$l_1 = 9{,}929{,}200$$

$$l_2 = 9{,}911{,}725$$

The d_x column shows that 70,800 of the persons in this group die while they are age zero (during the year after birth but before reaching age one). This is the same as saying that $d_0 = 70{,}800$. The same column shows that it is expected that 17,475 of them will die during the year they are age one, and 15,066 will die during the year they are age two. That is, the table shows

$$d_1 = 17{,}475$$

$$d_2 = 15{,}066$$

The probability of dying while age x, that is, during the year between age x and age $(x + 1)$, is sometimes called the probability of dying at age x. Likewise, the number so dying is sometimes called the number dying at age x.

EQUATIONS FOR INTERRELATIONSHIP. In general terms, it may be said that if the number dying in a given year (d_x) is subtracted from the number living at the beginning of that year (l_x), the result will represent the number still alive at the next higher age (l_{x+1}). In equation form, this is written:

$$l_{x+1} = l_x - d_x$$

To Illustrate—Calculate the value of l_{98} for the 1958 C.S.O. Table using the above equation.

Solution—

Basic equation

$$l_{x+1} = l_x - d_x$$

Substituting 97 for x (the age)

$$l_{98} = l_{97} - d_{97}$$

Substituting the values for l_{97} and d_{97} from the table

$$= 37{,}787 - 18{,}456$$

$$= 19{,}331$$

This value of l_{98} agrees with that given in the table.

In general terms, it may be said that if the number living at a certain age (l_x) is multiplied by the rate of mortality at that age (q_x), the result will represent the number expected to die during the year they are that age (d_x). In equation form, this is written

$$d_x = l_x q_x$$

To Illustrate—Calculate the value of d_{97} for the 1958 C.S.O. Table using the above equation.

Solution—

Basic equation

$$d_x = l_x q_x$$

Substituting 97 for x (the age)

$$d_{97} = l_{97} q_{97}$$

Substituting values for l_{97} and q_{97} from the table

$$= (37{,}787)(.48842)$$

Multiplying; rounding to nearest whole number

$$= 18{,}456$$

This value of d_{97} agrees with that given in the table.

In general terms, it may be said that if the number expected to die during the year in which they are a certain age (d_x) is divided by the number living at that age (l_x), the result will represent the rate of mortality at that age (q_x).

The equation, $d_x = l_x q_x$, may be solved for q_x by dividing both sides by l_x, giving this relationship in equation form:

$$\frac{d_x}{l_x} = q_x$$

To Illustrate—Calculate the value of q_2 for the 1958 C.S.O. Table using the above equation.

Solution—

Basic equation

$$q_x = \frac{d_x}{l_x}$$

Substituting 2 for x (the age)

$$q_2 = \frac{d_2}{l_2}$$

Substituting values for d_2 and l_2 from the table

$$= \frac{15{,}066}{9{,}911{,}725}$$

$$= .00152$$

This value of q_2 agrees with that given in the table.

It will be observed that the value for q_{99} shown in the 1958 C.S.O. Table is *certainty*, i.e., 1. This is done arbitrarily for the purpose of conveniently ending the table, and not because it was observed that everybody who reaches age 99 dies before reaching 100.

7.5 CONSTRUCTION OF A MORTALITY TABLE

After the rate of mortality, q_x, is established for each age, the other columns can be constructed. The youngest age in the table should be the youngest age for which it is expected the table will be used. In most cases, tables begin with age zero. The entire mortality table can be constructed by the following steps:

1. Assume an initial value for l_x (at the youngest age in the table). This is usually some large round number, such as 1,000,000 or 10,000,000.
2. Calculate the number of deaths between this age, x, and the next age, $(x + 1)$. This is done using the equation

   $$d_x = l_x q_x$$

3. Calculate the number living at the second age $(x + 1)$, using the equation

$$l_{x+1} = l_x - d_x$$

4. Repeat steps 2 and 3, successively, for each higher age.

By way of example, it can be seen how the columns of the 1958 C.S.O. Table were constructed by this process after the rates of mortality were known. The portions of the table appearing in Section 7.4 indicate that an initial value of l_x was chosen to be 10,000,000 at age zero. In other words,

$$l_0 = 10{,}000{,}000$$

The number of deaths between age zero and age one was calculated by applying the basic equation:

$$d_x = l_x q_x$$

Substituting 0 for x

$$d_0 = l_0 q_0$$

Substituting 10,000,000 for l_0, and the value for q_0 from the table

$$= (10{,}000{,}000)(.00708)$$

Multiplying; rounding to nearest whole number

$$= 70{,}800$$

Next, the number living at age one was calculated as follows:

Basic equation

$$l_{x+1} = l_x - d_x$$

Substituting 0 for x

$$l_1 = l_0 - d_0$$

Substituting 10,000,000 for l_0, and the value of d_0 calculated above

$$= 10{,}000{,}000 - 70{,}800$$

$$= 9{,}929{,}200$$

Repeating this process, the number of deaths at age one (between age one and age two) was calculated.

Basic equation

$$d_x = l_x q_x$$

Substituting 1 for x

$$d_1 = l_1 q_1$$

Substituting the value of l_1 calculated above, and the value for q_1

$$= (9{,}929{,}200)(.00176)$$

$$= 17{,}475$$

The number living at age two was then calculated as follows:

Basic equation

$$l_{x+1} = l_x - d_x$$

Substituting 1 for x

$$l_2 = l_1 - d_1$$

Substituting the values for l_1 and d_1 calculated above

$$= 9{,}929{,}200 - 17{,}475$$

$$= 9{,}911{,}725$$

All these values agree with those in the portion of the table shown earlier in this chapter. This process was repeated successively until the entire 1958 C.S.O. Table was constructed.

In constructing the Annuity Table for 1949, age 10 was chosen as the lowest age. As shown in Table II, 10,000,000 was chosen as the value of l_{10}. However, this table was later extended to begin at age 0. The values of l_x and d_x for ages under age 10 were then calculated in such a way as to produce this same value for l_{10}, namely 10,000,000. As a result, the initial figure, l_0, is 10,104,755.

EXERCISES

1 According to the Annuity Table for 1949 (see Table II in the Appendix of this book), what is the probability that a man age 60 will die before reaching age 61?

2 According to the 1958 C.S.O. Table (see Table III in the Appendix of this book), what is the rate of mortality at age 60? Express the answer as a fraction.

3 If the rate of mortality at a certain age is .00742, and the number of persons living at that age is 107,412, how many of them may be expected to die within a year?

4 Using Table III, calculate the probability that a man age 79 will live to age 80. (Hint: It is a certainty that he will either live or die that year.)

5 Using a "3-year setback" for females, what is the female rate of mortality at age 29, according to Table III? (Hint: Consider that a female is subject to the rate of mortality for a male 3 years younger.)

6 If a mortality table shows $l_{18} = 994{,}831$ and $d_{18} = 1{,}094$, calculate the value of l_{19}.

7 If a mortality table shows $l_{42} = 9{,}408{,}108$ and $l_{43} = 9{,}374{,}239$, calculate the value of d_{42}.

8 If a mortality table shows $l_{36} = 951{,}003$ and $q_{36} = .0022$, calculate the value of d_{36}.

9 Using the figures in Exercise 8, calculate the value of l_{37}.

10 If a mortality table shows $l_{75} = 4{,}940{,}810$ and $d_{75} = 361{,}498$, calculate the value for q_{75}.

11 Calculate the missing items in the following portion of a mortality table:

Age x	l_x	d_x	q_x
20	92,637	. . .	. . .
21	91,914	. . .	. . .
22	91,192	. . .	. . .
23	90,471		

7.6 PROBABILITIES OF LIVING AND DYING

PROBABILITIES OF LIVING OR DYING IN ONE YEAR. The probability that a person age x will live to reach $(x + 1)$ is represented by the symbol

$$p_x$$

That is, p with a subscript x. It is read "p sub x" or simply "p x." An example would be

$$p_{43}$$

which is read "p sub 43" or "p 43." It means the probability that a person age 43 will live to reach age 44, that is, will be alive for at least one whole year.

In general terms, it may be said that if the number living at age $(x + 1)$ is divided by the number living at age x, the result will be the probability that a person age x will live to reach age $(x + 1)$. In equation form, this is written

$$p_x = \frac{l_{x+1}}{l_x}$$

To Illustrate—Using the Annuity Table for 1949 (Table II), and the above equation, calculate the value of p_{95}.

Solution –

Basic equation

$$p_x = \frac{l_{x+1}}{l_x}$$

Substituting 95 for x

$$p_{95} = \frac{l_{96}}{l_{95}}$$

Substituting the values for l_{96} and l_{95} from Table II

$$= \frac{150{,}429}{220{,}194}$$

$$= .683166$$

The result shows that, according to this particular table, the probability that a person age 95 will live for at least one whole year is .683166.

It is a certainty that a person will either live for one year or die within that year. Since only one of those two events can occur, Rule 1 in Section 7.1 is applicable: the probability that one of the events will happen is the *total* of the probabilities of each individual event happening.

$$\begin{pmatrix}\text{Probability of}\\ \text{Living 1 Year}\end{pmatrix} + \begin{pmatrix}\text{Probability of}\\ \text{Dying within}\\ \text{1 Year}\end{pmatrix} = \begin{pmatrix}\text{Probability of}\\ \text{Either Living or}\\ \text{Dying That Year}\end{pmatrix}$$

Symbols can be substituted for each of the above expressions, as follows:

Substitute p_x for $\begin{pmatrix}\text{Probability of}\\ \text{Living 1 Year}\end{pmatrix}$

Substitute q_x for $\begin{pmatrix}\text{Probability of}\\ \text{Dying within 1 Year}\end{pmatrix}$

Substitute 1 (certainty) for $\begin{pmatrix}\text{Probability of Either}\\ \text{Living or Dying That Year}\end{pmatrix}$

Consequently, the equation is

$$p_x + q_x = 1$$

As an example, according to the 1958 C.S.O. Table, $q_{21} = .00183$. Expressed as a fraction, this is $\frac{183}{100{,}000}$. This means that, out of 100,000 persons all age 21, there will be 183 deaths during the year. If 183 persons out of 100,000 can be expected to die between the ages of 21 and

22, then 100,000 − 183 = 99,817 will survive to age 22. Therefore, the probability that a person age 21 will be living at age 22 is

$$\frac{99{,}817}{100{,}000}$$

or

$$.99817$$

In other words:

$$p_{21} = .99817$$

Using these figures, it can be shown that the equation $p_x + q_x = 1$ is applicable:

Basic equation

$$p_x + q_x = 1$$

Substituting 21 for x

$$p_{21} + q_{21} = 1$$

Substituting the values given above for p_{21} and q_{21}

$$.99817 + .00183 = 1$$

Adding; result verifies the equation

$$1.00000 = 1$$

The equation $p_x + q_x = 1$ can be used to calculate either p_x or q_x when the value of only one of these probabilities is known.

To Illustrate—Given that $p_{46} = .995138$, how many persons age 46 can be expected to die before reaching age 47 out of a group of 1,000,000? Out of a group of 100,000? Out of a group of 10,000?

Solution—

Basic equation

$$p_x + q_x = 1$$

Substituting 46 for x

$$p_{46} + q_{46} = 1$$

Substituting the given value for p_{46}

$$.995138 + q_{46} = 1$$

Subtracting .995138 from both sides

$$q_{46} = .004862$$

This result can also be written:

$$q_{46} = \frac{4{,}862}{1{,}000{,}000}$$

which means that out of 1,000,000 persons age 46, 4,862 can be expected to die in the succeeding year, before reaching age 47.

To find the number out of a group of 100,000, the numerator and denominator are each divided by 10. This is done by moving the decimal points one place to the left:

$$q_{46} = \frac{486.2}{100{,}000.0}$$

The numerator would seem to imply a number of persons dying which is not a whole number. This need not be confusing if it is remembered that such numbers are approximations for the exact number predicted to die, or averages based on observations of more than one year. Hence, this expression means that, out of 100,000 persons age 46, approximately 486 can be expected to die in the succeeding year.

To find the number out of a group of 10,000, the numerator and denominator are each divided by 10 again by the method of moving the decimal points one place to the left:

$$q_{46} = \frac{48.62}{10{,}000.00}$$

This expression means that, out of 10,000 persons age 46, about 48 or 49 can be expected to die in the succeeding year.

PROBABILITIES OF LIVING OR DYING IN n YEARS. The concepts presented above can be extended to include the probabilities of a person living for any number of years, or dying within any number of years. The probability that a person age x will live at least n more years, or that he will reach age $(x + n)$, is represented by the symbol

$$_np_x$$

That is, p with subscripts of n preceding and x following. It is read "n p x." An example would be

$$_{15}p_{20}$$

which is read "15 p 20." It represents the probability that a person age 20 will live at least 15 more years, that is, that he will reach age 35.

In general terms, the probability that a person age x will live at least n more years ($_np_x$) is found by dividing the number living at age $(x + n)$ by the number living at age x. In equation form this is written

$$_np_x = \frac{l_{x+n}}{l_x}$$

To Illustrate—Using Table II, calculate the probability that a man age 48 will live at least 6 more years. Show the answer to 5 decimal places.

Solution—

Basic equation

$${}_np_x = \frac{l_{x+n}}{l_x}$$

Substituting 48 for x, 6 for n

$${}_6p_{48} = \frac{l_{48+6}}{l_{48}}$$

$$= \frac{l_{54}}{l_{48}}$$

Substituting the values for l_{54} and l_{48} from Table II

$$= \frac{9{,}103{,}034}{9{,}493{,}401}$$

$$= .95888$$

To Illustrate Again—Using Table III with a "3-year setback" for females, calculate the probability that a woman age 36 will live to reach age 46. Show the answer to 5 decimal places.

Solution—Three years must be subtracted from the ages before using the table. This means using the table as if calculating the probability of a male age 33 reaching age 43. The number of years involved, n, is 10.

Basic equation

$${}_np_x = \frac{l_{x+n}}{l_x}$$

Substituting 33 for x, 10 for n

$${}_{10}p_{33} = \frac{l_{33+10}}{l_{33}}$$

$$= \frac{l_{43}}{l_{33}}$$

Substituting values for l_{43} and l_{33} from Table III

$$= \frac{9{,}135{,}122}{9{,}418{,}208}$$

$$= .96994$$

The probability that a person age x will die within n years, or will die before reaching age $(x + n)$, is represented by the symbol

$${}_nq_x$$

That is, q with subscripts of n preceding and x following. It is read "$n\ q\ x$." An example would be

$$_{12}q_{65}$$

which is read "12 q 65." It means the probability that a person age 65 will die within the next 12 years, that is, that he will die before reaching age 77.

In general terms, the probability that a person age x will die within n years ($_nq_x$) is found by dividing the difference between the number living at ages x and $(x + n)$ by the number living at age x. This is expressed in equation form as

$$_nq_x = \frac{l_x - l_{x+n}}{l_x}$$

The numerator equals the number who *die* between ages x and $(x + n)$ because the number living at age x is reduced by all those who die in the interval in order to arrive at the number still living at age $(x + n)$.

To Illustrate – Using Table II, calculate the probability that a man age 30 will die within the next 20 years. Show the answer to five decimal places.

Solution –

Basic equation

$$_nq_x = \frac{l_x - l_{x+n}}{l_x}$$

Substituting 30 for x, 20 for n

$$_{20}q_{30} = \frac{l_{30} - l_{30+20}}{l_{30}}$$

$$= \frac{l_{30} - l_{50}}{l_{30}}$$

Substituting values from Table II

$$= \frac{9{,}870{,}777 - 9{,}388{,}071}{9{,}870{,}777}$$

$$= \frac{482{,}706}{9{,}870{,}777}$$

$$= .04890$$

The number in the numerator, namely 482,706, is the number who die between ages 30 and 50. It is equal to the total of the numbers in the d_x column, beginning with d_{30} and ending with d_{49}.

It is a certainty that a person age x will either live at least n years or else die within n years. Therefore, the total of these two individual probabilities is equal to 1. In equation form, this is written as

$$ {}_np_x + {}_nq_x = 1 $$

This equation is similar to that discussed above for the relationship between the probabilities of living and/or dying for one year.

SOLVING FOR OTHER UNKNOWNS. The above equations for ${}_np_x$ or ${}_nq_x$, namely,

$$ {}_np_x = \frac{l_{x+n}}{l_x} $$

$$ {}_nq_x = \frac{l_x - l_{x+n}}{l_x} $$

can be solved for any desired unknown value which appears therein.

To Illustrate—Using Table III, to what age does a man age 24 have a 50–50 chance of living?

Solution—The question may be stated in another way by asking, "For what value of n is ${}_np_{24}$ equal to .50?"

Basic equation

$$ {}_np_x = \frac{l_{x+n}}{l_x} $$

Substituting .50 for ${}_np_x$, 24 for x

$$ .50 = \frac{l_{24+n}}{l_{24}} $$

Substituting the value for l_{24} from Table III

$$ .50 = \frac{l_{24+n}}{9{,}593{,}960} $$

Solving for l_{24+n} by multiplying both sides by 9,593,960

$$ 4{,}796{,}980 = l_{24+n} $$

The problem asks for the *age* for which $l_x = 4{,}796{,}980$; this age will equal $(24 + n)$. Reference to Table III shows that $l_{73} = 4{,}731{,}089$ is the nearest to the desired value. Hence, age 73 is the sought-after age. Since $73 - 24 = 49$, the sought-after number of years, n, equals 49.

PROBABILITIES INVOLVING MORE THAN ONE EVENT. Probabilities involving the happening of more than one event may be calculated using the rules given in Section 7.1.

To Illustrate—Using Table II, calculate the probability that a man age 30 will die either at age 50 or at age 51.

Solution—Since only one of the events can occur, Rule 1 given in Section 7.1 is applicable: the two individual probabilities are added. The probability that a man age 30 will die during the year he is age 50 is equal to the number so dying divided by the number living at age 30:

Basic equation

$$\begin{pmatrix}\text{Probability of}\\ \text{Dying at 50}\end{pmatrix} = \frac{d_{50}}{l_{30}}$$

Substituting the values for d_{50} and l_{30} from Table II

$$= \frac{61{,}558}{9{,}870{,}777}$$

$$= .00624$$

Similarly, the probability that a man age 30 will die during the year he is age 51 is

Basic equation

$$\begin{pmatrix}\text{Probability of}\\ \text{Dying at 51}\end{pmatrix} = \frac{d_{51}}{l_{30}}$$

Substituting the values for d_{51} and l_{30} from Table II

$$= \frac{67{,}869}{9{,}870{,}777}$$

$$= .00688$$

The desired probability equals the total of the two individual probabilities:

Basic equation

$$\begin{pmatrix}\text{Probability of}\\ \text{Dying at 50 or 51}\end{pmatrix} = \begin{pmatrix}\text{Probability of}\\ \text{Dying at 50}\end{pmatrix} + \begin{pmatrix}\text{Probability of}\\ \text{Dying at 51}\end{pmatrix}$$

Substituting the probabilities calculated above

$$= .00624 + .00688$$

$$= .01312$$

To Illustrate Again—Using Table III, calculate the probability that a man, age 50, and his son, age 20, will both live at least 15 more years.

Solution—Since the happening of one event has no effect upon the happening of the other, Rule 2 in Section 7.1 is applicable: the two individual probabilities are multiplied.

For the man:

Basic equation

$$_np_x = \frac{l_{x+n}}{l_x}$$

Substituting 50 for x, 15 for n

$$_{15}p_{50} = \frac{l_{50+15}}{l_{50}}$$

$$= \frac{l_{65}}{l_{50}}$$

Substituting values for l_{65} and l_{50} from Table III

$$= \frac{6{,}800{,}531}{8{,}762{,}306}$$

$$= .77611$$

For the son:

Basic equation

$$_np_x = \frac{l_{x+n}}{l_x}$$

Substituting 20 for x, 15 for n

$$_{15}p_{20} = \frac{l_{20+15}}{l_{20}}$$

$$= \frac{l_{35}}{l_{20}}$$

Substituting values for l_{35} and l_{20} from Table III

$$= \frac{9{,}373{,}807}{9{,}664{,}994}$$

$$= .96987$$

The desired probability that both will live at least 15 years equals the product of two individual probabilities multiplied together:

Basic equation

$$\begin{pmatrix}\text{Probability}\\ \text{Both Live}\end{pmatrix} = \begin{pmatrix}\text{Probability}\\ \text{Man Lives}\end{pmatrix}\begin{pmatrix}\text{Probability}\\ \text{Son Lives}\end{pmatrix}$$

Substituting the probabilities calculated above

$$= (.77611)(.96987)$$

$$= .75273$$

7.7 SELECT AND ULTIMATE MORTALITY TABLES

It was stated in Section 7.2 that the length of time which has elapsed since a person became insured affects his probability of dying. At the time a person becomes insured, it is established whether he is in good health (by a medical examination or otherwise). Those whose health is impaired may pay a higher insurance premium. It is customary for mortality tables to be based on the experience arising from those persons who were found to be in good health.

It has been observed that the rates of mortality for persons whose good health has just been established are lower than for other persons of the same age whose good health was established in the past. However, as the years go by, differences in rates of mortality between these two groups gradually disappear. The period of years during which there is a significant discernible difference in the rates of mortality is known as the *select period.* A mortality table which records the values of basic mortality functions during the select period is known as a *select mortality table.*

To indicate that a group consists of persons whose good health has just been established, it is customary to enclose the age in square brackets. Thus, instead of writing l_x, the number living at age x when all have just been established as being in good health is written

$$l_{[x]}$$

That is, l with a subscript $[x]$. The x in brackets is part of the whole symbol, and $l_{[x]}$ does not mean "l multiplied by x." An example would be

$$l_{[35]}$$

which means the assumed number of persons in a group, all of whom are age 35 and all of whom have just been established as being in good health.

The number of survivors of the $l_{[x]}$ group at the end of one, two, and three years is expressed by

$$l_{[x]+1}$$

$$l_{[x]+2}$$

$$l_{[x]+3}$$

respectively. Thus, the age at which good health was established remains a part of the symbol, enclosed in brackets. An example would be

$$l_{[24]+4}$$

which means the number still living four years after good health was established, which took place at age 24. In other words, there were $l_{[24]}$ persons in the group at age 24 when good health was just established. Now four years later (at age 28), $l_{[24]+4}$ of that original group are still living.

Beyond the select period, when the effects of the selection have worn off, the number of survivors of the original select group constitute the *ultimate mortality table.* The combination of these two tables is called a *select and ultimate mortality table.* An example of portions of such a table appears in Chart 7–3.

CHART 7–3

Portion of a Select and Ultimate Mortality Table (5-year select period)

	Select					*Ultimate*	
Age $[x]$	$l_{[x]}$	$l_{[x]+1}$	$l_{[x]+2}$	$l_{[x]+3}$	$l_{[x]+4}$	l_{x+5}	*Age* $x+5$
30	950,875	949,734	948,471	947,039	945,439	943,624	35
31	949,221	948,044	946,717	945,212	943,501	941,576	36
32	947,447	946,215	944,834	943,237	941,435	939,354	37
33	945,589	944,303	942,830	941,142	939,194	936,959	38
34	943,623	942,255	940,700	938,875	936,781	934,373	39
35	941,488	940,048	938,375	936,423	934,176	931,570	40
36	939,211	937,661	935,870	933,774	931,346	928,477	41
37	936,729	935,071	933,145	930,887	928,225	925,088	42
38	934,023	932,248	930,178	927,704	924,800	921,341	43
39	931,088	929,170	926,903	924,215	921,017	917,195	44

The first column records the various ages at which it may be assumed good health has just been established. The second column records the number assumed living in such a group for each such age, namely $l_{[x]}$. Starting at any age recorded in the first column, the number of survivors at successive ages is found by reading the table *horizontally to the right*. It will be seen that these columns to the right are labeled: $l_{[x]+1}$, $l_{[x]+2}$, $l_{[x]+3}$, $l_{[x]+4}$, and l_{x+5}. There are no brackets on the x in the l_{x+5} column. This is because persons still living five years after their good health was established are considered to be subject to the same rates of mortality as any other person of the same age. That is, the *select period* only lasts for five years (in this particular table). Hence, the l_{x+5} column may be considered by itself to be an *ultimate* mortality table. Accordingly, the ages represented by $(x+5)$ are recorded (in the right-hand column) beside the respective values of l_{x+5}.

For example, the $l_{[x]}$ column records 947,447 persons at age 32 whose good health has just been established. That is,

$$l_{[32]} = 947{,}447$$

Reading across the table horizontally to the right from there, the table records that 946,215 of them are still living one year later (at age 33). That is,

$$l_{[32]+1} = 946{,}215$$

Similarly, 944,834 of them are still living two years later, 943,237 three years later, and 941,435 four years later. Finally, the l_{x+5} column records that there are 939,354 of the original group still living five years later (at age 37). At this point it makes no difference at what age good health was established. It is only the current age which is used, and therefore the survivors in succeeding years are found by *reading down* the l_{x+5} column. The number still surviving at age 38 is 936,959, for example.

A select and ultimate mortality table may be used to calculate certain probabilities of living and dying.

To Illustrate—Calculate the probability that a person age 35 will be living at the end of one year, using the above table. First assume good health was established at age 35; then assume it was established at age 34; then at age 33; then at age 32; then at age 31; and finally assume it was established at age 30.

Solution—The equation $p_x = \frac{l_{x+1}}{l_x}$ may be used. The various ages will be expressed with the age at which good health was established enclosed in brackets.

Assuming Good Health Was Established at 35

Basic equation

$$p_x = \frac{l_{x+1}}{l_x}$$

Substituting [35] for x (person is age 35 and good health was just established)

$$p_{[35]} = \frac{l_{[35]+1}}{l_{[35]}}$$

Substituting the values for $l_{[35]+1}$ and $l_{[35]}$ from the table

$$= \frac{940{,}048}{941{,}488}$$

$$= .99847$$

Assuming Good Health Was Established at 34

Basic equation

$$p_x = \frac{l_{x+1}}{l_x}$$

Substituting [34] + 1 for x (person is age 35 and good health was established at age 34)

$$p_{[34]+1} = \frac{l_{[34]+2}}{l_{[34]+1}}$$

Substituting the values for $l_{[34]+2}$ and $l_{[34]+1}$ from the table

$$= \frac{940{,}700}{942{,}255}$$

$$= .99835$$

Assuming Good Health Was Established at 33

Basic equation

$$p_x = \frac{l_{x+1}}{l_x}$$

Substituting [33] + 2 for x (person is age 35 and good health was established at age 33)

$$p_{[33]+2} = \frac{l_{[33]+3}}{l_{[33]+2}}$$

Substituting values for $l_{[33]+3}$ and $l_{[33]+2}$ from the table

$$= \frac{941{,}142}{942{,}830}$$

$$= .99821$$

Assuming Good Health Was Established at 32

Basic equation

$$p_x = \frac{l_{x+1}}{l_x}$$

Substituting [32] + 3 for x (person is age 35, and good health was established at age 32)

$$p_{[32]+3} = \frac{l_{[32]+4}}{l_{[32]+3}}$$

Substituting values for $l_{[32]+4}$ and $l_{[32]+3}$ from the table

$$= \frac{941{,}435}{943{,}237}$$

$$= .99809$$

Assuming Good Health Was Established at 31

Basic equation

$$p_x = \frac{l_{x+1}}{l_x}$$

Substituting [31] + 4 for x (person is age 35 and good health was established at age 31)
In numerator l_{36} is shown instead of $l_{[31]+5}$ since 5 years puts it into the ultimate portion of the table

$$p_{[31]+4} = \frac{l_{36}}{l_{[31]+4}}$$

Substituting values for l_{36} and $l_{[31]+4}$ from the table

$$= \frac{941{,}576}{943{,}501}$$

$$= .99796$$

Assuming Good Health Was Established at 30

Basic equation

$$p_x = \frac{l_{x+1}}{l_x}$$

Substituting 35 for x (person is age 35; good health was established 5 years ago; hence l_x figures come entirely from ultimate portion of the table)

$$p_{35} = \frac{l_{36}}{l_{35}}$$

Substituting values for l_{36} and l_{35} from the l_{x+5} column (ultimate portion) of the table

$$= \frac{941,576}{943,624}$$

$$= .99783$$

This illustration demonstrates that the probability of a person age 35 living for one year diminishes as the number of years increases since he was established as being in good health, until the end of the select period. This is as might be expected.

To Illustrate Again—What is the probability that a person age 35, whose good health was established at age 32, will be living at the end of 5 years (at age 40)? Also, what is the probability that this person will die during those 5 years?

Solution—

Probability of Living

Basic equation

$${}_np_x = \frac{l_{x+n}}{l_x}$$

Substituting [32] + 3 for x (person is age 35 and good health was established at age 32)
Substituting 5 for n; in numerator l_{40} is shown instead of $l_{[32]+8}$ since 8 years puts it into the ultimate portion of the table

$${}_5p_{[32]+3} = \frac{l_{40}}{l_{[32]+3}}$$

Substituting values for l_{40} and $l_{[32]+3}$ from the table

$$= \frac{931,570}{943,237}$$

$$= .98763$$

Probability of Dying

Basic equation

$$_nq_x = \frac{l_x - l_{x+n}}{l_x}$$

Substituting [32] + 3 for x (person is age 35 and good health was established at age 32)
Substituting 5 for n; in numerator l_{40} is shown instead of $l_{[32]+8}$ since 8 years puts it into the ultimate portion of the table

$$_5q_{[32]+3} = \frac{l_{[32]+3} - l_{40}}{l_{[32]+3}}$$

Substituting values for $l_{[32]+3}$ and l_{40} from the table

$$= \frac{943{,}237 - 931{,}570}{943{,}237}$$

$$= \frac{11{,}667}{943{,}237}$$

$$= .01237$$

The total of the two probabilities above is

$$.98763 + .01237 = 1$$

This is the expected result, since the person is certain either to survive for 5 years or to die during the 5-year period.

EXERCISES

(Use Table III for Exercises 1 to 11)

1 What is the probability that a man age 20 will live for 1 year?
2 What is the probability that a man age 20 will live for 25 years?
3 What is the probability that a man age 30 will be living at age 50?
4 Using a "3-year setback" for females, calculate the probability that a female age 20 will survive to age 45.
5 How many men out of 10,000 men age 35 can be expected to live to age 65?
6 What is the probability that a man age 30 will die before reaching age 65?
7 Using a "3-year setback" for females, calculate the number of females out of 100,000 females age 27 who can be expected to die within 10 years.
8 To what age does a man age 21 have a $\frac{1}{3}$ chance of living?
9 What is the probability that two men, ages 30 and 40, will both survive 10 years?

10 What is the probability that two men, ages 30 and 40, will both die in the next 10 years?

11 What is the probability that a man age 20 will die either during the year he is age 70 or during the year he is age 80?

(Use the select and ultimate table in Section 7.7 for Exercises 12 to 16)

12 What is the probability that a person whose good health has just been established at age 38 will survive for 1 year?

13 What is the probability that a person age 38, whose good health was established at age 35, will survive for 1 year?

14 What is the probability that a person whose good health has just been established at age 30 will die during the next 10 years?

15 What is the probability that a person age 37, who was established as being in good health at age 35, will be living 5 years from now?

16 What is the probability that a person whose good health has just been established at age 32 and a person age 37, who was established as being in good health at age 35, will both die during the next 5 years?

8.

Life Annuities

8.1 INTRODUCTION

In Section 5.1, it was pointed out that there are two types of annuities: *annuities certain,* which involve a fixed number of payments, and annuities where the continuation of the payments depends upon the occurrence of some event. A *life annuity* is an example of the second type. Each payment in a life annuity is made only if a designated person is alive to pay or receive it.

Accumulated and present values of life annuities can be calculated in a way similar to the method used for annuities certain in Chapters 5 and 6. Accumulated and present values of just one payment will be considered first, as was done for payments certain in Chapters 3 and 4.

To ask the question:

> "How much should a man now age 35 pay for the right to receive $100 at age 60 if he is then alive to receive it?"

is the same as asking:

> "What is the present value to a man now age 35 of $100 payable at age 60, calculated with benefit of survivorship?"

The phrase *with benefit of survivorship* is used to distinguish this situation from one where only rates of interest are involved, as was the case in Chapter 4. If only rates of interest were involved in finding the present value, the answer would be

Basic equation for present value

$A = Sv^n$

Substituting $100 for S, 25 for n because 25 years are involved between age 35 and age 60

$= \$100v^{25}$

But now the element of survivorship is also involved, because the man must survive in order to receive the payment. *With benefit of survivorship*, then, means that payments will be made only if the designated payor or recipient is alive at the time the payment is due.

To begin solving the problem posed above, it is necessary to consult a mortality table. If Table II is used, the number shown as living at each of the two ages involved is

$l_{35} = 9{,}814{,}474$

$l_{60} = 8{,}465{,}043$

This means that if there is a group of 9,814,474 men alive at age 35, then 8,465,043 of this group will still be alive at age 60. In order to solve the problem, it must be assumed that all of these men are individually involved, that is, each one still alive at age 60 will receive $100. It is desired to know the present value of this money to men when they are age 35 (calculated with benefit of survivorship).

Since $100 is to be paid to each of the l_{60} men, the total amount that will be paid out altogether is

$$\$100(l_{60}) = (\$100)(8{,}465{,}043)$$
$$= \$846{,}504{,}300$$

Twenty-five years earlier, l_{35} men will pay the money in. The original question now may be stated: "How much will each pay?" The total amount paid in is

$$\begin{pmatrix}\text{Amount Each}\\ \text{Pays In}\end{pmatrix}(l_{35}) = \begin{pmatrix}\text{Amount Each}\\ \text{Pays In}\end{pmatrix}(9{,}814{,}474)$$

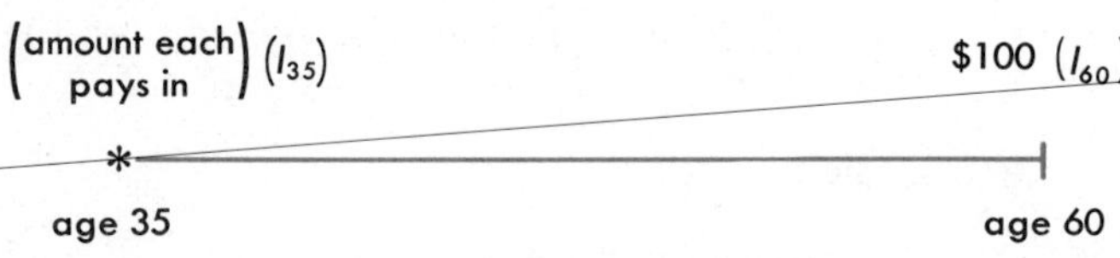

The money paid in will earn interest over the 25-year period. For this example, the rate will be assumed to be 2½%. The basic equation for finding present value can be used to show that *all the money paid in equals the present value of all the money to be paid out 25 years later*. The amount each pays in can then be found:

$$A = Sv^n$$

Substituting $\binom{\text{Amount Each}}{\text{Pays In}}(9{,}814{,}474)$ for A, \$846,504,300 for S, and the value of v^{25} at $2\frac{1}{2}\%$ from Table I

$$\binom{\text{Amount Each}}{\text{Pays In}}(9{,}814{,}474) = (\$846{,}504{,}300)(.539391)$$

$$\binom{\text{Amount Each}}{\text{Pays In}}(9{,}814{,}474) = \$456{,}596{,}801$$

$$\binom{\text{Amount Each}}{\text{Pays In}} = \$46.52$$

This \$46.52 is less than the present value calculated at interest only. The latter would be

$$\begin{aligned} A &= \$100(v^{25} \text{ at } 2\tfrac{1}{2}\%) \\ &= (\$100)(.539391) \\ &= \$53.94 \end{aligned}$$

\$53.94 is the amount each man would pay in if all were to receive \$100 25 years later (dead or alive). The \$46.52 payment with benefit of survivorship is smaller because in that case only those who survive are to receive their \$100.

It can be proved that \$46.52 is the desired present value, with benefit of survivorship, at age 35 of \$100 payable at age 60 as follows:

$$\begin{aligned} \text{Total amount paid in} &= \$46.52(l_{35}) \\ &= (\$46.52)(9{,}814{,}474) \\ &= \$456{,}569{,}330.48 \end{aligned}$$

Total amount accumulated at $2\frac{1}{2}\%$ for 25 years

$$\begin{aligned} &= (\$456{,}569{,}330.48)(1.025)^{25} \\ &= (\$456{,}569{,}330.48)(1.853944) \\ &= \$846{,}453{,}970.83 \end{aligned}$$

Amount payable to each survivor at age 60 (the accumulated fund divided by the number of survivors)

$$\begin{aligned} &= \$846{,}453{,}970.83 \div l_{60} \\ &= \$846{,}453{,}970.83 \div 8{,}465{,}043 \\ &= \$99.99 \end{aligned}$$

(The missing 1 cent is due to the fact that \$46.52 was rounded off to the nearest cent instead of using more decimal places.)

The present value, with benefit of survivorship, at age 35 of $100 payable at age 60 can be written as

$$\$100\left(\frac{l_{60}}{l_{35}}\right)v^{25}$$

or as

$$\frac{(\$100)(l_{60}v^{25})}{l_{35}}$$

Both these expressions permit interesting verbal interpretations. In the first, $\left(\frac{l_{60}}{l_{35}}\right)$ equals the probability that a person age 35 will live to age 60. Hence, the first expression says that the $100 is multiplied by the probability of surviving and also by the regular discounting factor for finding present values at interest. The second expression says that the $100 payable to each of l_{60} persons is discounted at interest for 25 years, and this amount is divided among the l_{35} persons to find out how much each must pay in.

In the numerical example, it was shown how compound interest and probability are combined in calculating contingent payments. Using more general terms, the equation is

$$\left(\begin{array}{c}\text{Present Value of \$1}\\ \text{Due in } n \text{ Years to a}\\ \text{Life Now Age } x\text{, with}\\ \text{Benefit of Survivorship}\end{array}\right) = \$1\left(\frac{l_{x+n}v^{n}}{l_x}\right)$$

To Illustrate—Using the 1958 C.S.O. Table (Table III) and 3% interest, calculate the present value at age 20 of $400 due in 15 years if the person is still alive; also due in 25 years.

Solution—

Due in 15 Years

Basic equation

$$\text{Present Value} = \$400\left(\frac{l_{x+n}v^{n}}{l_x}\right)$$

Substituting 20 for x (the evaluation age), 15 for n (the number of years)

$$= \$400\left(\frac{l_{35}v^{15}}{l_{20}}\right)$$

Substituting the values for the l's from Table III, for v^{15} from Table I (3%)

$$= \$400\left[\frac{(9{,}373{,}807)(.641862)}{9{,}664{,}994}\right]$$

$$= \$400\left(\frac{6{,}016{,}691}{9{,}664{,}994}\right)$$

$$= \$249.01$$

Due in 25 Years

Basic equation

$$\text{Present Value} = \$400\left(\frac{l_{x+n}v^{n}}{l_x}\right)$$

Substituting 20 for x, 25 for n

$$= \$400\left(\frac{l_{45}v^{25}}{l_{20}}\right)$$

Substituting the values for the l's from Table III, for v^{25} from Table I (3%)

$$= \$400\left[\frac{(9{,}048{,}999)(.477606)}{9{,}664{,}994}\right]$$

$$= \$400\left(\frac{4{,}321{,}856}{9{,}664{,}994}\right)$$

$$= \$178.87$$

As the number of years *increases* before the payment is to be made, the present value *decreases*. This is because there is a smaller probability that it will have to be paid, and because there will be a greater number of years in which to earn interest.

8.2 PRESENT VALUE OF A LIFE ANNUITY

CALCULATION OF PRESENT VALUES. An annuity is a series of payments. It is not difficult to find the present value of a series of payments where each payment is made only if the designated payor or recipient is alive to pay or receive it. The present value of the annuity is the *total* of the present values of each of the individual payments. The principles explained above can be used to find the present value of each individual payment.

For example, the present value at age 25 of a life annuity of $100 per year for three years, first payment due at age 26, can be represented by the following line diagram:

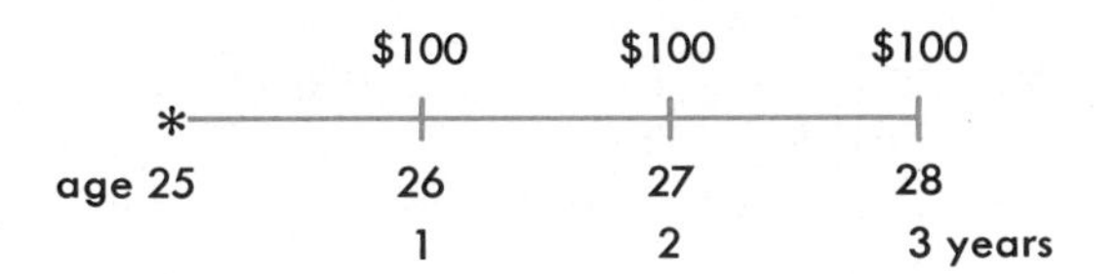

The present value of each of the three payments can be calculated individually, as follows:

The Payment Due at Age 26

Basic equation

$$\text{Present Value} = \$100\left(\frac{l_{x+n}v^n}{l_x}\right)$$

Substituting 25 for x, 1 for n (Exponent 1 need not be written)

$$= \$100\left(\frac{l_{26}v}{l_{25}}\right)$$

The Payment Due at Age 27

Basic equation

$$\text{Present Value} = \$100\left(\frac{l_{x+n}v^n}{l_x}\right)$$

Substituting 25 for x, 2 for n

$$= \$100\left(\frac{l_{27}v^2}{l_{25}}\right)$$

The Payment Due at Age 28

Basic equation

$$\text{Present Value} = \$100\left(\frac{l_{x+n}v^n}{l_x}\right)$$

Substituting 25 for x, 3 for n

$$= \$100\left(\frac{l_{28}v^3}{l_{25}}\right)$$

The present value at age 25 of this annuity is the total of these three expressions. The common multiplier ($100) can be factored out. The fractions to be added together have a common denominator (l_{25}). Hence, the present value of the annuity can be expressed as

$$\text{Present Value} = \$100\left(\frac{l_{26}v + l_{27}v^2 + l_{28}v^3}{l_{25}}\right)$$

The *numerator* of this expression represents the total to be paid out to the survivors at each age, with each such amount being discounted at interest to the evaluation date. The *denominator* represents the number of persons alive on the evaluation date, among whom this total present value to be paid in must be allocated.

If, for example, the 1958 C.S.O. Table and 3% interest were being used, the present value of the annuity would be calculated as follows:

From above

$$\text{Present Value} = \$100\left(\frac{l_{26}v + l_{27}v^2 + l_{28}v^3}{l_{25}}\right)$$

Substituting the values for the l's from Table III, for the v's from Table I (3%)

$$= \$100 \left[\frac{\begin{array}{l}(9{,}557{,}155)(.970874)\\ +(9{,}538{,}423)(.942596)\\ +(9{,}519{,}442)(.915142)\end{array}}{9{,}575{,}636} \right]$$

$$= \$100 \left(\frac{9{,}278{,}793 + 8{,}990{,}879 + 8{,}711{,}641}{9{,}575{,}636} \right)$$

$$= \$100 \left(\frac{26{,}981{,}313}{9{,}575{,}636} \right)$$

$$= \$281.77$$

It can be verified that the payment of $281.77 by each of the persons age 25 will provide $100 to each of the survivors at ages 26, 27, and 28, as follows (using the 1958 C.S.O. Table at 3%):

If each of the l_{25}, or 9,575,636, persons contributes $281.77, a fund is provided of

$$(\$281.77)(9{,}575{,}636) = \$2{,}698{,}126{,}955.72$$

During one year it will earn interest of

$$(\$2{,}698{,}126{,}955.72)(.03) = \$80{,}943{,}808.67$$

The total amount of money in the fund at the end of one year is then

$$\$2{,}698{,}126{,}955.72 + \$80{,}943{,}808.67 = \$2{,}779{,}070{,}764.39$$

Payments of $100 to each of the l_{26}, or 9,557,155, survivors will require

$$(\$100)(9{,}557{,}155) = \$955{,}715{,}500$$

This leaves a balance in the fund at the end of one year of

$$\$2{,}779{,}070{,}764.39 - \$955{,}715{,}500 = \$1{,}823{,}355{,}264.39$$

The continued progress of the fund can be traced in Chart 8–1.

CHART 8–1

(1) Year	(2) Fund at Beginning of Year	(3) Interest for One Year (Col. 2 × .03)	(4) Total Fund at End of Year before Annuity Payments Are Made (Col. 2 + Col. 3)	(5) Annuity Payments to Survivors	(6) Balance in Fund after Annuity Payments Are Made (Col. 4 – Col. 5)
1	$2,698,126,955.72	$80,943,808.67	$2,779,070,764.39	$955,715,500.00	$1,823,355,264.39
2	1,823,355,264.39	54,700,657.93	1,878,055,922.32	953,842,300.00	924,213,622.32
3	924,213,622.32	27,726,408.67	951,940,030.99	951,944,200.00	(–4,169.01)

The shortage of \$4,169.01 represents less than $\frac{1}{20}$th of a cent for each of the survivors, and results from rounding off the individual contribution, \$281.77, to two decimal places. If all calculations had been carried to more decimal places, the balance in the fund at the end of the third year would have been even closer to zero.

To Illustrate—Using the Annuity Table for 1949 and $2\frac{1}{2}\%$ interest, calculate the present value at age 40 of a life annuity of \$25 per year for 4 years, first payment due at age 41.

Solution—The line diagram for this life annuity appears as follows:

	\$25	\$25	\$25	\$25
*	+	+	+	+
age 40	41	42	43	44
	1	2	3	4 years

The expression for the present value will have a *numerator* representing the total to be paid out to the survivors at each age, with each such amount being discounted at interest to the evaluation date:

$$\$25(l_{41}v + l_{42}v^2 + l_{43}v^3 + l_{44}v^4)$$

The *denominator* is the number living on the evaluation date (l_{40}):

Basic equation

$$\text{Present Value} = \$25\left(\frac{l_{41}v + l_{42}v^2 + l_{43}v^3 + l_{44}v^4}{l_{40}}\right)$$

Substituting values for the l's from Table II, for the v's from Table I ($2\frac{1}{2}\%$)

$$= \$25\left[\frac{\begin{array}{l}(9{,}715{,}549)(.975610)\\+(9{,}693{,}980)(.951814)\\+(9{,}669{,}929)(.928599)\\+(9{,}642{,}815)(.905951)\end{array}}{9{,}735{,}263}\right]$$

$$= \$25\left(\frac{9{,}478{,}587 + 9{,}226{,}866 + 8{,}979{,}486 + 8{,}735{,}918}{9{,}735{,}263}\right)$$

$$= \$93.53$$

TYPES OF LIFE ANNUITIES. Life annuities may be either temporary life annuities or whole life annuities. In a *temporary life annuity*, each payment is made only if a designated person is then alive, but the payments are limited to a fixed number of years. In a *whole life annuity*, the payments continue for the entire lifetime of a designated person.

The three-year and four-year life annuities calculated above are examples of *temporary life annuities.* Each payment is made only if a designated person is then alive, but the number of such payments is limited to a definite number. The first payment is made one period following the date on which the present value is calculated.

There are also temporary life annuities in which the first payment is made at the *beginning,* that is, on the same date on which the present value is calculated. These are known as *temporary life annuities due.* The use of the word "due" is analogous to its use in annuities certain.

The line diagrams of two five-payment life annuities, one immediate and one due, look like this:

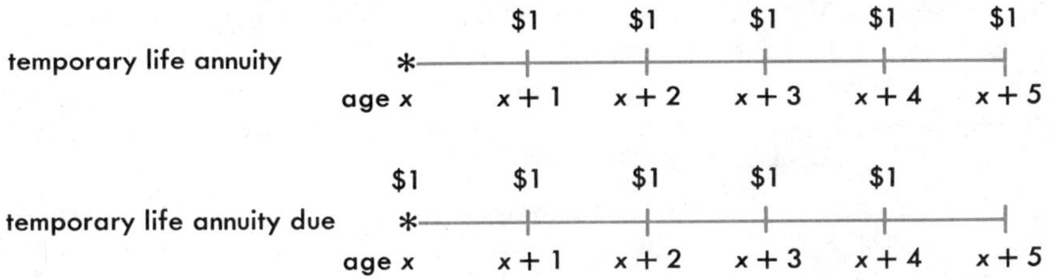

temporary life annuity		$1	$1	$1	$1	$1
	age x	x + 1	x + 2	x + 3	x + 4	x + 5

temporary life annuity due	$1	$1	$1	$1	$1	
	age x	x + 1	x + 2	x + 3	x + 4	x + 5

To Illustrate—Using the 1958 C.S.O. Table and 3% interest, calculate the present value at age 25 of a 3-year life annuity due of $100 per year.

Solution—The line diagram for this life annuity due appears as follows:

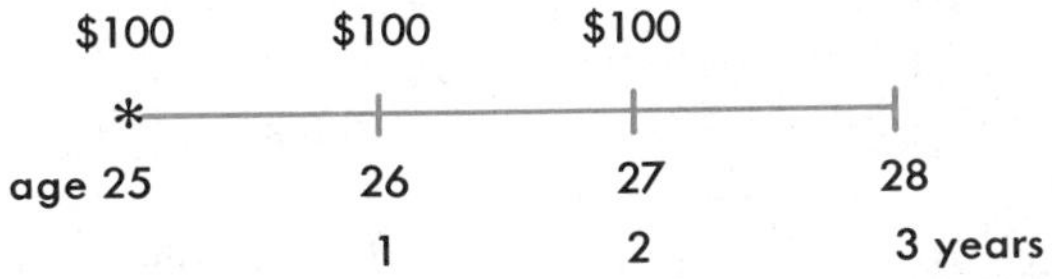

$100	$100	$100	
age 25	26	27	28
	1	2	3 years

The expression for the present value will have a *numerator* representing the total to be paid out to the survivors at each age, with each such amount being discounted at interest to the evaluation date. The first payment is due upon the evaluation date. Hence, its present value is simply $\$100(l_{25})$; it is not multiplied by any discounting factor. The *denominator* is the number living at the evaluation date:

Basic equation

$$\text{Present Value} = \$100\left(\frac{l_{25} + l_{26}v + l_{27}v^2}{l_{25}}\right)$$

Substituting values for the l's from Table III, for the v's from Table I (3%)

$$= \$100 \left[\frac{\begin{array}{l}(9{,}575{,}636) \\ +(9{,}557{,}155)(.970874) \\ +(9{,}538{,}423)(.942596)\end{array}}{9{,}575{,}636} \right]$$

$$= \$100 \left[\frac{9{,}575{,}636 + 9{,}278{,}793 + 8{,}990{,}879}{9{,}575{,}636} \right]$$

$$= \$290.79$$

The present value of a three-year life annuity identical to this one, except that the first payment was made at the *end* of the first year, was calculated earlier in this section to be $281.77. This value is less than the present value of the life annuity due ($290.79), because each payment in the annuity immediate is paid one year later than its counterpart in the annuity due. Hence, there is a smaller probability that it will have to be paid, and there is a greater number of years in which interest is earned.

Life annuities wherein the payments continue for the entire lifetime of a designated person are known as *whole life annuities*. Without the word "due," this name implies that the first payment is made one period following the date on which the present value is calculated. Whole life annuities in which the first payment is made at the *beginning*, that is, on the same date on which the present value is calculated, are known as *whole life annuities due*.

The present value of whole life annuities is calculated by exactly the same procedure as that shown above for temporary life annuities. In the case of whole life annuities, the payments are included to the end of the mortality table. It is thus assumed that all will die before a certain age; therefore, the number of payments to include in the calculation is actually a limited number, just as for temporary life annuities.

To Illustrate—Using the Annuity Table for 1949 and $2\frac{1}{2}\%$ interest, calculate the present value at age 106 of a whole life annuity of $50 per year.

Solution—The first payment is due 1 year after age 106 (at age 107). Payments will continue for the person's entire lifetime. However, the Annuity Table for 1949 (shown in Table II) assumes that no persons live beyond the age of 109. Hence, the line diagram for this annuity appears as follows:

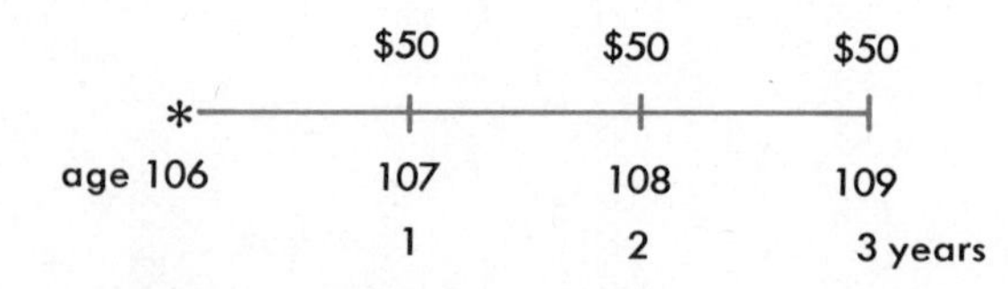

The expression for the present value will have a *numerator* representing the total to be paid out to the survivors at each age, with each such amount being discounted at interest to the evaluation date. The *denominator* is the number living on the evaluation date:

Basic equation

$$\text{Present Value} = \$50\left(\frac{l_{107}v + l_{108}v^2 + l_{109}v^3}{l_{106}}\right)$$

Substituting the values for the l's from Table II, for the v's from Table I ($2\frac{1}{2}\%$)

$$= \$50\left[\frac{\begin{array}{r}(54)(.975610)\\+(16)(.951814)\\+(\ 4)(.928599)\end{array}}{167}\right]$$

$$= \$50\left[\frac{52.6829 + 15.2290 + 3.7144}{167}\right]$$

$$= \$21.45$$

There is no rule for the number of decimal places to keep in rounding the answers obtained by the actual multiplications in the numerator. It is desirable to keep only a sufficient number of digits to have a meaningful answer. In the above illustration, each multiplication answer was rounded to four decimal places. In previous illustrations (involving much larger numbers for the l's), each multiplication answer was rounded to the nearest whole number.

The present value of the annuity calculated in the above illustration (\$21.45) is less than the amount of one year's payment (\$50). This is a phenomenon encountered when only the very high ages are being used. In this illustration it indicates that a considerable portion of those paying for the annuity at age 106 will die before receiving even one payment.

The calculation of the present value of whole life annuities at the younger ages would become very laborious if the above procedure were followed. Therefore, in actual practice this calculation is done by using *commutation functions*. This method will be explained later in Section 8.7.

A *deferred life annuity* is a life annuity in which the first payment is *postponed* one or more periods. Once payments commence, they may continue for the remaining lifetime of the designated person, or they may be limited to a specified number of payments.

As an example of a deferred life annuity, consider the problem of finding the present value at age 65 of a whole life annuity of \$100 per year, the first payment being made 38 years after the evaluation date. This means that the first payment is due at age $65 + 38 =$ age 103 (if the person is then alive). If the table used were the Annuity Table for

1949, the final payment would be at age 109, because this table shows none living after that age:

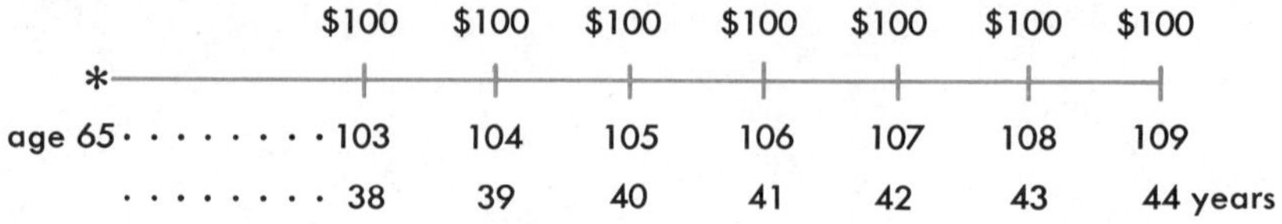

	$100	$100	$100	$100	$100	$100	$100
*							
age 65 ········	103	104	105	106	107	108	109
········	38	39	40	41	42	43	44 years

The total amount to be paid out to the survivors at age 103 would be

$$\$100(l_{103})$$

The present value is being calculated as of a time 38 years prior to the date of this payment. Hence, the present value is this total multiplied by the factor for finding present value:

$$\$100(l_{103}v^{38})$$

The present value of each of the payments is similarly calculated, and the total is divided by the number living at age 65 to derive the amount each must pay in. The expression for the present value of this deferred life annuity is

$$\$100\left(\frac{l_{103}v^{38} + l_{104}v^{39} + l_{105}v^{40} + l_{106}v^{41} + l_{107}v^{42} + l_{108}v^{43} + l_{109}v^{44}}{l_{65}}\right)$$

To Illustrate—Using the Annuity Table for 1949 and $2\frac{1}{2}\%$ interest, calculate the present value at age 40 of a temporary life annuity of $1,500 per year, first payment at age 50 and the last payment at age 53.

Solution—The line diagram for this life annuity appears as follows:

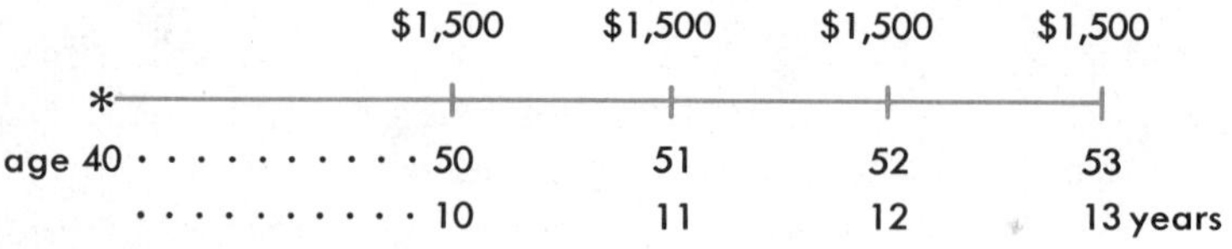

	$1,500	$1,500	$1,500	$1,500
*				
age 40 ··········	50	51	52	53
··········	10	11	12	13 years

The amount payable at age 50 is due 10 years after the evaluation date; the amount payable at age 51 is due 11 years after the evaluation date; etc. Following the above procedure of expressing the present value as the total of the present values of the individual payments:

Basic equation

$$\text{Present Value} = \$1{,}500\left(\frac{l_{50}v^{10} + l_{51}v^{11} + l_{52}v^{12} + l_{53}v^{13}}{l_{40}}\right)$$

Substituting the values for the l's from Table II, for the v's from Table I ($2\frac{1}{2}\%$)

$$= \$1{,}500\left[\frac{\begin{array}{l}(9{,}388{,}071)(.781198)\\+(9{,}326{,}513)(.762145)\\+(9{,}258{,}644)(.743556)\\+(9{,}184{,}223)(.725420)\end{array}}{9{,}735{,}263}\right]$$

$$= \$1{,}500\left[\frac{7{,}333{,}942 + 7{,}108{,}155 + 6{,}884{,}320 + 6{,}662{,}419}{9{,}735{,}263}\right]$$

$$= \$4{,}312.49$$

RELATIONSHIPS AMONG LIFE ANNUITIES. There are certain relationships among types of annuities which are important.

The first of these is the relationship between a *whole life annuity* and a *whole life annuity due.* The following line diagrams show a whole life annuity and a whole life annuity due, both evaluated at age x:

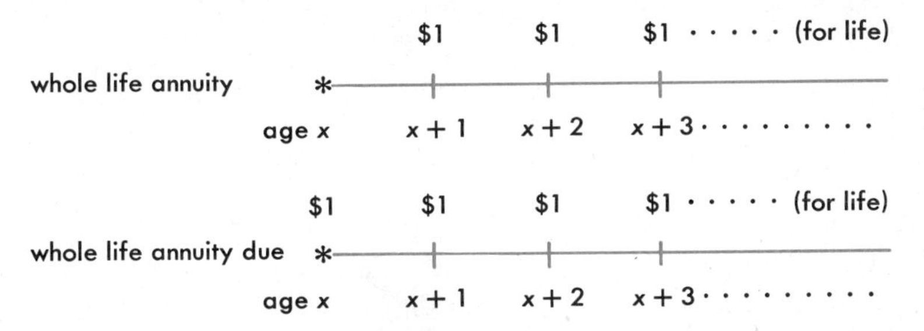

The diagrams show that the only difference between the two types is the one payment at age x in the second annuity. This illustrates that the *present value of the whole life annuity due is equal to the present value of the whole life annuity plus the amount of one payment.* In equation form, this is

$$\begin{pmatrix}\text{Present Value at Age } x\\ \text{of Whole Life Annuity Due}\end{pmatrix} = \begin{pmatrix}\text{Present Value at Age } x\\ \text{of Whole Life Annuity}\end{pmatrix} + 1$$

For a payment of $10 per year, the equation would be

$$\$10\begin{pmatrix}\text{Present Value at Age } x\\ \text{of Whole Life Annuity Due}\end{pmatrix} = \$10\left[\begin{pmatrix}\text{Present Value at Age } x\\ \text{of Whole Life Annuity}\end{pmatrix} + 1\right]$$

$$= \$10\begin{pmatrix}\text{Present Value at Age } x\\ \text{of Whole Life Annuity}\end{pmatrix} + \$10$$

To Illustrate—Using the Annuity Table for 1949 and $2\frac{1}{2}\%$ interest, calculate the present value at age 106 of a whole life annuity due of $50 per year.

Solution—The line diagram for this life annuity due appears as follows (with 109 being the highest age in this particular mortality table):

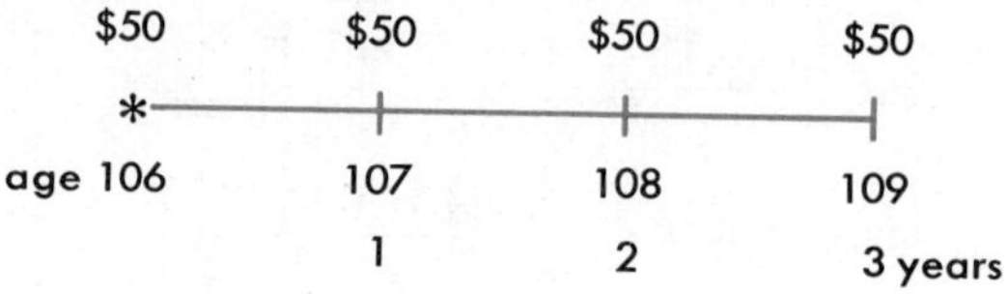

$50	$50	$50	$50
*	+	+	+
age 106	107	108	109
	1	2	3 years

In an earlier illustration, the present value at age 106 of a whole life annuity of $50 per year (first payment one year following age 106) was calculated to be $21.45. Hence, the above relationship can be used, with $21.45 substituted in the calculation.

Basic equation

$$\$50\begin{pmatrix}\text{Present Value at Age 106}\\ \text{of Whole Life Annuity Due}\end{pmatrix} = \$50\left[\begin{pmatrix}\text{Present Value at Age 106}\\ \text{of Whole Life Annuity}\end{pmatrix} + 1\right]$$

$$= \$50\begin{pmatrix}\text{Present Value at Age 106}\\ \text{of Whole Life Annuity}\end{pmatrix} + \$50$$

$$= \$21.45 + \$50$$

$$= \$71.45$$

This desired present value could also have been calculated by using the other procedure, as follows (remembering that since the first payment is due upon the evaluation date, it is not multiplied by any present value factor):

Basic equation

$$\text{Present Value} = \$50\left(\frac{l_{106} + l_{107}v + l_{108}v^2 + l_{109}v^3}{l_{106}}\right)$$

Substituting the values for the l's from Table II, for the v's from Table I ($2\frac{1}{2}\%$).

$$= \$50\left[\frac{\begin{array}{l}(167)\\ +(\ 54)(.975610)\\ +(\ 16)(.951814)\\ +(\ \ 4)(.928599)\end{array}}{167}\right]$$

$$= \$50\left[\frac{167.0000 + 52.6829 + 15.2290 + 3.7144}{167}\right]$$

$$= \$71.45$$

This answer agrees with that obtained by the use of the relationship between a whole life annuity and a whole life annuity due.

The second important relationship is that between *temporary life annuities* and *temporary life annuities due.* The following line diagrams show, as a specific example, a $500 19-year life annuity and a $500 20-year life annuity due, both evaluated at age 30:

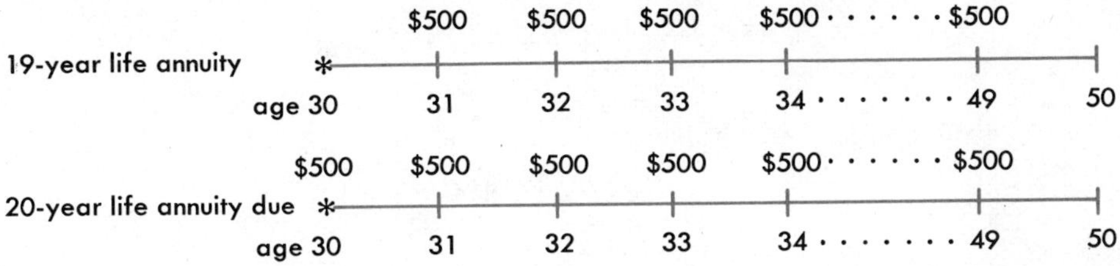

		$500	$500	$500	$500	$500	
19-year life annuity	*	+	+	+	+	+	⊣
	age 30	31	32	33	34	49	50
	$500	$500	$500	$500	$500	$500	
20-year life annuity due	*	+	+	+	+	+	⊣
	age 30	31	32	33	34	49	50

The only difference between them is the one payment of $500 on the evaluation date. This example illustrates that *the present value of a temporary life annuity due is equal to the present value of a temporary life annuity having one fewer total periods plus the amount of one payment.* In equation form, this is

$$\begin{pmatrix}\text{Present Value at Age } x\\ \text{of } n\text{-Year Life Annuity Due}\end{pmatrix} = \begin{pmatrix}\text{Present Value at Age } x\\ \text{of } (n-1)\text{-Year Life Annuity}\end{pmatrix} + 1$$

To Illustrate—Using the 1958 C.S.O. Table and 3% interest, calculate the present value at age 25 of a 4-year life annuity due of $100 per year.

Solution—The line diagram for this temporary life annuity due appears as follows:

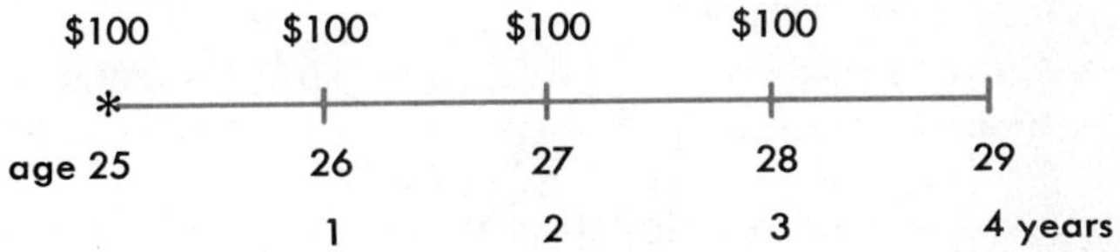

$100	$100	$100	$100	
*	+	+	+	⊣
age 25	26	27	28	29
	1	2	3	4 years

In an earlier illustration, the present value at age 25 of a 3-year life annuity of $100 per year (first payment due 1 year following age 25) was calculated to be $281.77. Using the above relationship and substituting $281.77, gives

Basic equation

$$\$100\begin{pmatrix}\text{Present Value at Age } x\\ \text{of } n\text{-Year Life Annuity Due}\end{pmatrix}$$

$$= \$100\left[\begin{pmatrix}\text{Present Value at Age } x\\ \text{of } (n-1)\text{-Year Life Annuity}\end{pmatrix} + 1\right]$$

Substituting 25 for x, 4 for n

$$\$100\begin{pmatrix}\text{Present Value at Age 25}\\ \text{of 4-Year Life Annuity Due}\end{pmatrix} = \$100\left[\begin{pmatrix}\text{Present Value at Age 25}\\ \text{of 3-Year Life Annuity}\end{pmatrix} + 1\right]$$

$$= \$100\begin{pmatrix}\text{Present Value at Age 25}\\ \text{of 3-Year Life Annuity}\end{pmatrix} + \$100$$

Substituting present value calculated above

$$= \$281.77 + \$100$$

$$= \$381.77$$

This desired present value could have been calculated by using the other procedure, as follows:

Basic equation

$$\text{Present Value} = \$100\left(\frac{l_{25} + l_{26}v + l_{27}v^2 + l_{28}v^3}{l_{25}}\right)$$

Substituting the values for the l's from Table III, for the v's from Table I (3%)

$$= \$100\left[\frac{(9{,}575{,}636) + (9{,}557{,}155)(.970874) + (9{,}538{,}423)(.942596) + (9{,}519{,}442)(.915142)}{9{,}575{,}636}\right]$$

$$= \$100\left(\frac{9{,}575{,}636 + 9{,}278{,}793 + 8{,}990{,}879 + 8{,}711{,}641}{9{,}575{,}636}\right)$$

$$= \$381.77$$

This answer agrees with that obtained by using the relationship between an n-year life annuity due and an $(n - 1)$-year life annuity.

The third important relationship involves *whole life annuities, temporary life annuities, and deferred life annuities.* This relationship is as follows: *A temporary life annuity plus a deferred life annuity (deferred the same number of years for which the temporary annuity runs) equals a whole life annuity.* The reasoning here is the same as that for annuities certain in Section 6.6 ("second method"). In equation form, this is

$$\begin{pmatrix}\text{Present Value}\\ \text{at Age } x \text{ of}\\ n\text{-Year Temporary}\\ \text{Life Annuity}\end{pmatrix} + \begin{pmatrix}\text{Present Value}\\ \text{at Age } x \text{ of}\\ \text{Life Annuity}\\ \text{Deferred } n \text{ Years}\end{pmatrix} = \begin{pmatrix}\text{Present Value}\\ \text{at Age } x \text{ of}\\ \text{Whole Life}\\ \text{Annuity}\end{pmatrix}$$

For example, a 5-year temporary life annuity plus a life annuity deferred 5 years equals a whole life annuity. This is shown in the following line diagram:

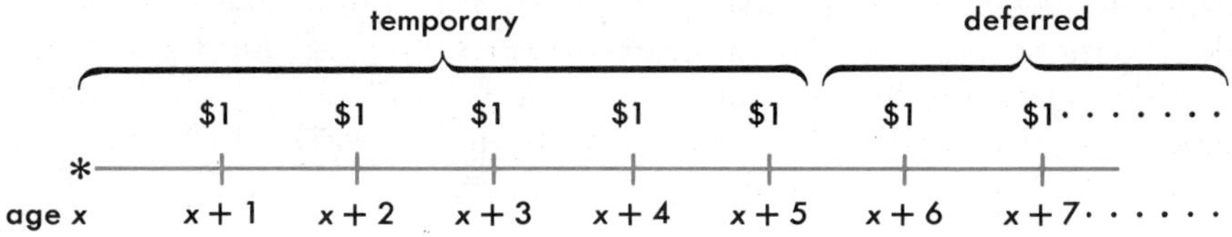

It is useful to know this relationship because published tables of life annuity values usually show only whole life annuities and temporary life annuities. The values of deferred life annuities must be obtained by some other means.

To Illustrate—If a published table gives the present value of a whole life annuity of $1 per year to a man age 40 as $18.80, and the present value of a 15-year temporary life annuity of $1 per year to a man age 40 as $12.84, find the present value of a $100 life annuity deferred for 15 years to a man age 40.

Solution—Using the present value relationship above:

Basic equation

$$\$100\begin{pmatrix}n\text{-Year}\\ \text{Temporary}\end{pmatrix} + \$100\begin{pmatrix}\text{Deferred}\\ n\text{-Years}\end{pmatrix} = \$100\text{ (Whole Life)}$$

Substituting 15 for n

$$\$100\begin{pmatrix}\text{15-Year}\\ \text{Temporary}\end{pmatrix} + \$100\begin{pmatrix}\text{Deferred}\\ \text{15 Years}\end{pmatrix} = \$100\text{ (Whole Life)}$$

Substituting the present values given

$$\$100\ (12.84) + \$100\begin{pmatrix}\text{Deferred}\\ \text{15 Years}\end{pmatrix} = \$100\ (18.80)$$

Subtracting $100 (12.84) from each side

$$\begin{aligned}\$100\begin{pmatrix}\text{Deferred}\\ \text{15 Years}\end{pmatrix} &= \$100\ (18.80) - \$100\ (12.84)\\ &= \$100\ (18.80 - 12.84)\\ &= \$100\ (5.96)\\ &= \$596\end{aligned}$$

Both life annuities (first payment at end of one period) and life annuities due (first payment at beginning) have considerable practical use in life insurance company operations. For example, annuities are widely sold whereby the buyer pays a lump sum to the insurance company, and the company then pays back a periodic income as long as the buyer lives. Here, the first payment is usually made to the buyer at the end of the first period. Hence, this is an example of a life annuity. An example of a life annuity due would be the payment of premiums on a life insurance policy. They constitute a life annuity due because money changes hands only if a designated person is alive at the time each premium is payable, this premium being payable at the beginning of each period.

EXERCISES

(Use Table II and $2\frac{1}{2}\%$ interest, unless specified differently)

1 Write an expression (using symbols) for the present value at age 10 of $250 due in 25 years, with benefit of survivorship.

2 Write an expression (using symbols) for the present value at age 65 of a 4-year temporary life annuity due of $50 per year.

3 Write an expression (using symbols) for the present value at age 20 of a deferred life annuity having 3 payments of $750 each, the first one of which is payable at age 42.

4 Write an expression (using symbols) for the present value at age 96 of a whole life annuity of $1,000 per year, assuming the mortality table which will be used is the 1958 C.S.O. Table.

5 Calculate the present value at age 70 of a $40 payment due at age 80, with benefit of survivorship.

6 If it is assumed that females will always show the same mortality experience as males 3 years younger, calculate the value for a female at age 25 of $100 due 15 years later, with benefit of survivorship. (Hint: The 3-year "setback" means that instead of using l_{25} and l_{40}, use l_{22} and l_{37}.)

7 Calculate the amount that a man age 22 should pay for the right to receive $10 per year, first payment due at age 30 and last payment due at age 33.

8 Calculate the present value at age 100 of a deferred life annuity of $1,000 per year, first payment at age 107 (payments continue for life).

9 Using the 1958 C.S.O. Table (Table III) and 3% interest, calculate the present value at age 97 of a whole life annuity due of $100 per year.

10 Calculate the present value at age 40 of a whole life annuity, deferred for 10 years, of $15 per year, using the following present value factors for 1 per year:

Present Value at Age 40 of Whole Life Annuity = 18.713
Present Value at Age 40 of 10-year Life Annuity = 8.509

8.3 ACCUMULATED VALUE OF LIFE ANNUITIES

The applications of the accumulated value of a life annuity are much less extensive than those of the present value. However, accumulated value is a useful tool in the calculation of reserves, to be presented in Chapter 11.

The *present value* of a life annuity means, in general, that amount which would be paid at the beginning to provide future payments, with benefit of survivorship. On the other hand, the *accumulated value* of a life annuity means, in general, that amount payable to a surviving person to which past payments have accumulated, with benefit of survivorship.

The development is similar to that shown for present values. To begin by accumulating a single payment, the question is asked:

> "If a man deposited $1 at age 35, how much money would he receive at age 60 if he must be alive to receive it?"

If Table II is used, the number shown as living at each of the two ages is

$$l_{35} = 9{,}814{,}474$$

$$l_{60} = 8{,}465{,}043$$

Since $1 is to be paid in by each of the l_{35} men, the total amount that will be paid in altogether is

$$\$1(l_{35}) = \$9{,}814{,}474$$

Twenty-five years later, l_{60} men will receive the money. The original question now may be stated: "How much will each receive?" The money paid in will earn interest over the 25-year period. If the rate of interest is $2\frac{1}{2}\%$, then the original $9,814,474 will accumulate as follows:

Basic equation for accumulating

$$S = A(1+i)^n$$

Substituting $9,814,474 for A, .025 for i, 25 for n

$$= \$9{,}814{,}474(1.025)^{25}$$

Substituting the value of $(1.025)^{25}$ from Table I

$$= (\$9{,}814{,}474)(1.853944)$$

$$= \$18{,}195{,}485.19$$

This sum is then divided among the l_{60} men:

$$\frac{\$18{,}195{,}485.19}{l_{60}} = \frac{\$18{,}195{,}485.19}{8{,}465{,}043}$$

$$= \$2.15$$

This \$2.15 is greater than the accumulated value calculated at interest only. The latter would be

$$S = \$1(1.025)^{25}$$
$$= \$1(1.853944)$$
$$= \$1.85$$

\$1.85 is the amount each man would receive at the end of the 25 years if all those who contributed originally were to share at the end. The \$2.15 payment with benefit of survivorship is larger because in that case only those who survive are to share in the accumulation.

In general terms, if x is the age when the deposit is made, and n is the number of years elapsed until the payment is returned to the survivors, then each survivor will receive

$$\$1\left[\frac{l_x(1+i)^n}{l_{x+n}}\right]$$

This expression states that \$1 deposited by each of the l_x persons accumulates at interest for n years, and the total is then divided among the l_{x+n} persons still alive. In equation form, this is written:

$$\left(\begin{array}{l}\text{Accumulated Value of \$1}\\ \text{at End of } n \text{ Years to a}\\ \text{Life age } x \text{ at the Beginning,}\\ \text{with Benefit of Survivorship}\end{array}\right) = \$1\left[\frac{l_x(1+i)^n}{l_{x+n}}\right]$$

This accumulation factor corresponds to $(1+i)^n$ used in Chapter 3, except that now *contingent* payments are being considered.

The factors for calculating present values and accumulated values of a single payment both with interest only and with benefit of survivorship are shown in Chart 8–2. In each case, n is the number of years involved, x is the age at the *beginning* of the time, and $x+n$ is the age at the *end* of the time:

CHART 8–2

	With Interest Only	*With Benefit of Survivorship*
Present Value Factor	$\frac{1}{(1+i)^n}$ or v^n	$\left(\frac{l_{x+n}}{l_x}\right)\left[\frac{1}{(1+i)^n}\right]$ or $\frac{l_{x+n}v^n}{l_x}$
Accumulation Factor	$(1+i)^n$	$\frac{l_x(1+i)^n}{l_{x+n}}$

The present value factor and the accumulation factor are the inverse of each other (i.e., numerator and denominator are switched). This is just as true when dealing with benefit of survivorship as when dealing with interest only.

The accumulated value of a series of payments may be handled as the total of accumulated value of each of the individual payments. For example, suppose it is desired to know the accumulated value, with benefit of survivorship, at age 65 for a three-year annuity due of $1. This means that $1 was deposited at the beginning of each of the last three years, and the accumulation will be paid to a designated person (at age 65) only if he is then alive to receive it. If he is then alive, how much will he receive? The deposits were made at ages 62, 63, and 64:

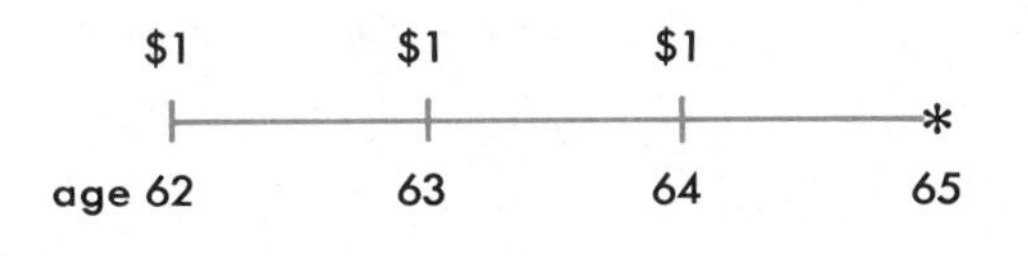

The accumulated value of each of the three payments can be calculated individually, as follows:

The Payment Due at Age 62

Basic equation

$$\text{Accumulated Value} = \$1\left[\frac{l_x(1+i)^n}{l_{x+n}}\right]$$

Substituting 62 for x (i.e., the age at the beginning), 3 for n (i.e., number of years), and .025 for i

$$= \$1\left[\frac{l_{62}(1.025)^3}{l_{65}}\right]$$

The Payment Due at Age 63

Basic equation

$$\text{Accumulated Value} = \$1\left[\frac{l_x(1+i)^n}{l_{x+n}}\right]$$

Substituting 63 for x, 2 for n, and .025 for i

$$= \$1\left[\frac{l_{63}(1.025)^2}{l_{65}}\right]$$

The Payment Due at Age 64

Basic equation

$$\text{Accumulated Value} = \$1\left[\frac{l_x(1+i)^n}{l_{x+n}}\right]$$

Substituting 64 for x, 1 for n, and .025 for i

$$= \$1\left[\frac{l_{64}(1.025)}{l_{65}}\right]$$

The accumulated value at age 65 of this annuity is the total of the three above expressions. The common multiplier ($1) can be factored out. The fractions to be added together have a common denominator (l_{65}). Hence, the accumulated value of the annuity can be expressed as

$$\text{Accumulated Value} = \$1\left[\frac{l_{62}(1.025)^3 + l_{63}(1.025)^2 + l_{64}(1.025)}{l_{65}}\right]$$

The *numerator* of this expression represents the total amount paid in by the survivors at each age, with each such amount being accumulated at interest to the evaluation date. The *denominator* represents the number of persons still alive on the evaluation date, among whom this total accumulated value will be allocated to be paid out.

To Illustrate—Using the Annuity Table for 1949 and $2\frac{1}{2}\%$ interest, calculate the accumulated value at age 40 of a life annuity of $15 per year for 4 years, first payment due at age 36.

Solution—The line diagram for this life annuity appears as follows:

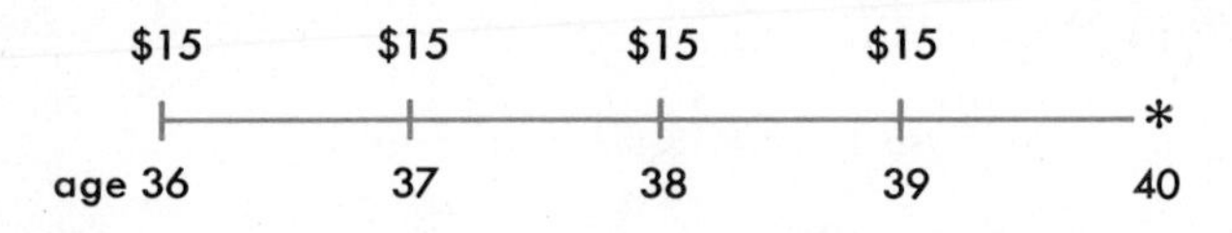

The expression for the accumulated value will have a *numerator* representing the total amount paid in by the survivors at each age, with each such amount being accumulated at interest to the evaluation date:

$$\$15[l_{36}(1+i)^4 + l_{37}(1+i)^3 + l_{38}(1+i)^2 + l_{39}(1+i)]$$

The *denominator* is the number living on the evaluation date (l_{40}).

Basic equation

$$\text{Accumulated Value} = \$15\left[\frac{l_{36}(1+i)^4 + l_{37}(1+i)^3 + l_{38}(1+i)^2 + l_{39}(1+i)}{l_{40}}\right]$$

Substituting values for the l's from Table II, for the $(1+i)$'s from Table I ($2\frac{1}{2}\%$)

$$= \$15\left[\frac{\begin{array}{l}(9{,}800{,}822)(1.103813)\\ +(9{,}786{,}180)(1.076891)\\ +(9{,}770{,}454)(1.050625)\\ +(9{,}753{,}522)(1.025000)\end{array}}{9{,}735{,}263}\right]$$

$$= \$15\left[\frac{10{,}818{,}275 + 10{,}538{,}649 + 10{,}265{,}083 + 9{,}997{,}360}{9{,}735{,}263}\right]$$

$$= \$64.13$$

This section on accumulated values of annuities has dealt only with the accumulations of temporary life annuities, because the accumulations of whole life or deferred life annuities have no application in practice.

8.4 LIFE ANNUITIES PAYABLE MORE THAN ONCE A YEAR

So far in this chapter, only life annuities payable once a year have been considered.

In actual practice, however, it is common for a series of payments (which are made only as long as the recipient is alive) to be paid more frequently than annually. Monthly social security benefits are one example. In life company operations, settlement option payments (to be presented in Section 8.5), which are most often made monthly, are another example.

Annuities of this type are difficult to analyze precisely because mortality tables generally do not record the number living at fractional intervals of a year. However, there is a simple method for calculating the present value of such annuities which gives an answer very close to the true present value.

For *whole life annuities*, the method involves calculating the present value as if payments were annual, and then *adding* a fractional part of a year's payments to this value.

For *whole life annuities due*, the method involves calculating the present value as if payments were annual, and then *subtracting* a fractional part of a year's payments from this value.

These fractions are as follows:

$\frac{1}{4}$ if payments are semiannual

$\frac{3}{8}$ if payments are quarterly

$\frac{11}{24}$ if payments are monthly

The fraction has a numerator which is always one less than the number of payments per year, and a denominator which is always two times the number of payments per year. (The mathematics by which this method was derived is beyond the scope of this book.)

To Illustrate—Using the Annuity Table for 1949 and $2\frac{1}{2}\%$ interest, calculate the present value at age 106 of a whole life annuity of $12.50 per quarter.

Solution—The total amount paid every year is ($12.50)(4) = $50. In Section 8.2, the present value at age 106 of a whole life annuity of $50 per year (with annual payments) was calculated to be $21.45. Since payments are made quarterly in this illustration, the rule states that $\frac{3}{8}$ of a year's payments must be added to this present value. Therefore, the present value of this annuity, when payments are quarterly, is

$$\begin{aligned}\text{Present Value} &= \begin{pmatrix}\text{Present Value as If}\\ \text{Payments Were Annual}\end{pmatrix} + \frac{3}{8}\begin{pmatrix}\text{A Year's}\\ \text{Payments}\end{pmatrix}\\ &= \$21.45 + \frac{3}{8}(\$50)\\ &= \$21.45 + \$18.75\\ &= \$40.20\end{aligned}$$

Since $\frac{3}{8}$ of a year's payments is added above, the present value is larger than it would be for payments being made annually, even though the total payments each year are of the same amount. This is logical, because in the particular year that the designated person dies, he may already have received one or more quarters' payments prior to his death, whereas he would have received nothing in that particular year if payments were being made annually (at the end of each year).

To Illustrate Again—Using the Annuity Table for 1949 and $2\frac{1}{2}\%$ interest, calculate the present value at age 106 of a whole life annuity *due* of $12.50 per quarter.

Solution—Here again the total amount paid every year is (12.50)(4) = $50. In Section 8.2, the present value at age 106 of a whole life annuity *due* of $50 per year (with annual payments) was calculated to be $71.45. Since payments are made quarterly in this illustration, the rule states that $\frac{3}{8}$ of a year's payments must be subtracted from this present value. Therefore, the present value of this annuity due, where payments are quarterly, is

$$\begin{aligned}\text{Present Value} &= \begin{pmatrix}\text{Present Value as If}\\ \text{Payments Were Annual}\end{pmatrix} - \frac{3}{8}\begin{pmatrix}\text{A Year's}\\ \text{Payments}\end{pmatrix}\\ &= \$71.45 - \frac{3}{8}(\$50)\\ &= \$71.45 - \$18.75\\ &= \$52.70\end{aligned}$$

Since $\frac{3}{8}$ of a year's payments is subtracted above, the present value is smaller than it would be for payments made annually, even though the total payments each year are of the same amount. This is logical, because in the particular year that the designated person dies, he may have received a few quarterly payments prior to his death, whereas he would have received a whole year's payment in that particular year if payments were being made annually (at the beginning of each year).

In actual practice, *temporary* life annuities payable more than once a year are seldom seen, but *deferred* whole life annuities payable more than once a year are of great importance. This is particularly true of settlement option payments.

The method used to evaluate *deferred* whole life annuities payable more than once a year makes use of the rules given above for evaluating whole life annuities payable more than once a year. Briefly, the present value is first found *as of the end of the deferred period,* and this present value is then discounted back to the true evaluation date by using the regular factor for finding present values (with benefit of survivorship):

$$\frac{l_{x+n}v^n}{l_x}$$

To Illustrate—Using the Annuity Table for 1949 and $2\frac{1}{2}\%$ interest, calculate the present value at age 45 of a whole life annuity of \$350 every half-year, first payment due at age 65. (It is given that the present value at age 65 of a whole life annuity due of 1 per year is 12.49597.)

Solution—The line diagram appears as follows:

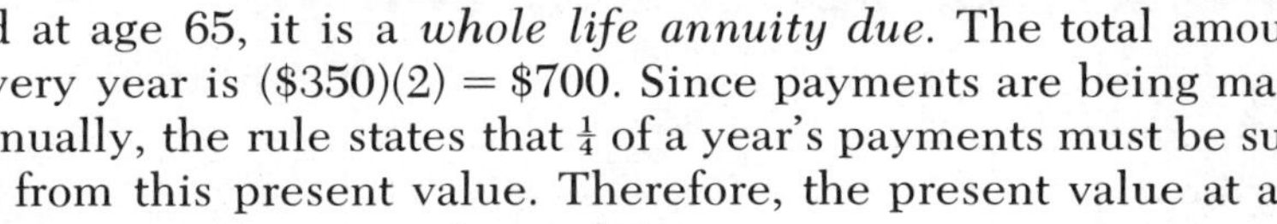

```
                         $350   $350   $350   $350   $350   $350 · · ·
  *────────────────────────┼──────┼──────┼──────┼──────┼──────┼─────
age 45 · · · · · · · · · · ·65            66            67 · · · · · · · ·
```

First, the present value will be calculated at age 65 instead of age 45. Viewed at age 65, it is a *whole life annuity due.* The total amount paid every year is (\$350)(2) = \$700. Since payments are being made semiannually, the rule states that $\frac{1}{4}$ of a year's payments must be subtracted from this present value. Therefore, the present value at age 65, when payments are semiannual, is

Basic equation

$$\begin{pmatrix}\text{Present Value}\\ \text{at Age 65}\end{pmatrix} = \begin{pmatrix}\text{Present Value as If}\\ \text{Payments Were Annual}\end{pmatrix} - \frac{1}{4}\begin{pmatrix}\text{A Year's}\\ \text{Payments}\end{pmatrix}$$

Using the given factor 12.49597 to calculate present value of an annual annuity

$$= \$700(12.49597) - \frac{1}{4}(\$700)$$

$$= \$8{,}747.18 - \$175.00$$

$$= \$8{,}572.18$$

This figure of $8,572.18 is the value *as of age* 65:

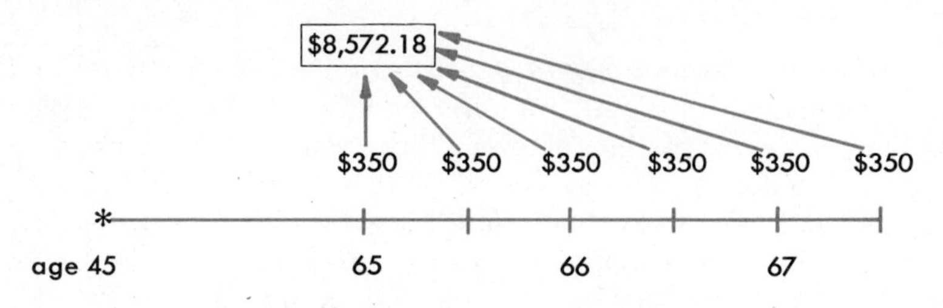

The problem is now similar to finding the present value (with benefit of survivorship) at age 45 of a *single payment* due in 20 years (at age 65):

Basic equation

$$\begin{pmatrix}\text{Present Value}\\ \text{at Age 45}\end{pmatrix} = \$8{,}572.18\left(\frac{l_{x+n}v^n}{l_x}\right)$$

Substituting 45 for x, 20 for n

$$= \$8{,}572.18\left(\frac{l_{65}v^{20}}{l_{45}}\right)$$

Substituting the values for the l's from Table II, for v^{20} from Table I ($2\frac{1}{2}\%$)

$$= \$8{,}572.18\left[\frac{(7{,}716{,}840)(.610271)}{9{,}612{,}083}\right]$$

$$= \$8{,}572.18\left[\frac{4{,}709{,}364}{9{,}612{,}083}\right]$$

$$= \$4{,}199.87$$

8.5 TABLES OF SETTLEMENT OPTIONS

At the time a settlement is made under a life insurance policy, as when a death claim is paid, the person who receives the proceeds may be entitled to receive the proceeds in periodic payments rather than in one sum. The *present value* of these periodic payments must be equal to the one-sum proceeds.

Life insurance policies contain a provision spelling out the exact types of periodic payments which are available, including either the mortality and interest assumptions to be used, or tables which incorporate these assumptions, or both. These tables are called "Tables of Settlement Options" and include options for periodic payments figured at interest only (payments *certain*) and also for periodic payments figured with benefit of survivorship (*contingent* payments).

Commonly, the options *involving interest only* are the following:

1. "Interest Option," which means that the company holds the proceeds and periodically pays out the interest thereon.
2. "Fixed Period Option," which means that the company pays out a series of equal payments for a certain period of time only, such as for 10 years (with no consideration of life contingencies). The recipient chooses the period of time, and the amount of the periodic payment is then so calculated that the present value of the series equals the proceeds.
3. "Fixed Payment Option," which means that the company pays out a series of equal payments of a certain amount, such as $100 per year (with no consideration of life contingencies). The recipient chooses the amount of the periodic payment, and the period of time is then so calculated that the present value of the series equals the proceeds.

As an example, the Tables of Settlement Options may provide that for each $1,000 of proceeds, the recipient may elect to receive instead $114.26 per year for 10 years. The $114.26 was calculated so that the present value of the 10 payments certain will equal $1,000 (using 2½% interest). This may be verified by multiplying $114.26 by the factor for $a_{\overline{10}|2\frac{1}{2}\%}$ from Table I, which is 8.752064. Calculating such tables is a common practical application of the principles of Section 6.7, "Amortization Payments."

These options must be calculated at fairly low interest rates, such as 2½%, because the company, by printing these tables in the policy, is actually guaranteeing that it will pay this rate of interest to somebody at some time many years in the future (if the recipient then wishes it). The actual interest rate which the company will be able to afford to pay many years in the future is unknown at the time these guaranteed figures are printed in the policy.

Commonly, the options *involving contingent payments* are the following:

1. "Life Income Option," which means that the company pays out a series of equal payments for as long as the recipient lives.
2. "Life Income Option with Period Certain," which means that the company pays out a series of equal payments for a designated period of time (such as 10 years or 20 years), these payments being *certain* and not contingent; thereafter payments will continue for as long as the recipient lives.
3. "Life Income Option with Refund," which means that the company pays out a series of equal payments, and the payments are *certain* until such time as the total paid out equals the proceeds; thereafter payments will continue for as long as the recipient lives.

As an example of the "Life Income Option," consider the accompanying portion of a table which might appear in the policy. It shows the annual payment available for each $1,000 of proceeds. The payments would continue for as long as the recipient lives. The amounts are dependent upon the age of the recipient at the time he applies for the proceeds:

Age	*Annual Payment*
.	.
.	.
.	.
63	$80.85
64	83.81
65	86.99
.	.
.	.

The above annual payments are calculated so that the present value of the whole life annuity will equal $1,000 using Table II. This may be verified for age 65 by multiplying $86.99 by the factor for the present value at age 65 of a whole life annuity of 1 per year, which is 11.49597. This example assumes the first payment is made at the end of the first period. In practice, payments are more often calculated to provide the first payment at the beginning.

The "Life Income Option with Period Certain" represents a combination of a *temporary annuity certain* and a *deferred life annuity.* An example would be annual payments for five years certain and as long thereafter as the recipient lives:

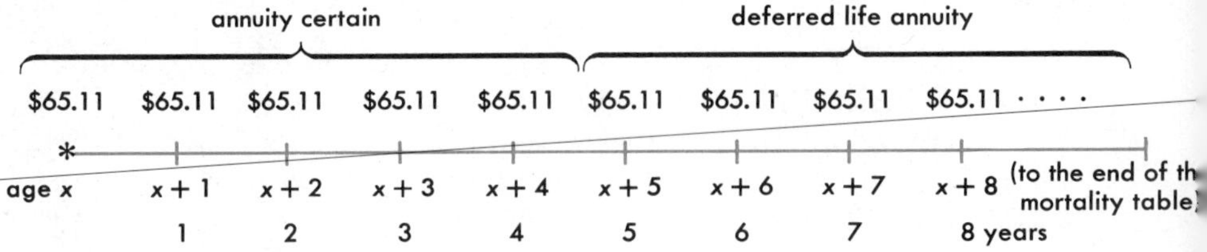

annuity certain | deferred life annuity

	$65.11	$65.11	$65.11	$65.11	$65.11	$65.11	$65.11	$65.11	$65.11 . . . .
age x	*	$x+1$	$x+2$	$x+3$	$x+4$	$x+5$	$x+6$	$x+7$	$x+8$ (to the end of the mortality table)
		1	2	3	4	5	6	7	8 years

The present value of the first five payments illustrated above, which are $65.11 each and constitute an annuity due, is

$$\$65.11\ddot{a}_{\overline{5}|i}$$

using interest only, because they are payments certain. The present value of the remainder of the payments is

$$\$65.11\left(\frac{l_{x+5}v^5 + l_{x+6}v^6 + l_{x+7}v^7 + \cdots \text{ to the end of the mortality table}}{l_x}\right)$$

The payments represent a deferred life annuity (first payment due at age $x + 5$). The total of these two present values, then, must be equal to the proceeds which the person is entitled to receive at age x.

The "Life Income Option with Refund" provides a life income to the original recipient; but if this recipient should die before an amount equal to the total proceeds has been paid out, income installments will be continued to a successor-payee until this amount has been paid. The payments are *certain* until all the proceeds have been "refunded." Thereafter, the payments are contingent on the life of the original recipient. Under this option, the period during which the payments are certain is determined by the size of each payment. Conversely, the size of each payment is determined by the period of time during which the payments are certain. This is because the present value of all the payments must equal the proceeds, and the number of payments affects this present value. Consequently, the calculation of a table showing installments payable under the Life Income Option with Refund requires the use of methods of higher mathematics. If a table is available showing the size of each payment, the period for which payments are certain is found by dividing the proceeds by the amount of each payment.

The "Life Income Option with Refund" described above is sometimes called the *Installment Refund* option. A slight variation of it is the *Cash Refund* option, which provides that if the recipient dies before the proceeds have been "refunded," the balance necessary to completely refund the proceeds is all paid at once by the company. The calculations involved in this second type are also beyond the scope of this text.

Since the present value of a *certain* payment is greater than the present value of a *contingent* payment, it follows that the amount of each payment will be smaller under options providing for more certain payments. For example, a typical Settlement Option Table might show the following monthly payments available at a certain age, per $1,000 of proceeds:

$6.68 Life Income (no payments certain)

$6.22 Life Income with 120 months certain

$5.15 Life Income with 240 months certain

As the number of certain payments *increases*, the amount of each payment *decreases*. In addition, the above table might show:

$5.78 Life Income with refund

The period during which these $5.78 payments are certain is found as follows:

$\$1{,}000 \div \$5.78 = \text{approximately } 173$

That is, in 173 months the $1,000 proceeds will have been "refunded." This also follows the above pattern, since the $5.78 falls between $6.22 (the 120-month payment) and $5.15 (the 240-month payment).

It is well to remember that in the complete array of figures printed in a Table of Settlement Options, every figure shares the common characteristic that the present value of those payments equals $1,000 (because the tables show figures per $1,000 of proceeds). In actual practice, companies are usually willing to set up payments in almost any manner the recipient desires, as long as the present value equals the proceeds available.

To Illustrate—Using the Annuity Table for 1949 and $2\frac{1}{2}\%$ interest, calculate the amount of annual payment for age 92, per $1,000 of proceeds, in a settlement option which provides payments for 15 years certain and for life thereafter.

Solution—If it is assumed that the first payment is made at the beginning, then the line diagram appears as follows:

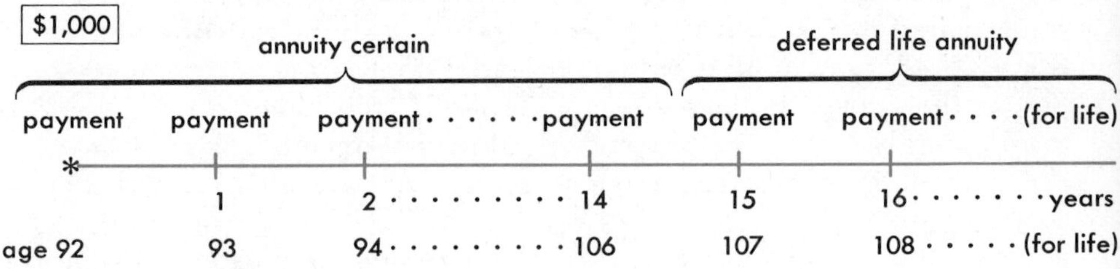

$1,000

annuity certain				deferred life annuity	
payment	payment	payment · · · · ·	· payment	payment	payment · · · · (for life)
*	1	2 · · · · · · · · ·	14	15	16 · · · · · · · years
age 92	93	94 · · · · · · · · ·	106	107	108 · · · · · (for life)

The present value of the 15 payments certain is

Basic equation

$$\text{Present Value} = (\text{Payment})\, \ddot{a}_{\overline{15}|2\frac{1}{2}\%}$$

Using the equation $\ddot{a}_{\overline{n}|i} = a_{\overline{n-1}|i} + 1$

$$= (\text{Payment})(a_{\overline{14}|2\frac{1}{2}\%} + 1)$$

Substituting the value for $a_{\overline{14}|2\frac{1}{2}\%}$ from Table I

$$= (\text{Payment})(11.690912 + 1)$$

$$= (\text{Payment})(12.690912)$$

The present value of the life annuity due, deferred 15 years (first payment at age 107), is

Basic equation (age 109 is highest age in Annuity Table for 1949)

$$\text{Present Value} = (\text{Payment})\left(\frac{l_{107}v^{15} + l_{108}v^{16} + l_{109}v^{17}}{l_{92}}\right)$$

Substituting the values for the l's from Table II, for the v's from Table I ($2\frac{1}{2}\%$)

$$= (\text{Payment})\left[\frac{\begin{array}{l}(54)(.690466)\\+(16)(.673625)\\+\ (4)(.657195)\end{array}}{565{,}326}\right]$$

$$= (\text{Payment})\left[\frac{37.2852 + 10.7780 + 2.6288}{565{,}326}\right]$$

$$= (\text{Payment})(.000090)$$

The total of the two present values must equal \$1,000:

$$(\text{Payment})(12.690912) + (\text{Payment})(.000090) = \$1{,}000$$

Factoring out the common multiplier, "Payment"

$$(\text{Payment})(12.690912 + .000090) = \$1{,}000$$

$$(\text{Payment})(12.691002) = \$1{,}000$$

$$\text{Payment} = \$78.80$$

In addition to the settlement options described in this section, options are sometimes available which are even more complicated, such as life annuities depending on one or more of several persons being alive.

8.6 LIFE ANNUITIES PAYABLE CONTINUOUSLY

Life annuities have been discussed which are payable more often than once a year, such as monthly. It is interesting to see what happens when the periodic payments become even more frequent than monthly. For instance, payments might be made weekly, or daily, or hourly, or every minute, etc. The ultimate frequency would be that payments would be made *continuously*. This concept is only theoretical and could not exist in practice, but there are places where this concept is used by life insurance companies in making certain calculations.

In evaluating life annuities payable more than once a year, the amount of the periodic payment has been multiplied by the number of payments per year to arrive at the total amount paid in a year's time. Obviously, this approach will not be possible in dealing with life annuities payable continuously, because the number of payments per year is infinitely large and the amount of each such payment is infinitesimally small. Instead, the total amount paid in a year's time must always be given. For example, "a whole life annuity of $25 payable continuously" means that the total of all the infinitesimally small payments being paid continuously is $25 each year.

To calculate the present value of such annuities, the same approximate method is applied that is used for other life annuities payable more than once a year. As set forth in Section 8.4, the fraction of a year's payments which is added or subtracted has a numerator which is always 1 less than the number of payments per year, and a denominator which is always 2 times the number of payments per year. As the number of payments per year gets bigger and bigger, this fraction gets closer and closer to being $\frac{1}{2}$. By using some methods of higher mathematics, it can be proved that when the payments are made continuously, the fraction does equal $\frac{1}{2}$. Hence, the fraction to be used in calculation is $\frac{1}{2}$ if payments are continuous.

To Illustrate—Using the Annuity Table for 1949 and $2\frac{1}{2}\%$ interest, calculate the present value at age 106 of a whole life annuity of $50 per year payable continuously.

Solution—When an annuity is payable continuously, it can be looked upon as either an annuity immediate or an annuity due; it makes no difference because the terms become meaningless. The calculation will be presented both ways to show that the answer is the same either way.

In Section 8.2, the present value at age 106 of a whole life annuity *immediate* of $50 per year (with annual payments) was calculated to be $21.45. Since payments are made continuously in this illustration, $\frac{1}{2}$ of a year's payments must be *added to this present value.* Therefore, the present value of this annuity, where payments are continuous, is

$$\text{Present Value} = \begin{pmatrix}\text{Present Value as If}\\ \text{Payments Were Annual}\end{pmatrix} + \frac{1}{2}\begin{pmatrix}\text{A Year's}\\ \text{Payments}\end{pmatrix}$$

$$= \$21.45 + \frac{1}{2}(\$50)$$

$$= \$21.45 + \$25$$

$$= \$46.45$$

Also in Section 8.2, the present value at age 106 of a whole life annuity *due* of $50 per year (with annual payments) was calculated to be $71.45. Since payments are made continuously in this illustration, $\frac{1}{2}$ of a year's payments must be *subtracted from this present value.*

Therefore, the present value of this annuity due, where payments are continuous, is

$$\text{Present Value} = \begin{pmatrix}\text{Present Value as If}\\ \text{Payments Were Annual}\end{pmatrix} - \frac{1}{2}\begin{pmatrix}\text{A Year's}\\ \text{Payments}\end{pmatrix}$$

$$= \$71.45 - \frac{1}{2}(\$50)$$

$$= \$71.45 - \$25$$

$$= \$46.45$$

This answer agrees with the first answer.

Calculation of the present value of a *deferred* life annuity payable continuously follows exactly the same method as shown for other life annuities. The present value is first calculated *as of the end of the deferred period* (so it is treated like a whole life annuity). Then the present value of this value at the evaluation age is found by multiplying by the factor for finding present value:

$$\frac{l_{x+n}v^n}{l_x}$$

EXERCISES

(Use Table II and $2\frac{1}{2}\%$ interest, unless specified differently)

1. Write an expression (using symbols) for the accumulated value at age 65 of $1,000 paid in at age 20, with benefit of survivorship.
2. Write an expression (using symbols) for the accumulated value at age 25 of a 4-year life annuity of $25 per year, first payment at age 21.
3. A man deposits $100 with an insurance company at age 65. What amount should the company pay him 5 years later, if the payment is conditioned on his being alive to receive it?
4. It is given that the present value at age 33 of a whole life annuity (immediate) of 1 per year is 24.764575. Calculate the present value of a whole life annuity (immediate) of $100 per year at age 33 if the payments are made: semiannually, quarterly, monthly, continuously.
5. Calculate the same present values requested in Exercise 4, but for an annuity due.
6. Using the factor given in Exercise 4, calculate the present value at age 20 of a whole life annuity due of $2 per month beginning at age 33.
7. Using the factor given in Exercise 4, calculate the amount of annual payment which would be shown in a Table of Settlement Options for the whole life annuity due option at age 33 (first payment at beginning).

8 If the beneficiary of a life insurance policy elects to receive the proceeds in yearly payments of $565 each (first payment at once) for 5 years certain, find the amount of the proceeds.

8.7 COMMUTATION FUNCTIONS

FOR EVALUATING A SINGLE PAYMENT. When dealing with payments *certain*, tabulated values for the present value and accumulated value factors (such as Table I) aid in performing calculations. When benefit of survivorship is involved, these factors are much more complicated. For example, the factor for the present value of a payment of 1 (with benefit of survivorship)

$$\frac{l_{x+n}v^n}{l_x}$$

is different for each *age* and *number of years*. Tabulated values of this factor, as well as factors for the present value of temporary and whole life annuities, are generally published for the common mortality tables and interest rates. Such tabulations are quite voluminous, however. In practice, another aid in performing calculations is widely used, namely, *commutation functions* (sometimes called *commutation symbols*).

To see how commutation functions are used and how they simplify the work, consider again the expression for finding present values of a contingent payment due in n years to a life now age x:

$$\frac{l_{x+n}v^n}{l_x}$$

As will be seen later, it will be very useful to have the numerator and denominator look similar to each other. This is accomplished by multiplying numerator and denominator both by v^x:

$$\frac{(l_{x+n}v^n)(v^x)}{(l_x)(v^x)} = \frac{l_{x+n}v^{x+n}}{l_xv^x}$$

The value of the fraction is unchanged by multiplying both the numerator and the denominator by the same amount. In the numerator, v^n multiplied by v^x equals v^{x+n} (adding exponents when multiplying). The numerator and denominator above now look similar to each other, since in each case the subscript of the l is the same as the exponent of the v.

Obviously, then, it would be extremely useful to have l_xv^x already calculated for all values of x (based on a desired mortality table and interest rate). This value of l_x multiplied by v^x is represented by the commutation symbol

$$D_x$$

The following, then, is the definition of the D_x symbol:

$$D_x = l_x v^x$$

In Table II and Table IV, columns of D_x are shown for the Annuity Table for 1949 at $2\frac{1}{2}\%$ and for the 1958 C.S.O. Table at 3%, respectively.

As an example, using age 20 in Table IV, the value of D_{20} can be verified by multiplying l_{20} (from Table III) by v^{20} at 3% (from Table I):

Basic equation

$$D_x = l_x v^x$$

Substituting 20 for x

$$D_{20} = l_{20} v^{20}$$

Substituting the values for l_{20} and v^{20} from the tables

$$= (9{,}664{,}994)(.553676)$$

$$= 5{,}351{,}275$$

The values of D_x in Table IV were derived using more decimal places in v^x. Nevertheless, the above answer is very close to that shown in the Table for D_{20}.

Above, the factor for finding present values of a contingent payment due in n years to a life now age x was finally expressed as

$$\frac{l_{x+n} v^{x+n}}{l_x v^x}$$

The numerator is equal to D_{x+n}, since the definition of a "D" is l multiplied by v (the subscript of the l being the same as the exponent of the v, and this then being the subscript of the D). The denominator is equal to D_x. Hence the factor for finding present values may be expressed

$$\begin{pmatrix} \text{Present Value of \$1} \\ \text{Due in } n \text{ Years to a} \\ \text{Life Now Age } x\text{, with} \\ \text{Benefit of Survivorship} \end{pmatrix} = \$1 \left(\frac{D_{x+n}}{D_x} \right)$$

In the above expression, the subscript of D in the *numerator* is the age when the contingent payment is to be made. The subscript of D in the *denominator* is the age at which the present value is being evaluated.

The value of this factor

$$\frac{D_{x+n}}{D_x}$$

is the same as the value of the factor used previously

$$\frac{l_{x+n}v^n}{l_x}$$

but the D's are easier to use in making calculations.

In the example given in Section 8.1, the present value at age 35 of \$100 payable at age 60 (with benefit of survivorship) would be

$$\$100\left(\frac{D_{60}}{D_{35}}\right)$$

Using values of D from Table II, this becomes

$$\$100\left(\frac{1{,}923{,}965}{4{,}135{,}535}\right) = \$46.52$$

The answer is the same as before, but the calculation is simplified.

To Illustrate—Using Table IV, calculate the present value at age 20 of \$400 due in 15 years if the person is then still alive.

Solution—This is the same problem as shown in the illustration in Section 8.1. The solution will now be given using commutation functions.

Basic equation

$$\text{Present Value} = \$400\left(\frac{D_{x+n}}{D_x}\right)$$

Substituting 20 for x, 15 for n

$$= \$400\left(\frac{D_{35}}{D_{20}}\right)$$

Substituting the values for D_{35} and D_{20} from Table IV

$$= \$400\left(\frac{3{,}331{,}295}{5{,}351{,}273}\right)$$

$$= \$249.01$$

This answer agrees with that calculated in Section 8.1.

The factor for calculating the *accumulated* value of a single payment by using commutation functions is the *inverse* of the *present value* factor (i.e., numerator and denominator are switched):

$$\begin{pmatrix}\text{Accumulated Value of \$1}\\ \text{at End of } n \text{ Years to a}\\ \text{Life Age } x \text{ at the Beginning}\\ \text{with Benefit of Survivorship}\end{pmatrix} = \$1\left(\frac{D_x}{D_{x+n}}\right)$$

Note that in this expression, it is still true that the subscript of D in the *numerator* is the age when the contingent payment is to be made. The subscript of D in the *denominator* is the age at which the accumulated value is being evaluated.

FOR EVALUATING AN ANNUITY. The present value at age x of a whole life annuity due of \$1 per year may be expressed as the total of the present values of the individual payments:

$$\text{Present Value} = \$1\left(\frac{D_x}{D_x}\right) + \$1\left(\frac{D_{x+1}}{D_x}\right) + \$1\left(\frac{D_{x+2}}{D_x}\right) + \cdots \text{ to the end of the mortality table}$$

The common multiplier (\$1) can be factored out. The fractions to be added together all have a common denominator (D_x). Hence, the present value of the annuity can be expressed as follows:

$$\text{Present Value} = \$1\left[\frac{D_x + D_{x+1} + D_{x+2} + \cdots \text{ to the end of the mortality table}}{D_x}\right]$$

In order to avoid the necessity of adding together all the D's to the end of the mortality table, this total is also tabulated. This total of the D's to the end of the mortality table is represented by the commutation symbol

$$N_x$$

the subscript of the N being the same as that of the first D in the series.

The following, then, is the definition of the N_x symbol:

$$N_x = (D_x + D_{x+1} + D_{x+2} + \cdots \text{ to the end of the mortality table})$$

In Table II and Table IV, columns of N_x are shown for the Annuity Table for 1949 at $2\frac{1}{2}\%$ and for the 1958 C.S.O. Table at 3%, respectively.

As an example, using age 104 in Table II, the value of N_{104} can be verified by adding the D's starting with D_{104} to the end of the mortality table:

Basic equation

$$N_x = (D_x + D_{x+1} + D_{x+2} + \cdots \text{ to the end of the mortality table})$$

Substituting 104 for x

$$N_{104} = D_{104} + D_{105} + D_{106} + D_{107} + D_{108} + D_{109}$$

Substituting the values for the D's from Table II

$$= 89 + 35 + 12 + 4 + 1 + 0$$

$$= 141$$

This value agrees with that shown in the Table for N_{104}.

The commutation function N_x can also be used to simplify the calculation of *temporary* life annuities. In the example given in Section 8.2, the present value at age 25 of a life annuity of $100 per year for three years, first payment due at age 26, would be

$$\$100\left(\frac{D_{26}+D_{27}+D_{28}}{D_{25}}\right)$$

Here the total of the D's to the end of the mortality table is not needed, but only the total for three years. This can be found by taking N_{26} (the total of the D's from age 26 to the end of the table) and *subtracting* N_{29} (the total of the D's from age 29 to the end of the table). What remains after the subtraction is $D_{26}+D_{27}+D_{28}$. That is,

$$\$100\left(\frac{D_{26}+D_{27}+D_{28}}{D_{25}}\right)=\$100\left(\frac{N_{26}-N_{29}}{D_{25}}\right)$$

Using values of N and D from Table IV, this becomes

$$\$100\left(\frac{108{,}616{,}223-95{,}729{,}800}{4{,}573{,}377}\right)=\$281.77$$

The answer is the same as that calculated in Section 8.2.

A general statement may be made that the factor to use in evaluating a life annuity will be of the form $\frac{N-N}{D}$, where the subscript of the first N is the age when the first payment is due, the subscript of the second N is the first age when there are no more payments due (i.e., one greater than the age when the last payment is due), and the subscript of the D is the age at which the annuity is being evaluated (or paid for). Also, the difference between the subscripts of the two N's equals the actual number of payments. If the payments are to be made for life, the second N does not appear.

To Illustrate—Using Table II, calculate the present value at age 40 of a deferred temporary life annuity of $1,500 per year, first payment at age 50 and last payment at age 53.

Solution—This is the same problem as shown in an illustration in Section 8.2. The solution will now be given by using commutation functions:

Basic equation; subscript of first N is age at first payment; subscript of second N is one age greater than when last payment is due; subscript of D is evaluation age

$$\text{Present Value}=\$1{,}500\left(\frac{N_{50}-N_{54}}{D_{40}}\right)$$

Substituting the values for N_{50}, N_{54}, and D_{40} from Table II

$$= \$1{,}500\left(\frac{51{,}853{,}713 - 41{,}429{,}812}{3{,}625{,}710}\right)$$

$$= \$4{,}312.49$$

This answer agrees with that calculated in Section 8.2.

One commutation symbol standing by itself has no usefulness. When commutation functions are used, they must be involved in a fraction; that is, one or more commutation functions must be divided by one or more other commutation functions. The reason underlying this is the fact that present values or accumulated values (with benefit of survivorship) always involve probabilities of living or dying. Such probabilities are calculated by dividing some number of persons living (or dying) by some number of persons living.

EXERCISES

(Use Table II, unless specified differently)

1 Write an expression (using commutation functions) for the present value at age 24 of $1,000 payable at age 62 (if alive); calculate the value.

2 Write an expression (using commutation functions) for the accumulated value, with benefit of survivorship, at age 63 of $500 deposited with an insurance company when a man is age 21; calculate the value.

3 Calculate the values of $\frac{D_x}{D_{25}}$ for $x = 35$, 40, 45 and 50. Compare the results with the corresponding values of the present value factor, v^n, for $n = 10$, 15, 20 and 25 at $2\frac{1}{2}\%$ using Table I.

4 If females will exhibit the same mortality as males who are 5 years younger, calculate the amount which a woman now age 30 would receive back 20 years later if she deposits $100 now, to accumulate with benefit of survivorship. (Hint: The 5-year "setback" means that instead of using $\frac{D_{30}}{D_{50}}$, use $\frac{D_{25}}{D_{45}}$.

5 Write expressions (using commutation functions) for the present value at age 23 of a whole life annuity of $1 per year, with the first payment at age 23; age 24; age 55. Calculate the values.

6 Write an expression (using commutation functions) for the present value at age 36 of a deferred 10-year life annuity of $100 per year, first payment due at age 46; calculate the value.

7 Calculate the value at age 35 of a whole life annuity due of $1,500 per year.

8 Calculate the amount a man age 45 should pay for a life annuity due of $1,000 per year, which has payments for 10 years only.

9 What is the present value to a man age 64 of a temporary life annuity of $100 per year for 3 years?

10 Construct a schedule showing that the value found in Exercise 9 will provide the benefits specified.

11 An insurance company has sold a life insurance policy to a man age 25 with premiums of $18.09 payable every year for life. What is the present value at the time the policy is sold of all the future premiums the company will receive?

12 State in words what each of the following expressions represents:

$$\$100\left(\frac{N_{69}}{D_{20}}\right)$$

$$\$100\left(\frac{N_{69}-N_{79}}{D_{20}}\right)$$

8.8 SYMBOLS FOR LIFE ANNUITIES

Chart 8–3 displays certain internationally used symbols, each of which represents the present value at age x of a life annuity of 1 per

CHART 8–3

Present Value at Age x of Life Annuity of 1 per Year

Type of Life Annuity	*Symbol for Present Value*	*Present Value Using Commutation Functions*
Whole Life Annuity	a_x	$\frac{N_{x+1}}{D_x}$
Whole Life Annuity Due	$\ddot{a}_x$	$\frac{N_x}{D_x}$
Temporary Life Annuity for n Years	$a_{x:\overline{n}\rceil}$	$\frac{N_{x+1}-N_{x+n+1}}{D_x}$
Temporary Life Annuity Due for n Years	$\ddot{a}_{x:\overline{n}\rceil}$	$\frac{N_x-N_{x+n}}{D_x}$
Whole Life Annuity, Deferred for m Years	$_{m\|}a_x$	$\frac{N_{x+m+1}}{D_x}$
Whole Life Annuity Due, Deferred for m Years	$_{m\|}\ddot{a}_x$	$\frac{N_{x+m}}{D_x}$
Temporary Life Annuity for n Years, Deferred for m Years	$_{m\|}a_{x:\overline{n}\rceil}$	$\frac{N_{x+m+1}-N_{x+m+n+1}}{D_x}$
Temporary Life Annuity Due for n Years, Deferred for m Years	$_{m\|}\ddot{a}_{x:\overline{n}\rceil}$	$\frac{N_{x+m}-N_{x+m+n}}{D_x}$

year. (These present values are also shown as they would be calculated using commutation functions.)

The use of "*a*" with the number of years under an "angle" is analogous with the symbol $a_{\overline{n}|i}$ given in Chapter 6 for the present value of an annuity certain. For life annuities, however, the age at which the present value is calculated also becomes a part of the symbol. For example, $a_{x:\overline{n}|}$ (read "a sub x angle n") represents the present value at age x of an n-year life annuity.

The use of two dots over the "*a*" is also analogous to the usage in annuities certain, indicating an annuity due.

Life annuity symbols wherein a *bar* is placed over the "*a*" represent annuities payable continuously. For example:

$$\bar{a}_x$$

is the internationally used symbol for the present value at age x of a whole life annuity of 1 per year payable continuously.

9. Life Insurance, Net Single Premiums

In Chapter 8, payments were discussed which are made only if a designated person is alive. Life insurance involves a payment to be made only when a designated person dies. The amount of such a payment is called the amount of insurance or the death benefit.

It is common in life insurance for all of the figures quoted in connection with such insurance to be based upon a death benefit of $1,000. Accordingly, for a policy with a $25,000 death benefit, all such figures would be multiplied by 25. This was seen in connection with Tables of Settlement Options in Section 8.5. In discussing premiums in this book, it will also be assumed that the unit policy is $1,000.

9.1 NET SINGLE PREMIUM FOR ONE YEAR OF LIFE INSURANCE—THE NATURAL PREMIUM

The present value of the benefits offered by a particular insurance policy is equal to the *net single premium.* This amount is calculated using a designated mortality table and a specified interest rate. The net single premium does not include any amount for expenses or profits.

It may be desired, for example, to calculate the net single premium that a man age 25 should pay for $1,000 of life insurance covering a one-year period. Under such insurance, if he dies before reaching age 26, $1,000 will be paid to his beneficiary. To begin solving the problem, it is necessary to consult a mortality table. If Table III is used, the numbers shown living and dying at age 25 are

$$l_{25} = 9{,}575{,}636$$

$$d_{25} = \quad 18{,}481$$

This means that if there is a group of 9,575,636 men alive at age 25, then 18,481 men of this group may be expected to die during the year (before reaching age 26). In order to find the net single premium, it is assumed that all of these men are individually involved, that is, that each one who dies that year will receive $1,000 (to be paid to the recipient designated). For purposes of simplifying some of the calculations, it is customary to assume that all such payments are made at the end of the year in which death occurs. In actual practice, however, such payments are made very soon after death occurs. The methods of calculation used when payments are assumed to be made "at the moment of death" will be described in Section 9.7.

Since a $1,000 benefit is to be paid for each of the d_{25} men, the total amount that will be paid out as benefits is

$$\$1{,}000d_{25} = (\$1{,}000)(18{,}481)$$
$$= \$18{,}481{,}000$$

One year earlier, l_{25} men will pay the money in. The original problem may now be stated: "How much will each pay?" The total amount paid in is

$$\begin{pmatrix}\text{Amount Each} \\ \text{Pays In}\end{pmatrix}(l_{25}) = \begin{pmatrix}\text{Amount Each} \\ \text{Pays In}\end{pmatrix}(9{,}575{,}636)$$

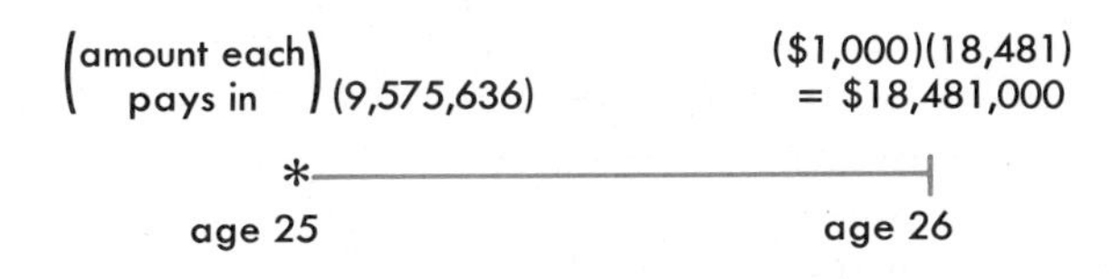

The money paid in will earn interest over the one-year period. For this example, the rate will be assumed to be 3%. The basic equation for finding present value can be used to show that *all the money paid in equals the present value of all the money to be paid out one year later*. The "amount each pays in" can then be solved for:

$$A = Sv^n$$

Substituting $\begin{pmatrix}\text{Amount Each}\\ \text{Pays In}\end{pmatrix}$(9,575,636) for A, \$18,481,000 for S and the value of v^1 at 3% from the table

$$\begin{pmatrix}\text{Amount Each}\\ \text{Pays In}\end{pmatrix}(9{,}575{,}636) = (\$18{,}481{,}000)(.970874)$$

$$\begin{pmatrix}\text{Amount Each}\\ \text{Pays In}\end{pmatrix}(9{,}575{,}636) = \$17{,}942{,}722$$

$$\begin{pmatrix}\text{Amount Each}\\ \text{Pays In}\end{pmatrix} = \$1.87$$

It can be demonstrated that \$1.87 is the desired net single premium at age 25 to provide \$1,000 of insurance for a one-year period, as follows:

$$\begin{aligned}\text{Total amount paid in} &= \$1.87(l_{25})\\ &= \$1.87(9{,}575{,}636)\\ &= \$17{,}906{,}439.32\end{aligned}$$

Total amount accumulated at 3% to the end of the year

$$\begin{aligned}&= \$17{,}906{,}439.32(1 + i)\\ &= \$17{,}906{,}439.32(1.03)\\ &= \$18{,}443{,}632.50\end{aligned}$$

Amount payable for each who dies during the year (the accumulated fund divided by the number who die)

$$\begin{aligned}&= \$18{,}443{,}632.50 \div d_{25}\\ &= \$18{,}443{,}632.50 \div 18{,}481\\ &= \$998 \text{ approximately}\end{aligned}$$

(The missing \$2 results from rounding off \$1.87 to the nearest cent, instead of using more decimal places.)

This net single premium for one year of life insurance at age 25 is also called the "natural premium" at age 25. It could be written as

$$\$1{,}000\left(\frac{d_{25}}{l_{25}}\right)v$$

or as

$$\frac{\$1{,}000 d_{25} v}{l_{25}}$$

Both these expressions for the natural premium permit interesting verbal interpretations. In the first, $\left(\frac{d_{25}}{l_{25}}\right)$ equals the probability that a person age 25 will die before reaching age 26 (q_{25}). The first expression says that the $1,000 is multiplied by the probability of dying and also by the regular factor for finding present values at interest. The second expression says that the $1,000 payable to each of d_{25} persons is discounted at interest for one year, and this amount is divided among the l_{25} persons to find out how much each must pay in.

Using more general terms, the equation for the natural premium is

$$\begin{pmatrix}\text{Net Single Premium for}\\ \text{\$1,000 Death Benefit}\\ \text{to a Life Age } x\text{, If}\\ \text{Death Occurs in 1 Year}\end{pmatrix} = \$1{,}000\left(\frac{d_x v}{l_x}\right)$$

To Illustrate—Using the 1958 C.S.O. Table (Table III) and 3% interest, calculate the net single premium for 1 year of life insurance of $1,000 at age 40; also at age 60; also at age 80.

At Age 40

Basic equation

$$\begin{pmatrix}\text{Net Single}\\ \text{Premium}\end{pmatrix} = \$1{,}000\left(\frac{d_x v}{l_x}\right)$$

Substituting 40 for x

$$= \$1{,}000\left(\frac{d_{40} v}{l_{40}}\right)$$

Substituting values from the tables

$$= \$1{,}000\left[\frac{(32{,}622)(.970874)}{9{,}241{,}359}\right]$$

$$= \$3.43$$

At Age 60

$$\begin{pmatrix}\text{Net Single}\\ \text{Premium}\end{pmatrix} = \$1{,}000\left(\frac{d_x v}{l_x}\right)$$

Substituting 60 for x

$$= \$1{,}000\left(\frac{d_{60} v}{l_{60}}\right)$$

Substituting values from the tables

$$= \$1{,}000\left[\frac{(156{,}592)(.970874)}{7{,}698{,}698}\right]$$

$$= \$19.75$$

At Age 80

Basic equation

$$\begin{pmatrix}\text{Net Single}\\\text{Premium}\end{pmatrix} = \$1{,}000\left(\frac{d_x v}{l_x}\right)$$

Substituting 80 for x

$$= \$1{,}000\left(\frac{d_{80} v}{l_{80}}\right)$$

Substituting values from the tables

$$= \$1{,}000\left[\frac{(288{,}848)(.970874)}{2{,}626{,}372}\right]$$

$$= \$106.78$$

It can be seen that the net single premium for one year of insurance, the natural premium, increases sharply at the older ages. This is similar to the age-by-age increase in the values of q_x (the probability of dying within one year) shown in Chapter 7.

9.2 NET SINGLE PREMIUMS FOR TERM INSURANCE

Life insurance which provides a benefit if death occurs during a specified period of years is known as *term insurance.* The one-year insurance considered in the above section is one-year term insurance.

To determine the net single premiums for life insurance for longer periods, the procedure is basically the same. For example, it may be desired to find the net single premium at age 25 for $1,000 of insurance during a period of three years (between ages 25 and 28), i.e., for three-year term insurance. The total amount to be paid out for those who die during the first year is

$$\$1{,}000 d_{25}$$

Assuming such payments are made at the *end of the year,* the present value at age 25 of those payments is

$$\$1{,}000 d_{25} v$$

The total amount to be paid out for those who die during the second year is

$$\$1{,}000 d_{26}$$

Assuming such payments are made at the end of the year, the present value at age 25 of those payments is

$$\$1{,}000 d_{26} v^2$$

The total amount to be paid out for those who die during the third year is

$$\$1{,}000d_{27}$$

Assuming such payments are made at the end of the year, the present value at age 25 of those payments is

$$\$1{,}000d_{27}v^3$$

(In each case the exponent of the v is the number of years between age 25 and the date when the death benefit is paid.)

The present value at age 25 of all the death benefits paid during the three-year period is the total of the three individual present values. The common multiplier (\$1,000) can be factored out:

$$\text{Present Value} = \$1{,}000(d_{25}v + d_{26}v^2 + d_{27}v^3)$$

This amount is paid in at age 25 by the l_{25} persons. Hence, the above expression should be divided by l_{25} to find out how much each must pay in (the net single premium):

$$\begin{pmatrix}\text{Net Single}\\ \text{Premium}\end{pmatrix} = \$1{,}000\left(\frac{d_{25}v + d_{26}v^2 + d_{27}v^3}{l_{25}}\right)$$

The *numerator* of this expression represents the total to be paid out for those who die in each of the three years, with each such amount being discounted at interest from the end of the year of death to the evaluation date. The *denominator* represents the number of persons alive on the evaluation date, among whom this total present value to be paid in must be allocated.

If, for example, the 1958 C.S.O. Table and 3% interest are used, the value of this net single premium can be calculated as follows:

From above

$$\begin{pmatrix}\text{Net Single}\\ \text{Premium}\end{pmatrix} = \$1{,}000\left(\frac{d_{25}v + d_{26}v^2 + d_{27}v^3}{l_{25}}\right)$$

Substituting values from the tables

$$= \$1{,}000\left[\frac{\begin{array}{r}(18{,}481)(.970874)\\ +(18{,}732)(.942596)\\ +(18{,}981)(.915142)\end{array}}{9{,}575{,}636}\right]$$

$$= \$1{,}000\left(\frac{17{,}943 + 17{,}657 + 17{,}370}{9{,}575{,}636}\right)$$

$$= \$5.53$$

It can be demonstrated that if each of the l_{25} persons pays \$5.53, the resulting fund will provide $1,000 (at the end of the year of death) for all who die before age 28. At the beginning of the first year, the amount paid in is

$$\$5.53 l_{25} = (\$5.53)(9{,}575{,}636)$$
$$= \$52{,}953{,}267.08$$

At the end of one year, interest earned on the fund is equal to

$$(\$52{,}953{,}267.08)(.03) = \$1{,}588{,}598.01$$

Hence, the total fund at that time is

$$\$52{,}953{,}267.08 + \$1{,}588{,}598.01 = \$54{,}541{,}865.09$$

From this total fund, $1,000 is deducted for each person who has died during the first year:

$$\$1{,}000 d_{25} = (\$1{,}000)(18{,}481)$$
$$= \$18{,}481{,}000$$

This leaves a balance in the fund of

$$\$54{,}541{,}865.09 - \$18{,}481{,}000 = \$36{,}060{,}865.09$$

The continued operation of the fund for succeeding years may be traced in the accompanying schedule (Chart 9–1). The final shortage in the fund represents less than $1 for each person dying the final year, and results from rounding off the net single premium to two decimal places.

CHART 9–1

(1) *Year*	(2) *Fund at Beginning of Year* *(Col. 6 of Previous Year)*	(3) *Interest for One Year* *(Col. 2 × .03)*	(4) *Total Fund at End of Year before Payment of Death Claims* *(Col. 2 + Col. 3)*	(5) *Claims Paid at End of Year* *(Number of Deaths × $1,000)*	(6) *Balance of Fund at End of Year After Payment of Claims* *(Col. 4 − Col. 5)*
1	$52,953,267.08	$1,588,598.01	$54,541,865.09	$18,481,000	$36,060,865.09
2	36,060,865.09	1,081,825.95	37,142,691.04	18,732,000	18,410,691.04
3	18,410,691.04	552,320.73	18,963,011.77	18,981,000	−17,988.23

To Illustrate—Using the 1958 C.S.O. Table (Table III) and 3% interest, calculate the net single premium at age 50 for $5,000 of 2-year term insurance.

Solution—The line diagram for this life insurance appears as follows:

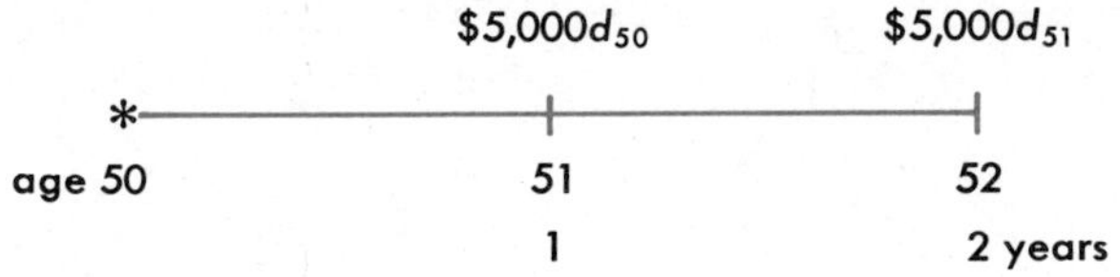

	$5,000$d_{50}$	$5,000$d_{51}$
*	+	+
age 50	51	52
	1	2 years

The expression for the net single premium is a fraction with a *numerator* equal to the total of the amounts to be paid out for those who die in each of the 2 years, discounted at interest from the end of each year of death to the evaluation date:

$$\$5000 d_{50} v + \$5000 d_{51} v^2$$

or

$$\$5000 (d_{50} v + d_{51} v^2)$$

The *denominator* of the fraction is the number living on the evaluation date at age 50:

Basic equation

$$\begin{pmatrix}\text{Net Single}\\ \text{Premium}\end{pmatrix} = \$5{,}000 \left(\frac{d_{50} v + d_{51} v^2}{l_{50}}\right)$$

Substituting values from the tables

$$= \$5{,}000 \left[\frac{(72{,}902)(.970874) + (79{,}160)(.942596)}{8{,}762{,}306}\right]$$

$$= \$5{,}000 \left(\frac{70{,}779 + 74{,}616}{8{,}762{,}306}\right)$$

$$= \$82.97$$

9.3 NET SINGLE PREMIUMS FOR WHOLE LIFE INSURANCE

Under whole life insurance, the death benefit will be paid whenever death occurs; that is, the period of years covered by the insurance extends to the end of the mortality table. Thus, whole life insurance may be looked upon as term insurance covering a period of years equal to those remaining in the mortality table.

The calculation of the net single premium for whole life insurance follows exactly the same procedure as that shown above for term insurance. In the case of whole life insurance, the years included extend to the end of the mortality table.

To Illustrate—Using the 1958 C.S.O. Table and 3% interest, calculate the net single premium at age 96 for $1,000 of whole life insurance.

Solution—The period of years covered by this insurance extends for the person's entire lifetime. However, since the 1958 C.S.O. Table assumes that no persons live beyond the age of 100, it is assumed that the insurance ends at age 100. The line diagram for this whole life insurance appears as follows:

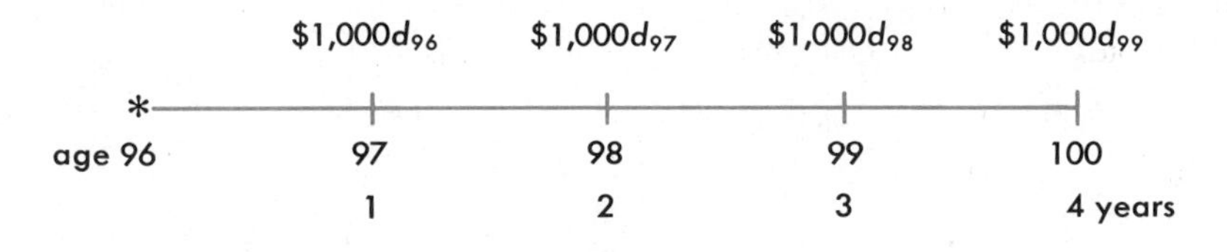

The expression for the net single premium is a fraction with a *numerator* representing the total to be paid out for those who die in each of the years, with each such amount being discounted at interest from the end of the year of death to the evaluation date. The *denominator* of the fraction is the number living on the evaluation date:

Basic equation

$$\begin{pmatrix}\text{Net Single}\\\text{Premium}\end{pmatrix} = \$1{,}000\left(\frac{d_{96}v + d_{97}v^2 + d_{98}v^3 + d_{99}v^4}{l_{96}}\right)$$

Substituting values from the tables

$$= \$1{,}000\left[\frac{\begin{array}{r}(25{,}250)(.970874)\\+(18{,}456)(.942596)\\+(12{,}916)(.915142)\\+(\ \ 6{,}415)(.888487)\end{array}}{63{,}037}\right]$$

$$= \$1{,}000\left(\frac{24{,}515 + 17{,}397 + 11{,}820 + 5{,}700}{63{,}037}\right)$$

$$= \$942.81$$

The calculation of net single premiums for whole life insurance at the younger ages would become very laborious if the above procedure were used. Therefore, in actual practice this calculation is usually done by using commutation functions. The commutation functions which apply in net single premium calculations will be explained in Section 9.8.

9.4 NET SINGLE PREMIUMS FOR A PURE ENDOWMENT

A *pure endowment* is an amount which is paid on a certain date only if a designated person is then alive to receive it. It is, therefore, the opposite of life insurance. It is, in fact, the same as a payment which is made with benefit of survivorship, as described in Chapter 8. Pure endowments are often combined with life insurance, as will be shown in Section 9.5. In that context, the term "net single premium for a pure endowment" is used instead of "present value of a single payment with benefit of survivorship."

Since the principles and equations for such a payment were presented in Section 8.1, the following equation will be given here without further explanation:

$$\begin{pmatrix}\text{Net Single Premium for}\\ \text{\$1,000 Pure Endowment to}\\ \text{a Life Age } x\text{, Due at the}\\ \text{End of } n \text{ Years}\end{pmatrix} = \$1{,}000\left(\frac{l_{x+n}v^{n}}{l_x}\right)$$

To Illustrate—Using the 1958 C.S.O. Table and 3% interest, calculate the net single premium for a female age 34 for a $5,000 pure endowment due in 25 years, using a "3-year setback" for females.

Solution—The line diagram for this pure endowment appears as follows:

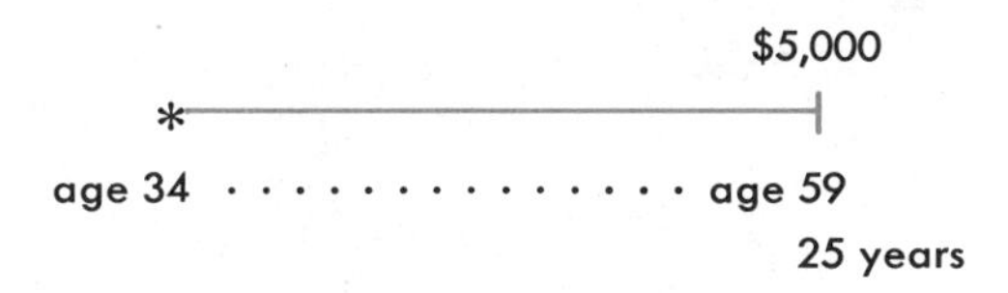

The female's age at the date the pure endowment is due is 34 + 25 = 59. The use of a "3-year setback" means that 3 years must be subtracted from the age before using the Table. The problem must be treated as if the age were 34 − 3 = 31, and the pure endowment were payable at age 59 − 3 = 56:

Basic equation

$$\begin{pmatrix}\text{Net Single}\\ \text{Premium}\end{pmatrix} = \$5{,}000\left(\frac{l_{x+n}v^{n}}{l_x}\right)$$

Substituting 31 for x, 25 for n

$$= \$5{,}000\left(\frac{l_{56}v^{25}}{l_{31}}\right)$$

Substituting values from the tables

$$= \$5{,}000\left[\frac{(8{,}223{,}010)(.477606)}{9{,}460{,}165}\right]$$

$$= \$2{,}075.73$$

9.5 NET SINGLE PREMIUMS FOR ENDOWMENT INSURANCE

Endowment insurance means that the benefit will be paid if death occurs during a specified number of years, or the benefit will be paid at the end of that period if the person is then alive. Therefore, endowment insurance is a combination of two benefits already presented: *term insurance* and *pure endowment*. The payment on death constitutes term insurance, while the payment on survival constitutes a pure endowment.

To Illustrate—Using the 1958 C.S.O. Table and 3% interest, calculate the net single premium at age 62 for a $7,500 endowment-at-age-65 insurance policy.

Solution—The policy provides that $7,500 will be paid if death occurs during the period between ages 62 and 65. It also provides that $7,500 will be paid at age 65 if the person is then alive. The line diagram for this endowment insurance policy appears as follows:

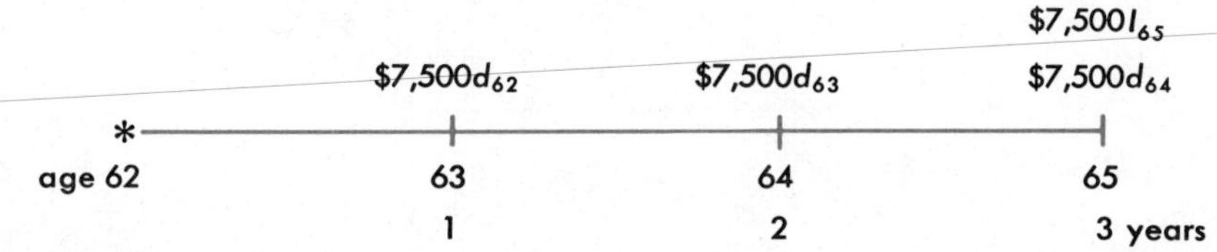

			$\$7{,}500 l_{65}$
	$\$7{,}500 d_{62}$	$\$7{,}500 d_{63}$	$\$7{,}500 d_{64}$
*	+	+	+
age 62	63	64	65
	1	2	3 years

The expression for the net single premium for the *term insurance part* has a *numerator* representing the total to be paid out for those who die each year, with each such amount being discounted at interest from the end of the year of death to the evaluation date. The *denominator* is the number living on the evaluation date. The common multiplier ($7,500) can be factored out:

$$\begin{pmatrix}\text{Net Single Premium for}\\ \text{Term Insurance Part}\end{pmatrix} = \$7{,}500\left(\frac{d_{62}v + d_{63}v^2 + d_{64}v^3}{l_{62}}\right)$$

The expression for the net single premium for the *pure endowment part* follows from the equation given in Section 9.4:

$$\begin{pmatrix}\text{Net Single Premium for}\\ \text{Pure Endowment Part}\end{pmatrix} = \$7{,}500\left(\frac{l_{x+n}v^n}{l_x}\right)$$

$$= \$7{,}500\left(\frac{l_{65}v^3}{l_{62}}\right)$$

The expression for the net single premium for the entire *endowment insurance policy* is the total of the above two expressions. The two expressions can be readily added, since they already have a common denominator (l_{62}). The common multiplier ($7,500) can be factored out:

Adding the above expressions

$$\begin{pmatrix}\text{Net Single}\\ \text{Premium}\end{pmatrix} = \$7{,}500\left(\frac{d_{62}v + d_{63}v^2 + d_{64}v^3 + l_{65}v^3}{l_{62}}\right)$$

Substituting values from the tables

$$= \$7{,}500\left[\frac{\begin{array}{l}(179{,}271)(.970874)\\ +(191{,}174)(.942596)\\ +(203{,}394)(.915142)\\ +(6{,}800{,}531)(.915142)\end{array}}{7{,}374{,}370}\right]$$

$$= \$7{,}500\left[\frac{174{,}050 + 180{,}200 + 186{,}134 + 6{,}223{,}452}{7{,}374{,}370}\right]$$

$$= \$6{,}879.06$$

It should be noted that the exponents on the last two v's are the same in the expression above. (d_{64} and l_{65} are both multiplied by v^3.) This is done because the two benefits are payable on the same date: the death benefit for those who die during the final year, and the pure endowment benefit for those still alive at the end of the final year.

The two separate parts of the net single premium for endowment insurance (term insurance and pure endowment) can be calculated separately if it is desired to know the relative contribution of each to the total net premium. For example, Chart 9–2 shows such figures (according to the 1958 C.S.O. Table at 3%) for 20-year endowment insurance issued at ages 20, 40, and 60.

CHART 9–2

Net Single Premiums per $1,000

	Age 20	*Age 40*	*Age 60*
20-Year Term	$ 31.77	$115.08	$474.22
20-Year Pure Endowment	529.41	461.25	188.88
TOTAL = 20-Year Endowment Policy	$561.18	$576.33	$663.10

9.6 THE ACCUMULATED COST OF INSURANCE

The net single premium which would have to be paid at the *end* of the term of coverage (by the survivors) to provide the death benefits for those who had died during the term is called the *accumulated cost of insurance.* Although this sort of arrangement may seem impractical, useful application of the accumulated cost of insurance will be demonstrated in Chapter 11.

It may be desired, for example, to calculate the accumulated cost of insurance at age 28 for $1,000 of insurance during a period of three years (i.e., between ages 25 and 28). The total amount to be paid out for those who die during the first year is

$$\$1{,}000d_{25}$$

Assuming the payments are made at the end of the year, these payments, accumulated at interest to the evaluation date (two years later at age 28), would amount to

$$\$1{,}000d_{25}(1+i)^2$$

The total amount to be paid for those who die during the second year is

$$\$1{,}000d_{26}$$

Accumulated at interest from the end of the year to the evaluation date (one year later at age 28), this would amount to

$$\$1{,}000d_{26}(1+i)$$

The total amount to be paid to those who die during the third year is

$$\$1{,}000d_{27}$$

Assuming such payments are made at the end of the year, the value at age 28 of those payments is

$$\$1{,}000d_{27}$$

because payment would be made upon the evaluation date (at age 28). In each case the exponent of the $(1+i)$ is the number of years between the date when the death benefit is paid and age 28.

The accumulated value at age 28 of all the death benefits paid during the three-year period is the total of the three individual accumulated values. The common multiplier ($1,000) can be factored out.

$$\text{Accumulated Value} = \$1{,}000\,[d_{25}(1+i)^2 + d_{26}(1+i) + d_{27}]$$

This amount is paid in at age 28 by the survivors. Hence, the above expression should be divided by l_{28} to find out how much each must pay in (the accumulated cost of insurance):

$$\begin{pmatrix}\text{Accumulated Cost}\\ \text{of Insurance}\end{pmatrix} = \$1{,}000\left[\frac{d_{25}(1+i)^2 + d_{26}(1+i) + d_{27}}{l_{28}}\right]$$

The *numerator* of this expression represents the total to be paid out for those who die in each of the years, with each such amount being accumulated at interest from the end of the year of death to the evaluation date. The *denominator* represents the number of persons alive on the evaluation date, among whom this total accumulated cost must be allocated to be paid in.

If, for example, the 1958 C.S.O. Table and 3% interest are used, the value of this accumulated cost can be calculated as follows:

Equation above

$$\begin{pmatrix}\text{Accumulated Cost}\\ \text{of Insurance}\end{pmatrix} = \$1{,}000\left[\frac{d_{25}(1+i)^2 + d_{26}(1+i) + d_{27}}{l_{28}}\right]$$

Substituting values from the tables

$$= \$1{,}000\left[\frac{\begin{array}{l}(18{,}481)(1.060900)\\ +(18{,}732)(1.030000)\\ +(18{,}981)\end{array}}{9{,}519{,}442}\right]$$

$$= \$1{,}000\left[\frac{19{,}606 + 19{,}294 + 18{,}981}{9{,}519{,}442}\right]$$

$$= \$6.08$$

In Section 9.2, the net single premium (payable at age 25) for this same term insurance was calculated to be $5.53. The accumulated cost calculated above (payable at age 28) can be verified by multiplying the net single premium by the factor for accumulating with benefit of survivorship (described in Section 8.3):

Basic equation

$$\begin{pmatrix}\text{Accumulated Cost}\\ \text{of Insurance}\end{pmatrix} = \begin{pmatrix}\text{Net Single}\\ \text{Premium}\end{pmatrix}\left[\frac{l_x(1+i)^n}{l_{x+n}}\right]$$

Substituting 25 for x, 3 for n

$$= \begin{pmatrix}\text{Net Single}\\ \text{Premium}\end{pmatrix}\left[\frac{l_{25}(1+i)^3}{l_{28}}\right]$$

Substituting $5.53 for net single premium, and values from the tables

$$= \$5.53\left[\frac{(9{,}575{,}636)(1.092727)}{9{,}519{,}442}\right]$$

$$= \$6.08$$

These two calculations agree.

To Illustrate— Using the 1958 C.S.O. Table and 3% interest, calculate the accumulated cost of insurance at age 65 for $15,000 of 2-year term insurance.

Solution—The line diagram for this life insurance appears as follows:

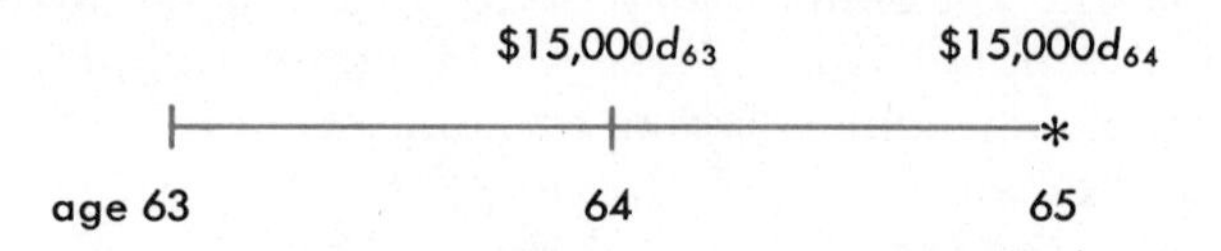

The expression for the accumulated cost will have a *numerator* representing the total to be paid out for those who die in each of the years, with each such amount being accumulated at interest from the end of the year of death to the evaluation date:

$$\$15{,}000 d_{63}(1+i) + \$15{,}000 d_{64}$$

The common multiplier ($15,000) can be factored out. The *denominator* is the number living on the evaluation date (l_{65}):

Basic equation

$$\begin{pmatrix}\text{Accumulated Cost}\\ \text{of Insurance}\end{pmatrix} = \$15{,}000\left[\frac{d_{63}(1+i)+d_{64}}{l_{65}}\right]$$

Substituting values from the tables

$$= \$15{,}000\left[\frac{(191{,}174)(1.030000) + (203{,}394)}{6{,}800{,}531}\right]$$

$$= \$15{,}000\left[\frac{196{,}909 + 203{,}394}{6{,}800{,}531}\right]$$

$$= \$882.95$$

9.7 INSURANCE PAYABLE AT THE MOMENT OF DEATH

The net single premiums and accumulated costs of insurance discussed so far in this chapter have involved the assumption that all payments for deaths are made at the *end of the year* in which death occurs. In actual practice, such payments are made very soon after death occurs.

If it is assumed that deaths are uniformly distributed throughout any year, then it is possible to assume that all deaths during any year occur at the middle of the year. The deaths during the first half of the year counterbalance those taking place in the last half of the year.

If all payments for deaths are made at the middle of the year, such payments are made one half-year earlier than at the end of the year of death. Consequently, the life insurance company is losing interest for one half of a year on the amount of the death benefit.

A common company procedure, which is approximately correct, is to calculate the net single premium on the basis of a death benefit which is increased by one-half year's interest. That is, when assuming that payments for deaths are made at the moment of death, the death benefit is multiplied by

$$\left(1+\frac{1}{2}i\right)$$

If, for example, the interest rate is .03, half of this interest rate is .015, and therefore the death benefit is multiplied by 1.015.

It is important to note, however, that in the case of endowment insurance the *pure endowment* part of the net single premium is not so multiplied. This is because the actual payment of this benefit always takes place at the end of the year.

To Illustrate—Using the 1958 C.S.O. Table and 3% interest, calculate the net single premium at age 25 for a $1,000 3-year term insurance policy, assuming the insurance is payable at the moment of death.

Solution—Assuming the insurance is payable at the moment of death, the death benefit ($1,000) is multiplied by $(1+\frac{1}{2}i)$ for purposes of calculation:

$$\begin{aligned}\text{Death Benefit} &= \$1{,}000\left(1+\frac{1}{2}i\right)\\ &= \$1{,}000\left(1+\frac{1}{2}\text{ of }.03\right)\\ &= \$1{,}000\,(1.015)\end{aligned}$$

The net single premium for this same 3-year term insurance policy, with the death benefit of $1,000 assumed to be paid at the end of the year, was calculated in Section 9.2 to be $5.53. Hence, if the death benefit is 1.015 times as great, the net single premium would be

$$(\$5.53)(1.015) = \$5.61$$

To Illustrate Again—Using the 1958 C.S.O. Table and 3% interest, calculate the net single premium at age 60 for a $1,000 20-year endowment policy, assuming the insurance is payable at the moment of death.

Solution—The *term insurance* part is payable at the moment of death. Therefore, its net single premium (calculated previously on the assumption that insurance is payable at the end of the year) is multiplied by $(1 + \frac{1}{2}i)$. The *pure endowment* part is payable at the end of the year (at age $60 + 20 = 80$). Therefore, its net single premium is not so multiplied.

The net single premiums for the two parts of this same $1,000 endowment policy, with the death benefit assumed to be paid at the end of the year, were given in Section 9.5 to be

Term Part	$474.22
Pure Endowment Part..........................	188.88

Hence, if the death benefit for purposes of net premium calculation is $(1 + \frac{1}{2}i)$ times as great, the net single premium would be

Term Part....................$474.22(1.015) =	$481.33
Pure Endowment Part..........................	188.88
Total	$670.21

EXERCISES

(Use Table III and 3% interest for all of the following)

1. Write an expression (using symbols) for the net single premium at age 25 for $4,000 of 1-year term insurance. Calculate this premium.
2. Write an expression (using symbols) for the net single premium at age 45 for $1,000 of 3-year term insurance. Calculate this premium.
3. Write an expression (using symbols) for the net single premium at age 97 for $10,000 of whole life insurance. Calculate this premium.
4. Write an expression (using symbols) for the net single premium at age 50 for a $1,000 pure endowment payable at age 65. Calculate this premium.
5. Write an expression (using symbols) for the net single premium at age 20 for a $5,000 3-year endowment insurance policy. Calculate this premium.
6. Calculate separately the term insurance part and the pure endowment part of the answer to Exercise 5.
7. Construct a schedule showing that the net single premium calculated in Exercise 5 is sufficient to provide all of the benefits of the policy.
8. Write an expression (using symbols) for the accumulated cost of insurance at age 22 for $1,000 of 3-year term insurance. Calculate this cost.
9. The net single premium at age 25 for $1,000 of whole life insurance (1958 C.S.O. Table with 3% interest) is $279.14. Calculate the net single premium for this same insurance policy, assuming that the insurance is payable at the moment of death.

10 Calculate the net single premium for the endowment insurance policy described in Exercise 5, assuming that the insurance is payable at the moment of death. (Hint: Use the information developed in working Exercise 6.)

9.8 COMMUTATION FUNCTIONS

FOR ONE-YEAR TERM INSURANCE. To see how commutation functions are used in calculating net single premiums, consider again the expression for the net single premium for a death benefit of 1 to a life age x if death occurs in one year (the natural premium):

$$\frac{d_x v^1}{l_x}$$

The same procedure is followed here as was shown in Chapter 8, namely, both the numerator and the denominator are multiplied by v^x:

$$\frac{(d_x v^1)(v^x)}{(l_x)(v^x)} = \frac{d_x v^{x+1}}{l_x v^x}$$

The value of the fraction is unchanged by multiplying both the numerator and the denominator by the same amount. In the numerator, v^1 multiplied by v^x equals v^{x+1} (adding exponents when multiplying).

Looking at the numerator, it is seen that it would be useful to have $d_x v^{x+1}$ already calculated for all values of x (based on a desired mortality table and interest rate). This value of d_x multiplied by v^{x+1} is represented by the commutation symbol:

$$C_x$$

The following, then, is the definition of the C_x symbol:

$$C_x = d_x v^{x+1}$$

In Table IV, columns of C_x are shown for the 1958 C.S.O. Table at 3%.

As an example, using age 20 in Table IV, the value of C_{20} can be verified by multiplying d_{20} (from Table III) by v^{21} at 3% (from Table I):

Basic equation

$$C_x = d_x v^{x+1}$$

Substituting 20 for x

$$C_{20} = d_{20} v^{21}$$

Substituting values from the tables

$$= (17{,}300)(.537549)$$

$$= 9{,}300$$

This agrees with the value given in Table IV.

Above, the factor for finding the net single premium for one year of insurance to a life age x was finally expressed as

$$\frac{d_x v^{x+1}}{l_x v^x}$$

The numerator is equal to C_x (because C_x is defined as d_x multiplied by v^{x+1}). The denominator is equal to D_x (because D_x is defined as l_x multiplied by v^x). Hence, the factor for finding the net single premium for one-year term insurance may be expressed

$$\begin{pmatrix}\text{Net Single Premium for}\\ \text{\$1,000 Death Benefit}\\ \text{to a Life Age } x\text{, If}\\ \text{Death Occurs in 1 Year}\end{pmatrix} = \$1{,}000\left(\frac{C_x}{D_x}\right)$$

The value of this factor

$$\frac{C_x}{D_x}$$

is the same as the value of the factor for the natural premium used previously:

$$\frac{d_x v^1}{l_x}$$

but the commutation functions are easier to use in making calculations.

In the example given in Section 9.1, the net single premium at age 25 for $1,000 of one-year term insurance would be

$$\$1{,}000\left(\frac{C_{25}}{D_{25}}\right)$$

Using values for the commutation functions from Table IV, this becomes

$$\$1{,}000\left(\frac{8{,}570}{4{,}573{,}377}\right) = \$1.87$$

The answer is the same as before, but the calculation is simplified.

To Illustrate—Using Table IV, calculate the net single premium at age 40 for one year of life insurance of $1,000.

Solution—This is the same problem as shown in the illustration in Section 9.1. The solution will now be given by using commutation functions:

Basic equation

$$\begin{pmatrix}\text{Net Single}\\ \text{Premium}\end{pmatrix} = \$1{,}000\left(\frac{C_x}{D_x}\right)$$

Substituting 40 for x

$$= \$1{,}000\left(\frac{C_{40}}{D_{40}}\right)$$

Substituting values from Table IV

$$= \$1{,}000\left(\frac{9{,}709}{2{,}833{,}002}\right)$$

$$= \$3.43$$

This answer agrees with that calculated in Section 9.1

FOR OTHER BENEFITS. The net single premium at age x for \$1,000 of *whole life insurance* may be expressed as the following total of the net single premiums for the individual years' insurance (with the subscripts of the D's all being the age at the evaluation date):

$$\begin{pmatrix}\text{Net Single}\\ \text{Premium}\end{pmatrix} = \$1{,}000\left(\frac{C_x}{D_x}\right) + \$1{,}000\left(\frac{C_{x+1}}{D_x}\right) + \$1{,}000\left(\frac{C_{x+2}}{D_x}\right) + \cdots \text{ to the end of the mortality table}$$

The common multiplier (\$1,000) can be factored out. The fractions to be added together all have a common denominator (D_x). Accordingly, the net single premium for the whole life insurance can be expressed as

$$\begin{pmatrix}\text{Net Single}\\ \text{Premium}\end{pmatrix} = \$1{,}000\left[\frac{C_x + C_{x+1} + C_{x+2} + \cdots \text{ to the end of the mortality table}}{D_x}\right]$$

In order to avoid the necessity of adding together all the C's to the end of the mortality table, this total is also tabulated. The total of the C's to the end of the mortality table is represented by the commutation symbol

$$M_x$$

the subscript of the M being the same as that of the first C in the series.

The following, then, is the definition of the M_x symbol:

$$M_x = (C_x + C_{x+1} + C_{x+2} + \cdots \text{ to the end of the mortality table})$$

In Table IV, columns of M_x are shown for the 1958 C.S.O. Table at 3%.

The commutation function M_x can also be used to simplify the calculation of *term insurance* and *endowment insurance* net single premiums. In the example given in Section 9.2, the net single premium at age 25 for $1,000 of three-year term insurance is

$$\$1{,}000\left(\frac{C_{25}+C_{26}+C_{27}}{D_{25}}\right)$$

Here the total of the C's to the end of the mortality table is not needed, but only the total for three years. This total can be found by taking M_{25} (the total of the C's from age 25 to the end of the table) and subtracting M_{28} (the total of the C's from age 28 to the end of the table). What remains after the subtraction is $C_{25}+C_{26}+C_{27}$. That is,

$$\$1{,}000\left(\frac{C_{25}+C_{26}+C_{27}}{D_{25}}\right)=\$1{,}000\left(\frac{M_{25}-M_{28}}{D_{25}}\right)$$

Using values of M and D from Table IV, this becomes

$$\$1{,}000\left(\frac{1{,}276{,}590-1{,}251{,}291}{4{,}573{,}377}\right)=\$5.53$$

The answer is the same as that calculated in Section 9.2.

A general statement may be made that the factor to use in calculating a net single premium or an accumulated cost of insurance will be of the form $\frac{M-M+D}{D}$, where the subscript of the first M is the age when the insurance coverage begins; the subscript of the second M is the age at which the insurance coverage stops (i.e., one greater than the last age covered); the subscript of the D in the numerator is the age at which a pure endowment would be paid; and the subscript of the D in the denominator is the age at which this net single premium or accumulated cost of insurance is paid. The difference between the subscripts of the M's equals the actual number of years of insurance coverage. If there is no pure endowment involved, the D in the numerator does not appear. If the insurance is for the whole of life, the second M does not appear.

To Illustrate—Using Table IV, calculate the net single premium at age 50 for $5,000 of 2-year term insurance.

Solution—This is the same problem as shown in the illustration in Section 9.2. The solution will now be given by using commutation functions. In the general expression given above, the D in the numerator will not appear, because there is no pure endowment involved:

Basic equation (subscripts of the M's define the period of coverage; subscript of D is the evaluation age)

$$\begin{pmatrix}\text{Net Single}\\ \text{Premium}\end{pmatrix} = \$5{,}000\left(\frac{M_{50} - M_{52}}{D_{50}}\right)$$

Substituting values from Table IV

$$= \$5{,}000\left(\frac{1{,}028{,}986 - 995{,}821}{1{,}998{,}744}\right)$$

$$= \$82.96$$

This answer is only 1 cent different from that calculated in Section 9.2.

To Illustrate Again—Using Table IV, calculate the net single premium at age 96 for \$1,000 of whole life insurance.

Solution—This is the same problem as shown in the illustration in Section 9.3. The solution will now be given by using commutation functions. In the general expression for net single premiums, the second M will not appear, because the insurance is for the whole of life. Also, the D in the numerator will not appear, because there is no pure endowment involved:

Basic equation

$$\begin{pmatrix}\text{Net Single}\\ \text{Premium}\end{pmatrix} = \$1{,}000\left(\frac{M_{96}}{D_{96}}\right)$$

Substituting values from Table IV

$$= \$1{,}000\left(\frac{3{,}481}{3{,}692}\right)$$

$$= \$942.85$$

This answer is only 4 cents different from that calculated in Section 9.3.

To Illustrate Again—Using Table IV, calculate the net single premium at age 62 for a \$7,500 endowment-at-age-65 insurance policy.

Solution—This is the same problem as shown in the illustration in Section 9.5. The solution will now be given by using commutation functions:

Basic equation (subscripts of the M's define the period of coverage; subscript of D in numerator is age of pure endowment; subscript of D in denominator is evaluation age)

$$\begin{pmatrix}\text{Net Single}\\ \text{Premium}\end{pmatrix} = \$7{,}500\left(\frac{M_{62} - M_{65} + D_{65}}{D_{62}}\right)$$

Substituting values from Table IV

$$= \$7{,}500\left(\frac{773{,}206 - 686{,}750 + 995{,}688}{1{,}179{,}823}\right)$$

$$= \$6{,}879.07$$

This answer is only one cent different from that calculated in Section 9.5.

The form $\frac{M - M + D}{D}$ is also used to compute the accumulated cost of insurance. However, the evaluation date for the accumulated cost of insurance is at the *end* of the term of coverage, whereas the net single premium is evaluated at the *beginning*. This is because the accumulated cost of insurance represents the amount that would have to be paid by the survivors at the end of the term of coverage, while the net single premium is the amount to be paid by those living at the beginning of the term of coverage. Therefore, when the accumulated cost is computed, the subscript of the D in the denominator is the highest age.

To Illustrate—Using Table IV, calculate the accumulated cost of insurance at age 28 for $1,000 of 3-year term insurance.

Solution—This is the same 3-year term policy for which the net single premium was calculated on page 208 to be $5.53. There the denominator used in the calculation was D_{25} because the net single premium is evaluated at the beginning of the insurance. Now to calculate the accumulated cost of insurance, the denominator is D_{28} because the evaluation date is at the end. (The D in the numerator will not appear, because there is no pure endowment involved.)

Basic equation (subscripts of the M's define the period of coverage; subscript of D is the evaluation age)

$$\begin{pmatrix}\text{Accumulated Cost}\\ \text{of Insurance}\end{pmatrix} = \$1{,}000\left(\frac{M_{25} - M_{28}}{D_{28}}\right)$$

Substituting values from Table IV

$$= \$1{,}000\left(\frac{1{,}276{,}590 - 1{,}251{,}291}{4{,}160{,}727}\right)$$

$$= \$6.08$$

This answer agrees with that calculated in Section 9.6 for the same policy without the use of commutation functions.

It should be noted that the accumulated cost of insurance ($6.08) is higher than the net single premium ($5.53). This is as expected since the number of persons paying in at the beginning of the term of coverage is greater than the number of survivors who would pay at the end.

EXERCISES

(Use Table IV for all of the following. Assume insurance is payable at the end of the year unless otherwise indicated.)

1 Write an expression (using commutation functions) for the net single

premium at age 10 for $10,000 of 1-year term insurance. Calculate the value.

2 Write an expression (using commutation functions) for the net single premium at age 10 for $10,000 of term-to-age-40 insurance. Calculate the value.

3 Write an expression (using commutation functions) for the net single premium at age 65 for $1,000 of whole life insurance. Calculate the value.

4 Write an expression (using commutation functions) for the net single premium at age 5 for a $2,000 pure endowment due 25 years thereafter. Calculate the value.

5 Write an expression (using commutation functions) for the net single premium at 40 for a $5,000 30-year endowment insurance policy. Calculate the value.

6 Write an expression (using commutation functions) for the accumulated cost at age 30 for a $10,000 12-year term insurance policy. Calculate the value.

7 Write an expression (using commutation functions) for the net single premium at age 15 for a $1,000 term-to-age-65 insurance policy, assuming the insurance is payable at the moment of death. Calculate the value.

8 Describe in words what is represented by each of the following expressions:

a) $\$1{,}000\left(\frac{C_{43}}{D_{43}}\right)$

b) $\$1{,}000\left(\frac{C_{43}+C_{44}+C_{45}+C_{46}}{D_{43}}\right)$

c) $\$1{,}000\left(\frac{M_{43}-M_{47}}{D_{43}}\right)$

d) $\$5{,}000\left(\frac{M_{62}}{D_{62}}\right)$

e) $\$15{,}000\left(\frac{M_{25}-M_{50}+D_{50}}{D_{25}}\right)$

f) $\$1{,}500\left(\frac{D_{65}}{D_{25}}\right)$

g) $\$1{,}500(1+\frac{1}{2}i)\left(\frac{M_0-M_{40}}{D_0}\right)$

9.9 SYMBOLS FOR NET SINGLE PREMIUMS

Chart 9–3 displays certain internationally used symbols, each of which represents the net single premium at age x for $1 of life insurance. (These net single premiums are also shown as they would be calculated using commutation functions.)

The capital letter "A" is used with a subscript for the evaluation age, and the number of years under an "angle." In general, the symbol $A_{x:\overline{n|}}$ refers to n-year endowment insurance. If the reference is to term insurance or to a pure endowment, then a "1" is placed over the age or the number of years, respectively.

CHART 9–3

Net Single Premium at Age x for $1 of Life Insurance

Type of Life Insurance	*Symbol for Net Single Premium*	*Net Single Premium Using Commutation Functions*
Whole Life Insurance	A_x	$\frac{M_x}{D_x}$
n-Year Term Insurance	$A^{1}_{x:\overline{n}\rceil}$	$\frac{M_x - M_{x+n}}{D_x}$
Pure Endowment Due in n Years	$A_{x:\overline{n}\rceil}^{\ \ 1}$	$\frac{D_{x+n}}{D_x}$
n-Year Endowment Insurance	$A_{x:\overline{n}\rceil}$	$\frac{M_x - M_{x+n} + D_{x+n}}{D_x}$

Net single premium symbols wherein a *bar* is placed over the "A" represent insurance payable at the moment of death. For example,

$$\bar{A}_x$$

is the internationally used symbol for the net single premium at age x for $1 of whole life insurance payable at the moment of death.

10. Life Insurance, Annual Premiums

10.1 INTRODUCTION

The purchase of life insurance by the payment of a single premium when the policy is issued is relatively uncommon, because few people are financially able to do so. The purchase of life insurance by payment of the one-year term insurance premium each year is also uncommon, because this premium increases sharply at the older ages.

A more practical procedure has been devised for paying premiums whereby the premium is paid annually but its amount is the same each year. The calculation of such annual level premiums is based on this principle: *at the date the policy is issued, the present value of the premiums must be equal to the present value of the benefits.*

Annual premiums so calculated are called *net annual premiums.* The word "net" means that the premium calculation involves only rates of interest and mortality, with no consideration of expenses or profits. (Annual premiums which do include an amount for expenses and profits are called *gross annual premiums.* These will be considered in Section 10.7.)

Life insurance policies may be issued on any date during a calendar year. The first annual premium is due on that date, the second annual premium is due one year later, etc. The period of time between such anniversaries is known as a *policy year,* to distinguish it from a calendar year (i.e., January 1 to December 31). In this book, references to "years" in connection with insurance policies will mean *policy years.*

Annual premiums are always paid at the beginning of the year, such payments taking place each year only if the person insured is then alive to pay. Therefore, annual premiums for a policy constitute a *life annuity due*. Such premiums may be paid for the same number of years as the insurance benefit covers, or a fewer number of years. Thus, they may constitute either a *whole life annuity due* or a *temporary life annuity due*. In describing a certain policy, if the premium-paying period is not specified, it is generally understood that premiums are payable for as long as there is life insurance coverage.

10.2 NET ANNUAL PREMIUMS FOR TERM INSURANCE

A term life insurance policy which covers a stated number of years normally requires an annual premium payable at the beginning of each of those years. The calculation of the net annual premiums is based upon the principle stated above: *at the date the policy is issued, the present value of the net premiums must be equal to the present value of the benefits.*

For example, it may be desired to calculate the net annual premium (per $1,000 of insurance) for a four-year term insurance policy issued to a person age 25. Since no premium-paying period is specified, it is understood that these premiums are payable for four years. In line diagram form, this series of net annual premiums appears as follows:

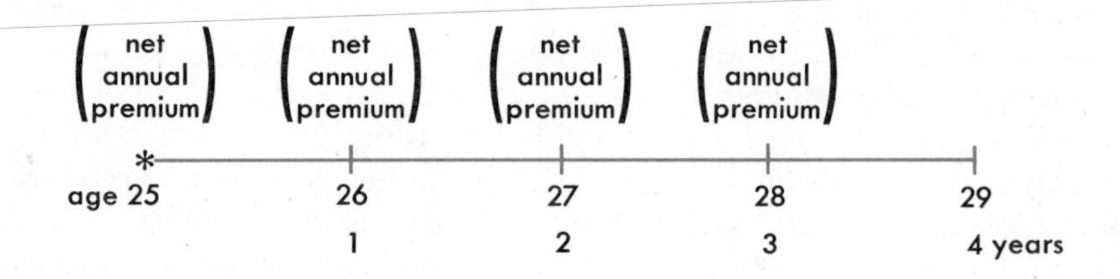

The net annual premiums constitute a *temporary life annuity due*. Their present value, at the date the policy is issued, may be calculated by consulting a mortality table and assuming that all persons enumerated therein are individually involved. At age 25, their present value is

$$\begin{pmatrix}\text{Present Value of}\\ \text{Net Annual Premiums}\end{pmatrix} = \begin{pmatrix}\text{Net Annual}\\ \text{Premium}\end{pmatrix}(l_{25} + l_{26}v + l_{27}v^2 + l_{28}v^3)$$

This equation shows that the present value of the net annual premiums equals the total of each of the net annual premiums paid by survivors at each age, with each such amount being discounted at interest to the evaluation date. The first item inside the parentheses, namely l_{25}, is not multiplied by any v factor because it represents those net annual premiums which are payable upon the evaluation date.

The above expression would be divided by the number living on the evaluation date (l_{25}) to find the present value per person (as was done in Chapter 8). However, in this case, this step is not necessary. The above expression represents a total present value for all the l_{25} persons. Calculations which follow will demonstrate how it is used to find a net annual premium per person.

Similarly, the present value of the *benefits* may be calculated. In line diagram form, the death benefits to be paid appear as follows:

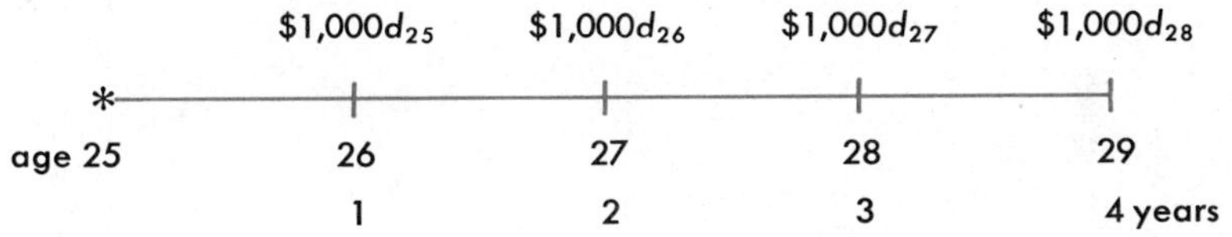

	$1,000$d_{25}$	$1,000$d_{26}$	$1,000$d_{27}$	$1,000$d_{28}$
*				
age 25	26	27	28	29
	1	2	3	4 years

At age 25, the present value is

$$\begin{pmatrix}\text{Present Value of}\\ \text{Benefits}\end{pmatrix} = \$1{,}000(d_{25}v + d_{26}v^2 + d_{27}v^3 + d_{28}v^4)$$

That is, the $1,000 death benefit is paid for those who die at each age, with each such amount being discounted at interest from the end of the year of death to the evaluation date.

The above expression would be divided by the number living on the evaluation date (l_{25}) to find this present value per person, i.e., the net single premium (as was done in Chapter 9). In this case, this step is not necessary. The above expression represents a total net single premium for all the l_{25} persons. It will be used in the calculation below to find a net annual premium per person.

The expression for the present value of net annual premiums is equal to the expression for the present value of the benefits:

$$\begin{pmatrix}\text{Present Value of}\\ \text{Net Annual Premiums}\end{pmatrix} = \begin{pmatrix}\text{Present Value of}\\ \text{Benefits}\end{pmatrix}$$

$$\begin{pmatrix}\text{Net Annual}\\ \text{Premium}\end{pmatrix}(l_{25} + l_{26}v + l_{27}v^2 + l_{28}v^3) = \$1{,}000(d_{25}v + d_{26}v^2 + d_{27}v^3 + d_{28}v^4)$$

The equation can be solved for the Net Annual Premium, which will be the net annual premium per person. If, for example, the 1958

C.S.O. Table and 3% interest were being used to calculate the above net annual premiums, the present value of the net annual premiums (the left side) would be evaluated as follows:

From above

$$\begin{pmatrix}\text{Present Value of}\\ \text{Net Annual Premiums}\end{pmatrix} = \begin{pmatrix}\text{Net Annual}\\ \text{Premium}\end{pmatrix}(l_{25} + l_{26}v + l_{27}v^2 + l_{28}v^3)$$

Substituting values for the l's from Table III, for the v's from Table I (3%)

$$= \begin{pmatrix}\text{Net Annual}\\ \text{Premium}\end{pmatrix}\begin{bmatrix}(9{,}575{,}636)\\ +(9{,}557{,}155)(.970874)\\ +(9{,}538{,}423)(.942596)\\ +(9{,}519{,}442)(.915142)\end{bmatrix}$$

$$= \begin{pmatrix}\text{Net Annual}\\ \text{Premium}\end{pmatrix}(9{,}575{,}636 + 9{,}278{,}793 + 8{,}990{,}879 + 8{,}711{,}641)$$

$$= \begin{pmatrix}\text{Net Annual}\\ \text{Premium}\end{pmatrix}(36{,}556{,}949)$$

The same mortality table and interest rate used to calculate the present value of the net annual premiums are used to calculate the present value of the benefits. The right side of the equation would be evaluated as follows:

From above

$$\begin{pmatrix}\text{Present Value of}\\ \text{Benefits}\end{pmatrix} = \$1{,}000(d_{25}v + d_{26}v^2 + d_{27}v^3 + d_{28}v^4)$$

Substituting values for the d's from Table III, for the v's from Table I (3%)

$$= \$1{,}000\begin{bmatrix}(18{,}481)(.970874)\\ +(18{,}732)(.942596)\\ +(18{,}981)(.915142)\\ +(19{,}324)(.888487)\end{bmatrix}$$

$$= \$1{,}000(17{,}943 + 17{,}657 + 17{,}370 + 17{,}169)$$

$$= \$70{,}139{,}000$$

The net annual premium per person can then be found:

Basic equation

$$\begin{pmatrix}\text{Present Value of}\\ \text{Net Annual Premiums}\end{pmatrix} = \begin{pmatrix}\text{Present Value of}\\ \text{Benefits}\end{pmatrix}$$

Substituting values calculated above

$$\begin{pmatrix}\text{Net Annual}\\ \text{Premium}\end{pmatrix}(36{,}556{,}949) = \$70{,}139{,}000$$

$$\begin{pmatrix}\text{Net Annual}\\ \text{Premium}\end{pmatrix} = \$1.92$$

In line diagram form, this series of net annual premiums appears as follows:

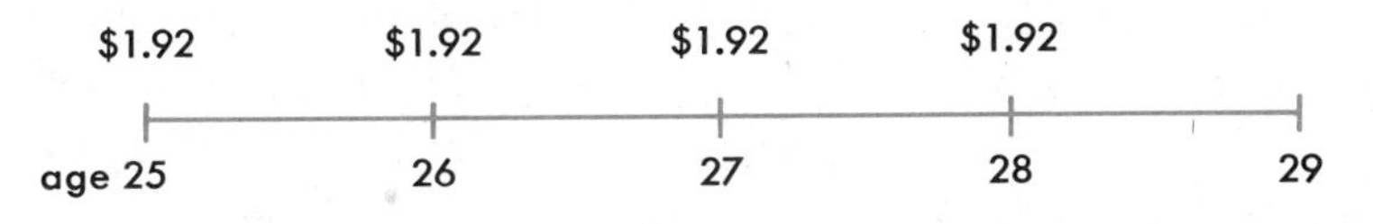

It can be demonstrated that the payment of these net annual premiums will provide $1,000 (at the end of the year of death) for all who die between ages 25 and 29. Using Table III, the amount of premium paid in at the beginning of the first year is

$$\$1.92(l_{25}) = \$1.92(9{,}575{,}636)$$
$$= \$18{,}385{,}221.12$$

At the end of one year, the accumulated value of this amount is

$$(\$18{,}385{,}221.12)(1.03) = \$18{,}936{,}777.75$$

From this fund is deducted $1,000 for each who have died during the first year:

$$\$1{,}000(d_{25}) = \$1{,}000(18{,}481)$$
$$= \$18{,}481{,}000$$

This leaves a balance in the fund of

$$\$18{,}936{,}777.75 - \$18{,}481{,}000 = \$455{,}777.75$$

The continued operation of the fund for succeeding years may be traced in the accompanying schedule (Chart 10–1). The final excess in the fund represents less than $3 for each person dying the final year,

CHART 10–1

(1) Year	(2) *Premiums Paid at Beginning of Year*	(3) *Total Fund at Beginning of Year (Col. 6, Previous Year, plus Col. 2)*	(4) *Fund Accumulated for One Year (Col. 3 × 1.03)*	(5) *Claims Paid at End of Year (Number of Deaths × $1,000)*	(6) *Balance in Fund at End of Year after Payment of Claims (Col. 4 – Col. 5)*
1	$18,385,221.12	$18,385,221.12	$18,936,777.75	$18,481,000	$455,777.75
2	18,349,737.60	18,805,515.35	19,369,680.81	18,732,000	637,680.81
3	18,313,772.16	18,951.452.97	19,519,996.56	18,981,000	538,996.56
4	18,277,328.64	18,816,325.20	19,380,814.96	19,324,000	56,814.96

and results from rounding off the net annual premium to two decimal places.

To Illustrate—Using Table III and 3% interest, calculate the net annual premium (per $1,000) for a 2-year term insurance policy issued at age 60.

Solution—In line diagram form, the *net annual premiums* for this policy appear as follows:

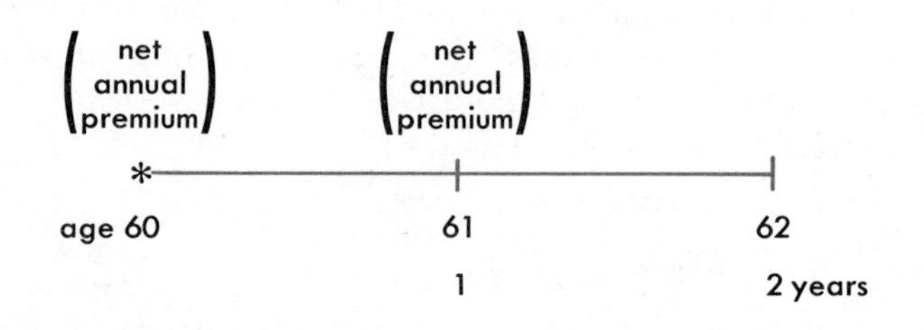

Their total present value is equivalent to the net annual premiums paid by the survivors at each age, with each such amount being discounted at interest to the evaluation date.

Basic equation

$$\begin{pmatrix}\text{Present Value of}\\ \text{Net Annual Premiums}\end{pmatrix} = \begin{pmatrix}\text{Net Annual}\\ \text{Premium}\end{pmatrix}(l_{60} + l_{61}v)$$

Substituting values from the tables

$$= \begin{pmatrix}\text{Net Annual}\\ \text{Premium}\end{pmatrix}\begin{bmatrix}(7{,}698{,}698)\\ +(7{,}542{,}106)(.970874)\end{bmatrix}$$

$$= \begin{pmatrix}\text{Net Annual}\\ \text{Premium}\end{pmatrix}(7{,}698{,}698 + 7{,}322{,}435)$$

$$= \begin{pmatrix}\text{Net Annual}\\ \text{Premium}\end{pmatrix}(15{,}021{,}133)$$

In line diagram form, the *benefits* for this policy appear as follows:

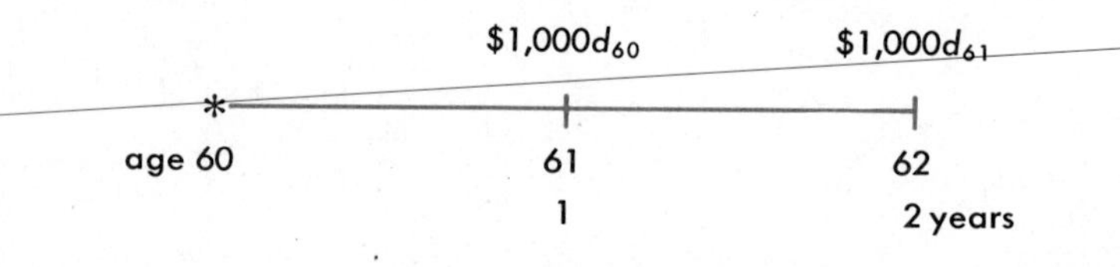

Their total present value is equivalent to the amounts paid for those who die at each age, with each amount being discounted at interest from the end of the year of death to the evaluation date.

Basic equation

$$\begin{pmatrix}\text{Present Value of}\\ \text{Benefits}\end{pmatrix} = \$1{,}000\,(d_{60}v + d_{61}v^2)$$

Substituting values from the tables

$$= \$1{,}000\begin{bmatrix}(156{,}592)(.970874)\\ +(167{,}736)(.942596)\end{bmatrix}$$

$$= \$1{,}000\,(152{,}031 + 158{,}107)$$

$$= \$310{,}138{,}000$$

The net annual premium is then found by substituting these values in the basic equation:

$$\begin{pmatrix}\text{Present Value of}\\ \text{Net Annual Premiums}\end{pmatrix} = \begin{pmatrix}\text{Present Value of}\\ \text{Benefits}\end{pmatrix}$$

$$\begin{pmatrix}\text{Net Annual}\\ \text{Premium}\end{pmatrix}(15{,}021{,}133) = \$310{,}138{,}000$$

$$\begin{pmatrix}\text{Net Annual}\\ \text{Premium}\end{pmatrix} = \$20.65$$

10.3 NET ANNUAL PREMIUMS FOR WHOLE LIFE INSURANCE

The net annual premiums for a whole life insurance policy may be paid either

1. For the entire lifetime of the person insured. They thus constitute a *whole life annuity due.* This kind of insurance policy is known as an *ordinary life* policy.

or

2. For a number of years which is *less* than the entire lifetime, say for n years. They thus constitute a *temporary life annuity due.* This kind of insurance is known as an *n-payment life* policy.

To Illustrate—Using the 1958 C.S.O. Table and 3% interest, calculate the net annual premium (per $1,000) for an ordinary life insurance policy issued at age 96; also for a 2-payment life policy issued at that age.

Solution—The *present value of the benefits* is the same for both policies because both provide insurance coverage for the whole of life. The line diagram for these benefits appears as follows (remembering that all persons die before age 100, according to the 1958 C.S.O. Table):

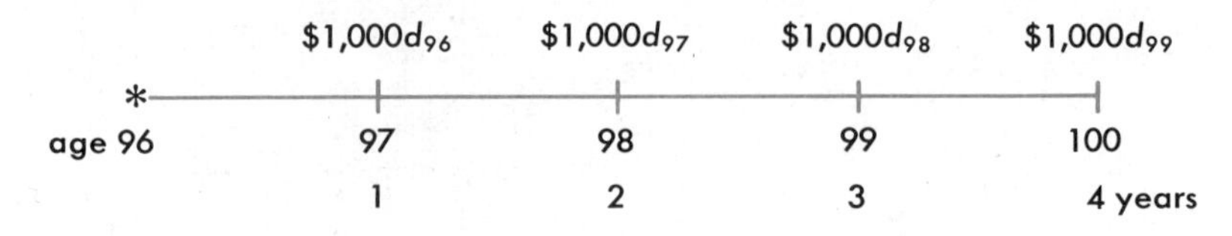

Their total present value is equivalent to the amounts of benefits paid for those who die at each age, with each such amount being discounted at interest from the end of the year of death to the evaluation date.

Basic equation

$$\begin{pmatrix}\text{Present Value of} \\ \text{Benefits}\end{pmatrix} = \$1{,}000\,(d_{96}v + d_{97}v^2 + d_{98}v^3 + d_{99}v^4)$$

Substituting values from the tables

$$= \$1{,}000 \begin{bmatrix} (25{,}250)(.970874) \\ +(18{,}456)(.942596) \\ +(12{,}916)(.915142) \\ +(\ 6{,}415)(.888487) \end{bmatrix}$$

$$= \$1{,}000\,(24{,}515 + 17{,}397 + 11{,}820 + 5{,}700)$$

$$= \$59{,}432{,}000$$

The line diagrams for the *net annual premiums* for these two policies appear as follows:

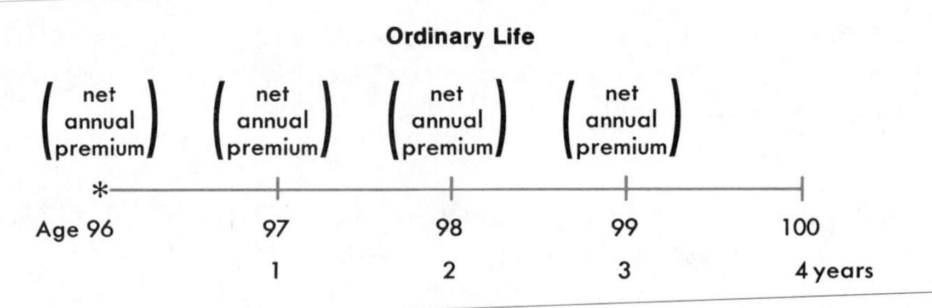

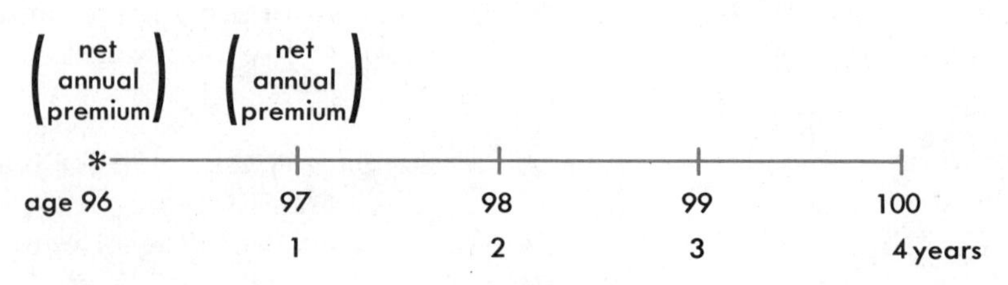

In each case, their total present value is equivalent to the net annual premiums paid by the survivors at each age, with each such amount being discounted at interest to the evaluation date.

Ordinary Life

Basic equation

$$\begin{pmatrix}\text{Present Value of}\\ \text{Net Annual Premiums}\end{pmatrix} = \begin{pmatrix}\text{Net Annual}\\ \text{Premium}\end{pmatrix}(l_{96} + l_{97}v + l_{98}v^2 + l_{99}v^3)$$

Substituting values from the tables

$$= \begin{pmatrix}\text{Net Annual}\\ \text{Premium}\end{pmatrix}\begin{bmatrix}(63{,}037)\\ +(37{,}787)(.970874)\\ +(19{,}331)(.942596)\\ +(\ 6{,}415)(.915142)\end{bmatrix}$$

$$= \begin{pmatrix}\text{Net Annual}\\ \text{Premium}\end{pmatrix}(63{,}037 + 36{,}686 + 18{,}221 + 5{,}871)$$

$$= \begin{pmatrix}\text{Net Annual}\\ \text{Premium}\end{pmatrix}(123{,}815)$$

Two-Payment Life

Basic equation

$$\begin{pmatrix}\text{Present Value of}\\ \text{Net Annual Premiums}\end{pmatrix} = \begin{pmatrix}\text{Net Annual}\\ \text{Premium}\end{pmatrix}(l_{96} + l_{97}v)$$

Substituting values from the tables

$$= \begin{pmatrix}\text{Net Annual}\\ \text{Premium}\end{pmatrix}\begin{bmatrix}(63{,}037)\\ +(37{,}787)(.970874)\end{bmatrix}$$

$$= \begin{pmatrix}\text{Net Annual}\\ \text{Premium}\end{pmatrix}(63{,}037 + 36{,}686)$$

$$= \begin{pmatrix}\text{Net Annual}\\ \text{Premium}\end{pmatrix}(99{,}723)$$

The net annual premium for each policy is then solved for, as follows:

Ordinary Life

Basic equation

$$\begin{pmatrix}\text{Present Value of}\\ \text{Net Annual Premiums}\end{pmatrix} = \begin{pmatrix}\text{Present Value of}\\ \text{Benefits}\end{pmatrix}$$

Substituting values calculated above

$$\begin{pmatrix}\text{Net Annual}\\ \text{Premium}\end{pmatrix}(123{,}815) = \$59{,}432{,}000$$

$$\begin{pmatrix}\text{Net Annual}\\ \text{Premium}\end{pmatrix} = \$480.01$$

Two-Payment Life

Basic equation

$$\begin{pmatrix}\text{Present Value of}\\ \text{Net Annual Premiums}\end{pmatrix} = \begin{pmatrix}\text{Present Value of}\\ \text{Benefits}\end{pmatrix}$$

Substituting values calculated above

$$\begin{pmatrix}\text{Net Annual}\\ \text{Premium}\end{pmatrix}(99{,}723) = \$59{,}432{,}000$$

$$\begin{pmatrix}\text{Net Annual}\\ \text{Premium}\end{pmatrix} = \$595.97$$

As the premium-paying period is shortened, the amount of the net annual premium for the same benefits increases. This can be seen by comparing the net annual premium for the ordinary life policy above ($480.01) with the net annual premium for the two-payment life policy ($595.97).

The calculation of net annual premiums for whole life insurance at the younger ages would become very laborious if the procedure described were used. In actual practice, calculations for all kinds of net annual premiums are usually simplified by using commutation functions. How commutation functions are used to compute net annual premiums will be explained in Section 10.6.

10.4 NET ANNUAL PREMIUMS FOR ENDOWMENT INSURANCE

The net annual premiums for an endowment insurance policy may be paid either

1. For the same number of years as the insurance covers, say for n years. They thus constitute a *temporary life annuity due for n years.* This kind of insurance policy is known as an *n-year endowment* policy.

or

2. For a number of years which is *less* than the period that the insurance covers, say for m years (with the insurance coverage for n years). They thus constitute a *temporary life annuity due for m years.* This kind of insurance policy is known as an *m-payment n-year endowment* policy.

To Illustrate—Using the 1958 C.S.O. Table and 3% interest, calculate the net annual premium for a $1,000 2-payment endowment-at-age-65 policy issued to a man age 61. Construct a schedule proving that this premium will provide the benefits of the policy.

Solution—The number of years of insurance equals $65 - 61 = 4$. Hence, this is a 2-payment 4-year endowment policy. In line diagram form, the *net annual premiums* appear as follows:

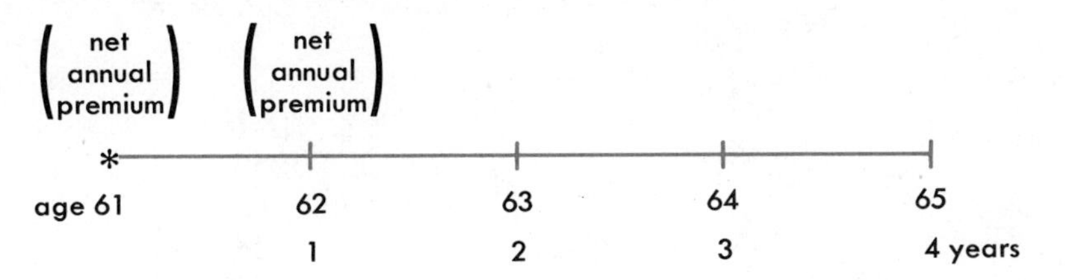

Their total present value is equivalent to the net annual premiums paid by the survivors at each age, with each such amount being discounted at interest to the evaluation date.

Basic equation

$$\begin{pmatrix}\text{Present Value of} \\ \text{Net Annual Premiums}\end{pmatrix} = \begin{pmatrix}\text{Net Annual} \\ \text{Premium}\end{pmatrix}(l_{61} + l_{62}v)$$

Substituting values from the tables

$$= \begin{pmatrix}\text{Net Annual} \\ \text{Premium}\end{pmatrix}\begin{bmatrix}7{,}542{,}106 \\ +(7{,}374{,}370)(.970874)\end{bmatrix}$$

$$= \begin{pmatrix}\text{Net Annual} \\ \text{Premium}\end{pmatrix}(7{,}542{,}106 + 7{,}159{,}584)$$

$$= \begin{pmatrix}\text{Net Annual} \\ \text{Premium}\end{pmatrix}(14{,}701{,}690)$$

In line diagram form, the *benefits* for this policy appear as follows:

$\$1{,}000l_{65}$

$\$1{,}000d_{61}$ $\$1{,}000d_{62}$ $\$1{,}000d_{63}$ $\$1{,}000d_{64}$

age 61 62 63 64 65

1 2 3 4 years

The amounts paid for those who die at each age are payable at the end of the year of death. The pure endowment is paid to the survivors at the end of the 4-year period. All amounts paid are discounted at interest to the evaluation date. Notice that in the expression below, the exponents on the last two v's are the same. Both d_{64} and l_{65} are multiplied by v^4. This is because the two benefits are payable on the same date: the death benefit for those who die during the final year, and the pure endowment benefit to those still alive at the end of the final year.

Basic equation

$$\begin{pmatrix}\text{Present Value of}\\ \text{Benefits}\end{pmatrix} = \$1{,}000\,(d_{61}v + d_{62}v^2 + d_{63}v^3 + d_{64}v^4 + l_{65}v^4)$$

Substituting values from the tables

$$= \$1{,}000\begin{bmatrix}(167{,}736)(.970874)\\ +(179{,}271)(.942586)\\ +(191{,}174)(.915142)\\ +(203{,}394)(.888487)\\ +(6{,}800{,}531)(.888487)\end{bmatrix}$$

$$= \$1{,}000\,(162{,}851 + 168{,}980 + 174{,}951 + 180{,}713 + 6{,}042{,}183)$$

$$= \$6{,}729{,}678{,}000$$

The net annual premium is then found:

Basic equation

$$\begin{pmatrix}\text{Present Value of}\\ \text{Net Annual Premiums}\end{pmatrix} = \begin{pmatrix}\text{Present Value of}\\ \text{Benefits}\end{pmatrix}$$

Substituting values calculated above

$$\begin{pmatrix}\text{Net Annual}\\ \text{Premium}\end{pmatrix}(14{,}701{,}690) = \$6{,}729{,}678{,}000$$

$$\begin{pmatrix}\text{Net Annual}\\ \text{Premium}\end{pmatrix} = \$457.75$$

The accompanying schedule (Chart 10–2) demonstrates that this premium will provide the benefits of the policy.

CHART 10–2

(1) Year	(2) Premiums Paid at Beginning of Year	(3) Total Fund at Beginning of Year (Col. 6 Previous Year, plus Col. 2)	(4) Fund Accumulated for One Year (Col. 3 × 1.03)	(5) Claims Paid at End of Year (Number of Deaths × $1,000)	(6) Balance in Fund at End of Year after Payment of Claims (Col. 4 − Col. 5)
1	$3,452,399,021.50	$3,452,399,021.50	$3,555,970,992.15	$167,736,000	$3,388,234,992.
2	3,375,617,867.50	6,763,852,859.65	6,966,768,445.44	179,271,000	6,787,497,445
3	None	6,787,497,445.44	6,991,122,368.80	191,174,000	6,799,948,368
4	None	6,799,948,368.80	7,003,946,819.86	203,394,000	6,800,552,819.

At the end of the four years, the number of survivors is

$$l_{65} = 6{,}800{,}531$$

Therefore, the total pure endowments to be paid to the survivors at that time is

$$\$1{,}000(6{,}800{,}531) = \$6{,}800{,}531{,}000$$

This leaves a balance in the fund, after the pure endowments are paid, equal to

$$\$6{,}800{,}552{,}819.86 - \$6{,}800{,}531{,}000 = \$21{,}819.86$$

This represents only about $\frac{1}{3}$ of a cent for each of the survivors, and is the result of rounding off the net annual premium to 2 decimal places.

10.5 RELATIONSHIPS BETWEEN NET PREMIUMS AND LIFE ANNUITIES

The basis for the derivation of all the net annual premiums discussed in this chapter has been the principle: *at the date the policy is issued, the present value of the net annual premiums must be equal to the present value of the benefits.* The calculations above were made on a total basis, that is, the total present values for all persons living on the evaluation date.

Net premiums can also be calculated on a per person basis. The present value of the net annual premiums may be expressed as the net annual premium multiplied by the present value at age x of a temporary life annuity due of 1. This latter present value is known as the "annuity factor." Tables of such life annuity factors at various ages have been prepared and are usually available.

This relationship can be expressed by the following equation:

$$\begin{pmatrix}\text{Net Annual}\\ \text{Premium}\end{pmatrix}\begin{pmatrix}\text{Annuity}\\ \text{Factor}\end{pmatrix} = \begin{pmatrix}\text{Present Value of Net}\\ \text{Annual Premiums}\end{pmatrix}$$

Since the present value of the benefits is the same as the net single premium, the basic statement of equality may be written:

$$\begin{pmatrix}\text{Net Annual}\\ \text{Premium}\end{pmatrix}\begin{pmatrix}\text{Annuity}\\ \text{Factor}\end{pmatrix} = \begin{pmatrix}\text{Net Single}\\ \text{Premium}\end{pmatrix}$$

From this equation, the value of any one of the items in the equation may be calculated if the values of the other two are known.

To Illustrate—Calculate the present value at age 40 of a 10-year life annuity due of 1 per year (the annuity factor), given the following values:

$57.84 = Net Annual Premium per $1,000 at Age 40 for a 10-Payment Life Policy

$502.64 = Net Single Premium per $1,000 at Age 40 for Whole Insurance

Solution—

Basic equation

$$\begin{pmatrix}\text{Net Annual}\\ \text{Premium}\end{pmatrix}\begin{pmatrix}\text{Annuity}\\ \text{Factor}\end{pmatrix}=\begin{pmatrix}\text{Net Single}\\ \text{Premium}\end{pmatrix}$$

Substituting values given

$$\$57.84\begin{pmatrix}\text{Annuity}\\ \text{Factor}\end{pmatrix}=\$502.64$$

$$\begin{pmatrix}\text{Annuity}\\ \text{Factor}\end{pmatrix}=8.69$$

To Illustrate Again—Calculate the net single premium per $1,000 at age 40 for a 10-year pure endowment, given the following values:

$90.68 = Net Annual Premium per $1,000 at Age 40 for a 10-Year Endowment Policy

$70.90 = Net Single Premium per $1,000 at Age 40 for a 10-Year Term Insurance Policy

8.69 = Present Value at Age 40 of a 10-Year Life Annuity Due of 1 per Year (Annuity Factor)

Solution—It must be remembered that the net single premium for a 10-year endowment policy consists of two parts:

1. Net single premium for term insurance

and

2. Net single premium for a pure endowment

The value of the first part is given; the value of the second part must be solved for.

Basic equation, showing net single premium in two parts

$$\begin{pmatrix}\text{Net Annual}\\ \text{Premium}\end{pmatrix}\begin{pmatrix}\text{Annuity}\\ \text{Factor}\end{pmatrix}=\begin{pmatrix}\text{Net Single Premium}\\ \text{for Term Insurance}\end{pmatrix}+\begin{pmatrix}\text{Net Single Premium}\\ \text{for Pure Endowment}\end{pmatrix}$$

Substituting values given

$$(\$90.68)(8.69)=\$70.90+\begin{pmatrix}\text{Net Single Premium}\\ \text{for Pure Endowment}\end{pmatrix}$$

$$(\$90.68)(8.69)-\$70.90=\begin{pmatrix}\text{Net Single Premium}\\ \text{for Pure Endowment}\end{pmatrix}$$

$$\$717.11=\begin{pmatrix}\text{Net Single Premium}\\ \text{for Pure Endowment}\end{pmatrix}$$

EXERCISES

1 Write an equation (using symbols) showing the present value of the net annual premiums being equal to the present value of the benefits for each of the following $1,000 policies (on a *total* basis, not per person): Solve each equation for the net annual premium per person (using Table III and 3% interest):

a) A 1-year term insurance policy issued at age 75
b) A 3-year term insurance policy issued at age 69
c) An ordinary life policy issued at age 97
d) A 2-payment life policy issued at age 97
e) A 3-year endowment insurance policy issued at age 10
f) A 4-year endowment insurance policy issued at age 25, wherein premiums stop at age 27 (i.e., last premium is payable at age 26)

2 Construct a schedule for the policy in Exercise 1, part (*f*), showing the adequacy of the net annual premium to provide the benefits.

3 Given the following values, calculate the net annual premium per $1,000 at age 69 for an ordinary life insurance policy:

$808.41 = Net Single Premium per $1,000 at Age 69 for Whole Life Insurance

10.772 = Present Value at Age 69 of a Whole Life Annuity Due of 1 per Year

4 Calculate the present value of a 20-year life annuity due of 1 per year, given the following values:

$808.41 = Net Single Premium per $1,000 at Age 69 for Whole Life Insurance

$102.15 = Net Annual Premium per $1,000 at Age 69 for a 20-Payment Life Insurance Policy

5 If the following values are given, calculate the net single premium per $1,000 at age 30 for endowment-at-age-65 insurance:

$21.18 = Net Annual Premium per $1,000 at Age 30 for an Endowment-at-Age-65 Policy

19.47 = Present Value at Age 30 of a 35-Year Life Annuity Due of 1 per Year

10.6 COMMUTATION FUNCTIONS

The commutation functions explained in Chapters 8 and 9 can be used to calculate net annual premiums and will generally simplify the work.

The basis for the calculation is the equation given in Section 10.5:

$$\begin{pmatrix}\text{Net Annual}\\ \text{Premium}\end{pmatrix}\begin{pmatrix}\text{Annuity}\\ \text{Factor}\end{pmatrix}=\begin{pmatrix}\text{Net Single}\\ \text{Premium}\end{pmatrix}$$

The $1,000 four-year term insurance policy issued at age 25, discussed in Section 10.2, will be used as an example. The left-hand side of the above equation may be written

$$\begin{pmatrix}\text{Net Annual}\\ \text{Premium}\end{pmatrix}\left(\frac{N_{25}-N_{29}}{D_{25}}\right)$$

This follows from the general statement made in Chapter 8 that the factor to use in evaluating a *life annuity* will be of the form $\frac{N-N}{D}$, where the subscript of the first N is the age when the first payment is due, the subscript of the second N is the first age when there are no more payments due, and the subscript of the D is the age at which the annuity is being evaluated.

The right-hand side of the above equation (Net Single Premium) may be written

$$\$1{,}000\left(\frac{M_{25}-M_{29}}{D_{25}}\right)$$

This follows from the general statement made in Chapter 9 that the factor to use in calculating a *net single premium* will be of the form $\frac{M-M+D}{D}$, where the subscript of the first M is the age when the insurance coverage begins, the subscript of the second M is the age at which the insurance coverage stops, the subscript of the D in the numerator is the age at which a pure endowment would be paid, and the subscript of the D in the denominator is the age at which this net single premium is evaluated. (In this particular case, the D in the numerator does not appear, because no pure endowment is involved.)

The entire equation then appears as follows:

$$\begin{pmatrix}\text{Net Annual}\\ \text{Premium}\end{pmatrix}\left(\frac{N_{25}-N_{29}}{D_{25}}\right)=\$1{,}000\left(\frac{M_{25}-M_{29}}{D_{25}}\right)$$

The commutation symbol D_{25} appears in the denominator on both sides of the equation. If both sides are multiplied by D_{25}, the denominators are eliminated. The equation can then be solved for (Net Annual Premium) by dividing both sides by $(N_{25}-N_{29})$. The result is

$$\begin{pmatrix}\text{Net Annual}\\ \text{Premium}\end{pmatrix}=\$1{,}000\left(\frac{M_{25}-M_{29}}{N_{25}-N_{29}}\right)$$

Using values of M and N from Table IV, this becomes

$$\binom{\text{Net Annual}}{\text{Premium}} = \$1{,}000\left(\frac{1{,}276{,}590 - 1{,}243{,}091}{113{,}189{,}600 - 95{,}729{,}800}\right)$$

$$= \$1.92$$

The answer is the same as that calculated in Section 10.2.

A general statement may be made that the factor to use in calculating a *net annual premium* will be of the form $\frac{M - M + D}{N - N}$, where the subscripts in the numerator define the benefits and follow the rule given in Chapter 9 for calculating net single premiums, and the subscripts of the N's in the denominator define the premium-paying period and follow the rule given in Chapter 8 for calculating life annuity factors.

To Illustrate—Using Table IV, calculate the net annual premium (per $1,000) for a 2-year term insurance policy issued at age 60.

Solution—This is the same problem as the illustration in Section 10.2. The solution will now be given by using commutation functions. In the general expression given above, the D in the numerator will not appear, because there is no pure endowment involved.

Basic equation; subscripts of the M's define the period of coverage; subscripts of the N's define the premium-paying period

$$\binom{\text{Net Annual}}{\text{Premium}} = \$1{,}000\left(\frac{M_{60} - M_{62}}{N_{60} - N_{62}}\right)$$

Substituting values from Table IV

$$= \$1{,}000\left(\frac{825{,}847 - 773{,}206}{16{,}510{,}076 - 13{,}960{,}493}\right)$$

$$= \$1{,}000\left(\frac{52{,}641}{2{,}549{,}583}\right)$$

$$= \$20.65$$

This answer agrees with that calculated in Section 10.2.

To Illustrate Again—Using Table IV, calculate the net annual premium (per $1,000) for an ordinary life policy issued at age 96.

Solution—This is the same problem as the illustration in Section 10.3. The solution will now be given by using commutation functions. In the general expression for net annual premiums, the second M in the numerator will not appear, because the insurance is for the whole of life. Also, the D in the numerator will not appear, because there is no pure endowment involved. In the denominator, the second N will not appear, because the premium payments are to be made for life.

Basic equation

$$\binom{\text{Net Annual}}{\text{Premium}} = \$1{,}000\left(\frac{M_{96}}{N_{96}}\right)$$

Substituting values from Table IV

$$= \$1{,}000\left(\frac{3{,}481}{7{,}251}\right)$$

$$= \$480.07$$

This answer is only 6 cents different from that calculated in Section 10.3. The difference is due to the fact that the commutation functions as shown in the tables are rounded off to the nearest whole number.

To Illustrate Again—Using Table IV, calculate the net annual premium for a $1,000 2-payment endowment-at-age-65 policy issued to a man age 61.

Solution—This is the same problem as the illustration in Section 10.4. The solution will now be given by using commutation functions.

Basic equation; subscripts of the M's define the period of coverage; subscript of D is age of pure endowment; subscripts of the N's define the premium-paying period

$$\binom{\text{Net Annual}}{\text{Premium}} = \$1{,}000\left(\frac{M_{61} - M_{65} + D_{65}}{N_{61} - N_{63}}\right)$$

Substituting values from Table IV

$$= \$1{,}000\left(\frac{800{,}042 - 686{,}750 + 995{,}688}{15{,}203{,}352 - 12{,}780{,}670}\right)$$

$$= \$1{,}000\left(\frac{1{,}108{,}980}{2{,}422{,}682}\right)$$

$$= \$457.75$$

This answer agrees with that calculated in Section 10.4.

EXERCISES

(Use Table IV for all of the following.)

1 Write an expression (using commutation functions) for the *net annual premium* (per $1,000) for each of the following policies. (If a student wishes, he can calculate the value of each.)

a) A 20-year term insurance policy issued at age 25
b) A 1-year term insurance policy issued at age 65
c) A term-to-age-65 insurance policy issued at age 40
d) An ordinary life policy issued at age 0

e) A 30-payment life policy issued at age 21

f) A whole life insurance policy issued at age 30, wherein premiums stop at age 70 (i.e., last premium is payable at age 69)

g) A 25-year endowment insurance policy issued at age 28

h) A 20-payment 30-year endowment insurance policy issued at age 15

i) A 30-payment endowment-at-age-70 policy issued at age 22

2 Calculate the net annual premium for a $20,000 ordinary life insurance policy issued to a girl age 15. Use a "3-year setback" for females.

3 Calculate the net annual premium for a $1,000 20-payment life policy issued at age 5, assuming the insurance is payable at the moment of death.

4 State in words what each of the following represents:

a) $\$1{,}000\left(\frac{M_5 - M_{35} + D_{35}}{N_5 - N_{25}}\right)$

b) $\$1{,}000\left(\frac{M_{60}}{N_{60} - N_{80}}\right)$

c) $\$1{,}000\left(\frac{M_{14} - M_{24}}{N_{14} - N_{19}}\right)$

d) $(\$5{,}000)(1.015)\left(\frac{M_{25} - M_{65}}{N_{25} - N_{65}}\right) + \$5{,}000\left(\frac{D_{65}}{N_{25} - N_{65}}\right)$

10.7 GROSS ANNUAL PREMIUMS

The *net* annual premiums considered thus far are sufficient, in terms of mortality and assumed interest rates, to provide the benefits guaranteed in the policy. However, they make no provision for the life insurance company's expenses of conducting business. Therefore, an amount called the *loading* must be added to these net premiums to provide for expenses, profits, and the possibility of unforeseen adversities. The total of the net premium and the loading is known as the *gross premium*. It is the gross premium which the policyowner pays to the insurance company.

Where the policy is "participating" (receives policy dividends), it is not necessary to have great refinement in the calculation of the loading. Savings from operations can be returned to the policyowners of participating policies in the form of dividends, and the dividend calculations can be changed when necessary to meet changing conditions. However, the amount of the loading must be reasonably conservative.

Where a policy is "nonparticipating," however, very detailed analysis of probable expenses is employed in calculating the loading. Because no policy dividends are returned to policyowners, the insurance company has no means of adjusting its income to allow for changes in expenses subsequent to issue of the policy.

The gross annual premium may be calculated by a variety of

methods. Companies use many different formulas for computing loadings, some very simple, some complex. As a result, the equations for calculating the gross premiums vary.

The expenses of a life insurance company fall into three principal categories:

1. Those expenses which are relatively *constant for each policy* regardless of the amount of the policy. These include the cost of issuing the policy, collecting the premiums, paying the claims, etc.
2. Those expenses which *vary with the amount of the premium.* These include state premium taxes and agents' commissions.
3. Those expenses which *vary with the amount of insurance,* i.e., those expenses which are usually higher for larger amount policies. These include costs of establishing whether applicants are in good health (such as medical examiners' fees), drawing up directions for payment of proceeds, etc.

Expenses which are relatively constant regardless of policy size (category 1) are frequently provided for by adding a certain charge for each policy, regardless of the amount of the policy. This is known as a "policy charge" or "policy fee." However, prior to about 1957, this method of loading was generally considered illegal because state laws prohibiting "discrimination between different policyholders of the same class" were interpreted to prohibit such a method of calculation. Therefore, a method of calculation was used in those days which was based on the determination of the amount of an average-size policy. The gross premiums per $1,000 were so calculated that such an average-size policy would yield the amount needed to pay for these particular expenses. The result was that large policies yielded more than enough to cover their expenses, while small policies yielded an insufficient amount. In total, however, approximately the correct amount was collected.

A compromise between the "old" and "new" methods of providing for these expenses which are relatively constant regardless of policy size is sometimes used. Under this method, gross premiums per $1,000 are quoted which vary according to the size group into which the policy falls. For example, these groups might be

Policies of less than $5,000 face amount
Policies of $5,000 to $9,999 face amount
Policies of $10,000 to $24,999 face amount
Policies of $25,000 to $99,999 face amount
Policies of $100,000 and over face amount

Within each such size group, an average-size policy is used to calculate the gross premium per $1,000 for that group, such that the loading for this average-sized policy will cover the particular expenses referred to in category 1. The result is that the smaller-sized policies require a larger gross premium per $1,000 than the larger policies. This method is known as "band grading," or simply "banding."

In providing for those expenses which vary with the amount of the premium (category 2), a simple method is to add a percentage of the gross annual premium per $1,000 to the net annual premium. In equation form, this would be

$$\text{Gross} = \text{Net} + \text{Percent of Gross}$$

To Illustrate—Calculate the gross annual premium per $1,000 for a policy for which the net annual premium per $1,000 is $12.49, and a loading is needed of 25% of the gross annual premium. What gross annual premium would the policyowner pay for a $5,000 policy, assuming a charge is also made of $7.50 per policy?

Solution—Before computing the premium which the policyowner pays, it is necessary to find the gross premium *per $1,000* of insurance. The policyowner's gross premium is this gross premium per $1,000 multiplied by the number of thousands of insurance, plus any policy charge which is added by the company.

The calculation is first made to find the gross annual premium per $1,000:

Basic equation

$$\text{Gross} = \text{Net} + \text{Percent of Gross}$$

Substituting $12.49 for net, .25 for percent

$$\text{Gross} = \$12.49 + (.25)(\text{Gross})$$

Subtracting (.25)(Gross) from each side

$$\text{Gross} - (.25)(\text{Gross}) = \$12.49$$

$$\text{Gross}\ (1 - .25) = \$12.49$$

$$\text{Gross}\ (.75) = \$12.49$$

$$\text{Gross} = \$16.65$$

For the $5,000 policy, the gross annual premium would be 5 times $16.65, plus the $7.50 charge:

$$\begin{pmatrix}\text{Gross Premium}\\ \text{for } \$5{,}000\end{pmatrix} = (5)(\$16.65) + \$7.50$$

$$= \$90.75$$

A common method of providing for those expenses which vary with the amount of insurance (category 3) is to use a constant amount per $1,000 of insurance. The expenses referred to in category 2, which vary with the amount of the premium, are then provided for by a percentage of gross annual premium. In equation form, this total would be

$$\text{Gross} = \text{Net} + \text{Constant} + \text{Percent of Gross}$$

To Illustrate—Calculate the gross annual premium per \$1,000 for a policy for which the net annual premium per \$1,000 is \$31.28, if it is to be loaded \$3 per \$1,000 plus 20% of the gross annual premium. What would the gross annual premium be for a \$15,000 policy, assuming a charge is also made of \$10 per policy?

Solution—The calculation is first made to find the gross annual premium per \$1,000:

Basic equation

$$\text{Gross} = \text{Net} + \text{Constant} + \text{Percent of Gross}$$

Substituting \$31.28 for net, \$3 for constant, and .20 for percent

$$\text{Gross} = \$31.28 + \$3.00 + (.20)(\text{Gross})$$

$$\text{Gross} - (.20)(\text{Gross}) = \$31.28 + \$3.00$$

$$\text{Gross}\ (1 - .20) = \$31.28 + \$3.00$$

$$\text{Gross}\ (.80) = \$34.28$$

$$\text{Gross} = \$42.85$$

For the \$15,000 policy, the gross annual premium paid by the policyowner would be 15 times \$42.85, plus the \$10 charge:

$$\begin{pmatrix}\text{Gross Premium}\\ \text{for } \$15{,}000\end{pmatrix} = (15)(\$42.85) + \$10.00$$

$$= \$652.75$$

In this case, the total \$652.75 gross annual premium which the policyowner pays is made up of the net annual premium plus loading, as follows:

$$\begin{pmatrix}\text{Net Annual}\\ \text{Premium}\end{pmatrix} = (15)(\$31.28) \qquad = \$469.20$$

$$\begin{pmatrix}\text{Expenses Constant}\\ \text{per Policy}\end{pmatrix} = \$10.00 \qquad = \quad 10.00$$

$$\begin{pmatrix}\text{Expenses Varying}\\ \text{with Premium}\end{pmatrix} = (15)(.20)(\$42.85) = \quad 128.55$$

$$\begin{pmatrix}\text{Expenses Varying}\\ \text{with Amount}\\ \text{of Insurance}\end{pmatrix} = (15)(\$3.00) \qquad = \quad 45.00$$

\$652.75 Total

Since each insurance company determines its own method for calculating the loading, not all insurance companies use loading formulas which add loadings of each of the types described above. Companies sometimes use loading methods involving only one or two of the types of additions described, rather than all three, or they may use very complex methods of loading which are not given in this book.

10.8 FRACTIONAL PREMIUMS

Instead of paying for life insurance by annual premiums, many people prefer to pay premiums in installments during the year, either semiannually, quarterly, or monthly. These installments are known as *fractional premiums*. When premiums are paid in this manner, the company cannot invest the premium income so soon and thereby loses some interest. Also, the company incurs additional expenses for postage, clerical work, etc. The loss of interest and the additional expenses properly should be borne by the policyowners who pay such fractional premiums. Therefore, the semiannual premium charged will be more than one half of the annual premium, and the quarterly and monthly premiums will likewise be more than one fourth or one twelfth of the annual premium, respectively. The amount of the additional charges vary by company.

One practice that may be followed to obtain the gross *semiannual* premium is to increase the total gross annual premium (including any policy charge) by some percentage of itself, and divide the result by 2.

To Illustrate—If the gross annual premium for a certain policy is \$34.89, calculate the semiannual premium. Assume that it is $\frac{1}{2}$ of the gross annual premium increased by $2\frac{1}{2}\%$.

Solution—The gross annual premium increased by $2\frac{1}{2}\%$ is

$$(\$34.89)(1.025) = \$35.76$$

The semiannual premium is $\frac{1}{2}$ of this:

$$\text{Semiannual Premium} = \frac{1}{2}(\$35.76)$$

$$= \$17.88$$

If a great many semiannual premiums are to be calculated, it would be desirable to shorten the calculation by first dividing 1.025 by 2. This equals .5125. Each gross annual premium can be multiplied by this factor. By this procedure, only one multiplication is required to calculate each semiannual premium. The solution for the above illustration would then be written:

$$\text{Semiannual Premium} = (\$34.89)(.5125)$$
$$= \$17.88$$

This is the same answer as above.

To determine the *quarterly* premium, the gross annual premium may be increased by some larger percentage, such as 5%, and the result divided by 4.

To Illustrate—If the gross annual premium for a certain policy is \$34.89, calculate the quarterly premium. Assume that it is $\frac{1}{4}$ of the gross annual premium increased by 5%.

Solution—The gross annual premium increased by 5% is

$$(\$34.89)(1.05) = \$36.63$$

The quarterly premium is $\frac{1}{4}$ of this:

$$\text{Quarterly Premium} = \frac{1}{4}(\$36.63)$$
$$= \$9.16$$

Or, if 1.05 is divided by 4, the factor .2625 is obtained. The gross annual premium can be multiplied by this factor:

$$\text{Quarterly Premium} = (\$34.89)(.2625)$$
$$= \$9.16$$

The answer is the same by both methods.

To determine the *monthly* premium, the gross annual premium may be increased by a still greater percentage, such as 8%, and the result divided by 12.

To Illustrate—If the gross annual premium for a certain policy is \$34.89, calculate the monthly premium. Assume that it is $\frac{1}{12}$ of the gross annual premium increased by 8%.

Solution—The gross annual premium increased by 8% is

$$(\$34.89)(1.08) = \$37.68$$

The monthly premium is $\frac{1}{12}$ of this:

$$\text{Monthly Premium} = \frac{1}{12}(\$37.68)$$
$$= \$3.14$$

Or, if 1.08 is divided by 12, the factor .09 is obtained. The gross annual premium can be multiplied by this factor:

$$\text{Monthly Premium} = (\$34.89)(.09)$$
$$= \$3.14$$

The answer is the same by both methods.

EXERCISES

1 The net annual premium for a certain policy is $12.05 per $1,000. Calculate the gross annual premium per $1,000 by loading the net premium 20% of the gross premium.

2 Using the answer to Exercise 1, calculate the gross annual premium for a $10,000 policy, assuming an $8 policy charge is added to the premium.

3 Calculate the gross annual premium per $1,000 for a certain policy, given the following:

Net annual premium per $1,000 = $21.05
Loading (Except policy charge) = $2.50 per $1,000, plus 10% of gross premium

4 Using the answer to Exercise 3, calculate the gross annual premium for a $15,000 policy, assuming a charge of $6 per policy is added.

5 Calculate the gross annual premium for a $10,000 policy for which the net annual premium per $1,000, $49.20, is to be loaded $5 per $1,000 plus 15% of the gross premium, and finally $10 per policy is added.

6 A certain company does not make an additional charge per policy, but instead charges a different gross annual premium per $1,000 for different-sized policies, as follows:

20-Payment Life; Age 30

Amount of Policy	*Gross Premium per $1,000*
Less than $10,000	$33.28
$10,000 to $49,999	32.02
$50,000 and over	31.86

What would be the gross annual premium for a $25,000 20-payment life policy issued at age 30?

7 If the gross annual premium for a certain policy is $314.95, calculate the monthly premium. Assume that it is $\frac{1}{12}$ of the gross annual premium increased by 5%.

8 If the gross annual premium for a certain policy is $14.10 per $1,000, plus a charge of $5 per policy, calculate the semiannual premium for a $10,000 policy. Assume that it is $\frac{1}{2}$ of the gross annual premium increased by 4%.

10.9 SYMBOLS FOR NET ANNUAL PREMIUMS

Chart 10–3 displays certain internationally used symbols, each of which represents the net annual premium for $1 of life insurance issued at age x. (These net annual premiums are also shown as they would be calculated using commutation functions.)

The capital letter "P" is used with a subscript for the issue age, and the number of years under an "angle." In this respect, the subscripts are identical to those shown in Section 9.9 which appear with "A" for the various types of net single premiums. However, there is an additional subscript shown at the lower *left* of the "P" whenever the premium-paying period is shorter than the benefit period. For example, the symbol ${}_mP_{x:\overline{n}|}$ represents the net annual premium for a $1 m-payment n-year endowment policy issued at age x.

CHART 10–3

Net Annual Premium for $1 of Life Insurance Issued at Age x

Type of Life Insurance	*Symbol for Net Annual Premium*	*Net Annual Premium Using Commutation Functions*
Ordinary Life	P_x	$\frac{M_x}{N_x}$
m-Payment Life	${}_mP_x$	$\frac{M_x}{N_x - N_{x+m}}$
n-Year Term Insurance	$P^{1}_{x:\overline{n}|}$	$\frac{M_x - M_{x+n}}{N_x - N_{x+n}}$
m-Payment n-Year Term Insurance	${}_mP^{1}_{x:\overline{n}|}$	$\frac{M_x - M_{x+n}}{N_x - N_{x+m}}$
n-Year Endowment Insurance	$P_{x:\overline{n}|}$	$\frac{M_x - M_{x+n} + D_{x+n}}{N_x - N_{x+n}}$
m-Payment n-Year Endowment Insurance	${}_mP_{x:\overline{n}|}$	$\frac{M_x - M_{x+n} + D_{x+n}}{N_x - N_{x+m}}$

11. Net Level Premium Reserves

11.1 TERMINAL RESERVES

It was pointed out in Section 9.1 that the net premium for one-year term insurance increases each year with the age of the insured. In Chapter 10 a method of calculating premiums under which the net premium remains uniform throughout the premium-paying period was described. Under the method, known as the *net level premium method,* the person is paying net premiums in the early policy years which are higher than required to pay death claims in those years. The excess accumulates from year to year to produce a fund known as the *net level premium reserve.* Because this fund will be needed to help pay benefits in later years, the total of the reserves for all the individual policies in force at any time represents the principal liability of a life insurance company. Since the insurance company has invested the premium income, it has accumulated assets which have a value at least large enough to provide for this liability.

As the name implies, such a reserve fund is calculated by using *net* level premiums, not gross premiums. The same mortality table and interest rate on which net premiums are based are used to compute the reserve. (Whenever the word "reserve" is used in this chapter, it will mean "net level premium reserve." Reserves calculated by other than net level premiums will be described in Chapter 12.)

In Chapter 10, two schedules were shown which illustrated the year-by-year accumulation of such a fund (Sections 10.2 and 10.4).

The fund shown at the end of each year could be divided by the number of persons living at the end of that year to determine a reserve *per person* (per $1,000 of insurance). In this way, a reserve is actually determined each year for an individual policy.

Such reserves are calculated as of the end of each policy year, after payment of the year's death claims. They are, therefore, known as *terminal reserves*.

As an example, consider a five-payment 10-year endowment policy issued to a person age 21. The net level annual premium per $1,000 is $158.752, rounding off to three decimal places for this example, instead of the customary two. Using Table III and 3% interest, and assuming that each person in the Table has $1,000 of such insurance, the schedule which follows may be constructed. The premium income for each of the first five years is calculated by multiplying $158.752 by the number living. The death claims each year are calculated by multiplying $1,000 by the number dying. It can then be seen how the total fund accumulates year by year. Column (8) of the schedule is the reserve per person (per $1,000 of insurance). It is calculated each year by dividing the total fund at the *end* of the year by the number of persons living at the *end* of the year (by the number living at the *beginning* of the *following* year). See Chart 11–1.

An inspection of the figures in column (8) shows that the reserve per person grows year by year until it reaches exactly $1,000 on the date when the $1,000 pure endowment is payable. It is also interesting to note that each person pays a premium the first year of $158.752, and that the reserve at the end of that year is $161.98. Since 3% interest is being credited, the $158.752 premium would have accumulated to

$$\$158.752(1.03) = \$163.51$$

using interest only. The difference represents the contribution which each person makes to pay that year's death claims:

$$\$163.51 - \$161.98 = \$1.53$$

To Illustrate—Using the 1958 C.S.O. Table and 3% interest, calculate the terminal reserve per $1,000 for a 4-year term insurance policy issued at age 25.

Solution—This is the same policy which was considered in Section 10.2. In that section, the year-by-year fund was calculated, and the schedule is repeated in Chart 11–2, which is shown on page 242. This schedule assumes that each person has $1,000 of insurance. To derive the terminal reserve per $1,000, the balance in the fund at the

CHART 11–1

Age 21 – 5-Pay 10-Year Endowment (1958 C.S.O. 3%)

(1) Age x	(2) l_x	(3) Premium Income (Premium × l_x)	(4) Total Fund Beginning of Year (Col. 3 + Col. 7 Previous Yr.)	(5) Fund Accumulated for 1 year (Col. 4 × 1.03)	(6) Death Claims ($1,000 d_x)	(7) Total Fund at End of Year (Col. 5 – Col. 6)	(8) Reserve per Person (Col. 7 ÷ Col. 2 Following Yr.)
21	9,647,694	$1,531,590,718	$1,531,590,718	$1,577,538,440	$17,655,000	$1,559,883,440	$ 161.98
22	9,630,039	1,528,787,951	3,088,671,391	3,181,331,533	17,912,000	3,163,419,533	329.11
23	9,612,127	1,525,944,386	4,689,363,919	4,830,044,837	18,167,000	4,811,877,837	501.55
24	9,593,960	1,523,060,338	6,334,938,175	6,524,986,320	18,324,000	6,506,662,320	679.50
25	9,575,636	1,520,151,366	8,026,813,686	8,267,618,097	18,481,000	8,249,137,097	863.14
26	9,557,155	0	8,249,137,097	8,496,611,210	18,732,000	8,477,879,210	888.81
27	9,538,423	0	8,477,879,210	8,732,215,586	18,981,000	8,713,234,586	915.31
28	9,519,442	0	8,713,234,586	8,974,631,624	19,324,000	8,955,307,624	942.65
29	9,500,118	0	8,955,307,624	9,223,966,853	19,760,000	9,204,206,853	970.87
30	9,480,358	0	9,204,206,853	9,480,333,059	20,193,000	9,460,140,059	1000.00
31	9,460,165	—	—	—	—	—	—

CHART 11–2

Age 25—4-Year Term Insurance (1958 C.S.O. 3%)

(1) Year	(2) Premiums Paid at Beginning of Year	(3) Total Fund at Beginning of Year (Col. 6 Previous Year + Col. 2)	(4) Fund Accumulated for One Year (Col. 3 × 1.03)	(5) Claims Paid at End of Year (Number of Deaths × $1,000)	(6) Balance in Fund at End of Year After Payment of Claims (Col. 4 − Col. 5)
1	$18,385,221.12	$18,385,221.12	$18,936,777.75	$18,481,000	$445,777.75
2	18,349,737.60	18,805,515.35	19,369,680.81	18,732,000	637,680.81
3	18,313,772.16	18,951,452.97	19,519,996.56	18,981,000	538,996.56
4	18,277,328.64	18,816,325.20	19,380,814.96	19,324,000	56,814.96

(Note: The final balance in the fund would be even closer to zero if the net annual premium were rounded off to more decimal places.)

end of each year is divided by the number living at the end of that year (by the number living at the beginning of the following year):

At the End of First Year

Balance in Fund = $455,777.75

Age at That Time = 26

$$\text{Number Living at That Time} = l_{26}$$

$$= 9{,}557{,}155$$

$$\text{Terminal Reserve per } \$1{,}000 = \frac{\text{Balance in Fund}}{\text{Number Living}}$$

$$= \frac{\$455{,}777.75}{9{,}557{,}155}$$

$$= \$.05$$

At the End of Second Year

Balance in Fund = $637,680.81

Age at That Time = 27

$$\text{Number Living at That Time} = l_{27}$$

$$= 9{,}538{,}423$$

$$\text{Terminal Reserve per } \$1{,}000 = \frac{\text{Balance in Fund}}{\text{Number Living}}$$

$$= \frac{\$637{,}680.81}{9{,}538{,}423}$$

$$= \$.07$$

At the End of Third Year

Balance in Fund = \$538,996.56

Age at That Time = 28

Number Living at That Time = l_{28}

= 9,519,442

$$\text{Terminal Reserve per \$1,000} = \frac{\text{Balance in Fund}}{\text{Number Living}}$$

$$= \frac{\$538{,}996.56}{9{,}519{,}442}$$

= \$.06

At the End of Fourth Year

Balance in Fund = \$56,814.96

Age at That Time = 29

Number Living at That Time = l_{29}

= 9,500,118

$$\text{Terminal Reserve per \$1,000} = \frac{\text{Balance in Fund}}{\text{Number Living}}$$

$$= \frac{\$56{,}814.96}{9{,}500{,}118}$$

= \$.01, but would be zero if net annual premium were rounded off to more decimal places

The terminal reserves on this term policy are much smaller than those calculated above on the endowment policy. The final reserve on this term policy is zero. This is logical because, at the end of the term, all of the net premium income should have been used to pay death claims. The company owes nothing further in benefits.

It is interesting to consider the accumulation of such a fund on a policy where the insurance extends for the whole of life. All mortality tables are constructed to show the number dying in the *final year* equal to the number living at the beginning of that year, leaving none living at the end. The accumulated fund will normally provide, therefore, exactly enough money in that final year to pay all these death claims, leaving no balance in the fund. From this viewpoint, a whole life insurance policy can be considered as a "term to age 100" policy, when based on the 1958 C.S.O. Table, which ends at age 100. If, as sometimes happens, an insured person actually lives to age 100, it is customary for the insurance company to pay the amount of insurance at that time.

11.2 THE RETROSPECTIVE METHOD

The method explained above for calculating terminal reserves requires that a year-by-year accumulation be performed. To find the terminal reserve for any year, one must know the accumulations for all the preceding years. However, by another method, reserves may be calculated for any year desired without such a requirement. This second method uses the principle that the terminal reserve, at any specified time, is equal to the accumulated value of all the net premiums which have been received, less the accumulated cost of the insurance which has been provided.

This method is known as the *retrospective method,* because it involves the use of past happenings ("looking backwards"). In equation form, it may be written:

$$\begin{pmatrix}\text{Terminal}\\\text{Reserve}\end{pmatrix}=\begin{pmatrix}\text{Accumulated Value}\\\text{of Net Premiums}\\\text{Received}\end{pmatrix}-\begin{pmatrix}\text{Accumulated}\\\text{Cost of}\\\text{Insurance}\end{pmatrix}$$

The two items on the right side of the equation make direct use of principles previously presented. The "accumulated value of net premiums received" represents the accumulated value of a temporary life annuity due (since premium payments are made each year only if the person insured is then alive), as discussed in Section 8.3. The "accumulated cost of insurance" was presented in Section 9.6.

To Illustrate—Using the 1958 C.S.O. Table and 3% interest, calculate the 4th terminal reserve for a \$1,000 5-payment 10-year endowment policy issued at age 21, with a net annual premium of \$158.752.

Solution—This is the same policy for which terminal reserves were calculated in Section 11.1 by a year-by-year accumulation. The 4th terminal reserve (at attained age 25) will now be calculated by the retrospective method. The accumulated value of the net premiums received will be considered first. The line diagram of the net premiums *received during these first 4 years* appears as follows:

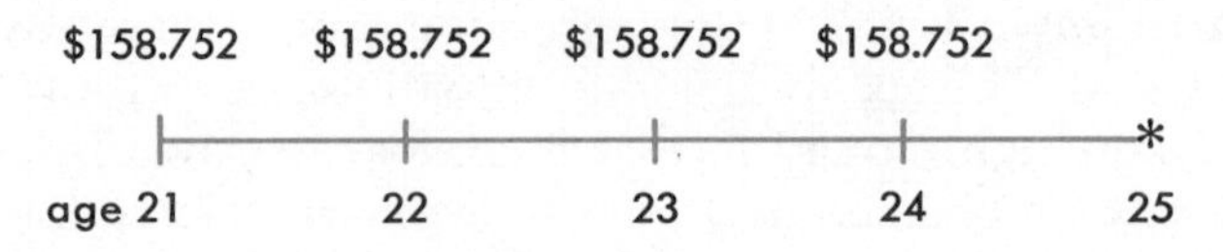

The expression for their accumulated value will have a *numerator* representing the total amount paid in by the survivors at each age, with each such amount being accumulated at interest to the evaluation date. The *denominator* is the number living on the evaluation date:

Basic equation

$$\begin{pmatrix}\text{Accumulated Value}\\ \text{of Net Premiums}\\ \text{Received}\end{pmatrix} = \$158.752\left[\frac{l_{21}(1+i)^4 + l_{22}(1+i)^3 + l_{23}(1+i)^2 + l_{24}(1+i)}{l_{25}}\right]$$

Substituting values from the tables

$$= \$158.752\left[\frac{\begin{array}{c}9{,}647{,}694(1.125509)\\ +9{,}630{,}039(1.092727)\\ +9{,}612{,}127(1.060900)\\ +9{,}593{,}960(1.030000)\end{array}}{9{,}575{,}636}\right]$$

$$= \$158.752\left[\frac{10{,}858{,}566 + 10{,}523{,}004 + 10{,}197{,}506 + 9{,}881{,}779}{9{,}575{,}636}\right]$$

$$= \$687.37$$

The accumulated cost of insurance will be considered next. The line diagram of the life insurance benefits *paid during these first 4 years* appears as follows:

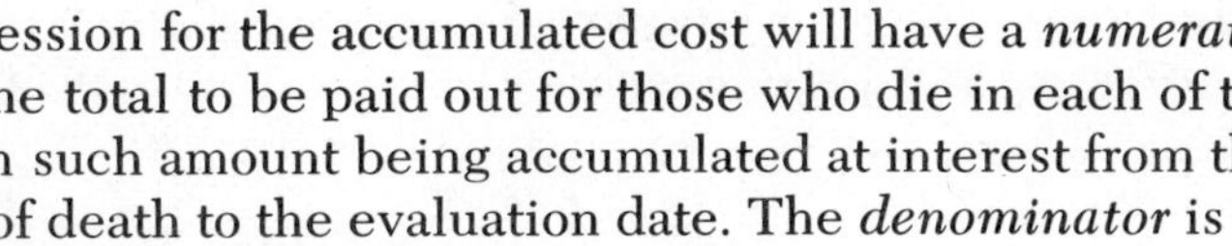

age 21	22	23	24	25
	\$1,000d_{21}	\$1,000d_{22}	\$1,000d_{23}	\$1,000d_{24} *

The expression for the accumulated cost will have a *numerator* representing the total to be paid out for those who die in each of the years, with each such amount being accumulated at interest from the end of the year of death to the evaluation date. The *denominator* is the number living on the evaluation date:

Basic equation

$$\begin{pmatrix}\text{Accumulated}\\ \text{Cost of}\\ \text{Insurance}\end{pmatrix} = \$1{,}000\left[\frac{d_{21}(1+i)^3 + d_{22}(1+i)^2 + d_{23}(1+i) + d_{24}}{l_{25}}\right]$$

Substituting values from the tables

$$= \$1{,}000 \left[\frac{17{,}655(1.092727) + 17{,}912(1.060900) + 18{,}167(1.030000) + 18{,}324}{9{,}575{,}636} \right]$$

$$= \$1{,}000 \left[\frac{19{,}292 + 19{,}003 + 18{,}712 + 18{,}324}{9{,}575{,}636} \right]$$

$$= \$7.87$$

Hence, the 4th terminal reserve, calculated by the retrospective method, is

Basic equation

$$\begin{pmatrix}\text{Terminal}\\ \text{Reserve}\end{pmatrix} = \begin{pmatrix}\text{Accumulated Value}\\ \text{of Net Premiums}\\ \text{Received}\end{pmatrix} - \begin{pmatrix}\text{Accumulated}\\ \text{Cost of}\\ \text{Insurance}\end{pmatrix}$$

Substituting values calculated above

$$= \$687.37 - \$7.87$$

$$= \$679.50$$

This answer agrees with the figure shown in column (8) for the 4th terminal reserve.

11.3 THE PROSPECTIVE METHOD

Terminal reserves can also be calculated by looking into the future of a life insurance policy. This method of calculating reserves is known as the *prospective method* ("looking ahead").

At any particular time during the life of a policy, the company may look ahead at the benefits it will have to pay on that policy in the future. The money necessary to pay those future benefits will come from two sources: the *reserve* currently being held, and the *future net premiums*. The following equation may be written to express this fact:

$$\begin{pmatrix}\text{Present Value}\\ \text{of Future Benefits}\end{pmatrix} = \begin{pmatrix}\text{Terminal}\\ \text{Reserve}\end{pmatrix} + \begin{pmatrix}\text{Present Value of}\\ \text{Future Net Premiums}\end{pmatrix}$$

Solving for the terminal reserve results in the following equation which expresses the prospective method:

$$\begin{pmatrix}\text{Terminal}\\ \text{Reserve}\end{pmatrix} = \begin{pmatrix}\text{Present Value}\\ \text{of Future Benefits}\end{pmatrix} - \begin{pmatrix}\text{Present Value of}\\ \text{Future Net Premiums}\end{pmatrix}$$

This is equivalent to the equation:

$$\begin{pmatrix}\text{Terminal}\\ \text{Reserve}\end{pmatrix} = \begin{pmatrix}\text{Net Single Premium}\\ \text{at Attained Age}\end{pmatrix} - \begin{pmatrix}\text{Present Value of}\\ \text{Future Net Annual}\\ \text{Premiums at}\\ \text{Attained Age}\end{pmatrix}$$

The reserves calculated by the prospective method are equal to those calculated by the retrospective method.

It should be stressed that the two items on the right side of the equation for the terminal reserve are calculated at the *attained age,* and take into account only those benefits and premiums, respectively, which will be in effect *after* the date of the particular reserve which is being calculated. Both make direct use of principles previously presented. The "present value of future benefits" is the *net single premium,* presented in Chapter 9. In this case, it is the net single premium at the *attained age* for those benefits then remaining. The "present value of future net premiums" represents the present value of a life annuity due. The present value is calculated at the *attained age,* and includes only those premiums still to be paid. These principles were presented in Chapter 8.

For example, if the third terminal reserve were being calculated for a 20-payment 30-year endowment insurance policy issued at age 25, the attained age would be $25 + 3 = 28$. The future benefits at age 28 would be the same as for a 27-year endowment insurance policy at that age. The future net premiums at age 28 would be 17 in number (three premiums having already been collected).

To Illustrate – Using the 1958 C.S.O. Table and 3% interest, calculate the 4th terminal reserve for a \$1,000 5-payment 10-year endowment policy issued at age 21, with a net annual premium of \$158.752.

Solution – This is the same policy for which the terminal reserves were calculated in Section 11.1 by a year-by-year accumulation, and in Section 11.2 by the retrospective method. This reserve will now be derived by the prospective method. If the 4th terminal reserve is to be calculated, then the *attained age* is $21 + 4 = 25$. The present value of future benefits will be considered first. This present value will be the net single premium at the attained age of 25 for a 6-year endowment policy. In line diagram form, these future benefits (those coming after the end of the 4th year) appear as follows:

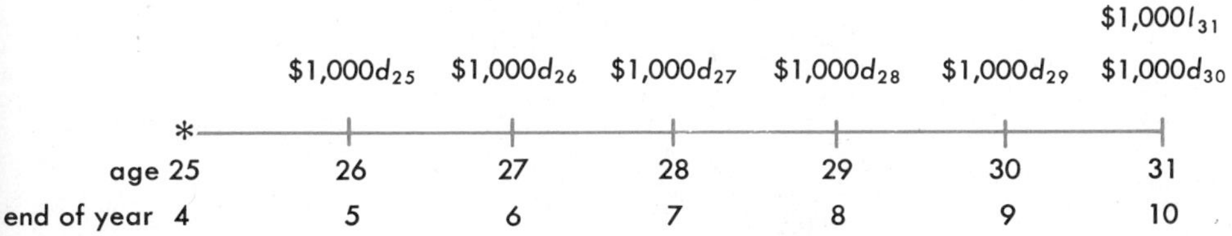

						$\$1{,}000l_{31}$
	$\$1{,}000d_{25}$	$\$1{,}000d_{26}$	$\$1{,}000d_{27}$	$\$1{,}000d_{28}$	$\$1{,}000d_{29}$	$\$1{,}000d_{30}$
*						
age 25	26	27	28	29	30	31
end of year 4	5	6	7	8	9	10

The expression for the present value of these future benefits (the net single premium at the attained age) will have a *numerator* representing the total paid out for those who die each year, with each such amount being discounted at interest from the end of the year of death to the evaluation date, plus the total pure endowments paid to the survivors at the end of the period, discounted at interest to the evaluation date. The *denominator* is the number living on the evaluation date:

Basic equation

$$\begin{pmatrix}\text{Present Value}\\ \text{of Future Benefits}\end{pmatrix}$$

or

$$\begin{pmatrix}\text{Net Single Premium}\\ \text{at Attained Age 25}\end{pmatrix}$$

$$= \$1{,}000\left(\frac{d_{25}v + d_{26}v^2 + d_{27}v^3 + d_{28}v^4 + d_{29}v^5 + d_{30}v^6 + l_{31}v^6}{l_{25}}\right)$$

Substituting values from the tables

$$= \$1{,}000\left[\frac{\begin{array}{l} 18{,}481(.970874)\\ +18{,}732(.942596)\\ +18{,}981(.915142)\\ +19{,}324(.888487)\\ +19{,}760(.862609)\\ +20{,}193(.837484)\\ +\ 9{,}460{,}165(.837484)\end{array}}{9{,}575{,}636}\right]$$

$$= \$1{,}000\left(\frac{17{,}943 + 17{,}657 + 17{,}370 + 17{,}169 + 17{,}045 + 16{,}911 + 7{,}922{,}737}{9{,}575{,}636}\right)$$

$$= \$838.256$$

The present value of future net annual premiums at the attained age will be considered next. The net annual premium was given as \$158.752. The present value of future net annual premiums will be the present value at age 25 of a life annuity due of \$158.752 per year for *one year.* (Since the policy requires only five premium payments, there is only one remaining at the end of four years.) In line diagram form, the future net annual premiums (those coming after the end of the 4th year) appear as follows:

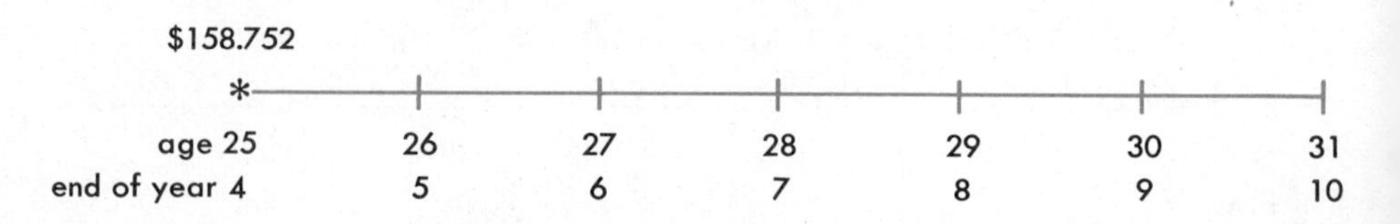

The expression for their present value will have a *numerator* representing the total amount paid in by the survivors at each age, with each such amount being discounted at interest to the evaluation date. The *denominator* is the number living on the evaluation date:

$$\begin{pmatrix}\text{Present Value of}\\ \text{Future Net Premiums}\end{pmatrix} = \$158.752\left(\frac{l_{25}}{l_{25}}\right)$$

In this instance, there is only one age to consider in the numerator. The item in the numerator is not multiplied by any v factor because it represents those net annual premiums which are payable upon the evaluation date. These particular premiums payable on the evaluation date are not discounted at interest for any period of time. Since the entire fraction in the parentheses equals 1, it can be dropped from this calculation.

$$\begin{pmatrix}\text{Present Value of}\\ \text{Future Net Premiums}\end{pmatrix} = \$158.752$$

Hence, the 4th terminal reserve, as calculated by the prospective method, is

Basic equation

$$\begin{pmatrix}\text{Terminal}\\ \text{Reserve}\end{pmatrix} = \begin{pmatrix}\text{Present Value}\\ \text{of Future Benefits}\end{pmatrix} - \begin{pmatrix}\text{Present Value of}\\ \text{Future Net Premiums}\end{pmatrix}$$

$$= \begin{pmatrix}\text{Net Single Premium}\\ \text{at Attained Age}\end{pmatrix} - \begin{pmatrix}\text{Present Value of}\\ \text{Future Net Annual Premiums}\end{pmatrix}$$

Substituting values calculated above

$$= \$838.256 - \$158.752$$

$$= \$679.50$$

This answer agrees with both the figure shown in column (8) of the schedule in Section 11.1 and the figure calculated in Section 11.2 by use of the retrospective method.

It is interesting to consider the equation for the terminal reserve (using the prospective method) at the end of *zero years*, that is, at the time the policy is issued. The usual equation, as given before, is

$$\begin{pmatrix}\text{Terminal}\\ \text{Reserve}\end{pmatrix} = \begin{pmatrix}\text{Present Value}\\ \text{of Future Benefits}\end{pmatrix} - \begin{pmatrix}\text{Present Value of}\\ \text{Future Net Premiums}\end{pmatrix}$$

However, *at the time the policy is issued* the two items on the right side are equal to each other. This is because the basis for the calculation of net annual premiums is the principle that, *at the time the policy is issued*

$$\begin{pmatrix}\text{Present Value}\\ \text{of Future Benefits}\end{pmatrix} = \begin{pmatrix}\text{Present Value of}\\ \text{Future Net Premiums}\end{pmatrix}$$

This equality is only true at the time the policy is issued, and hence at that time the value of the terminal reserve is zero.

Having two different methods for calculating terminal reserves (retrospective and prospective) enables one to choose the method which is simpler for the case at hand. Where the future benefits are complicated, it is often simpler to use the *retrospective* method (provided the net premium is known). On the other hand, if the reserve is desired at a date when there are no more premiums due (such as the 25th reserve on a 20-payment life policy), the *prospective* method is usually simpler because the "present value of future net premiums" is then zero. Other examples of situations for which the prospective method is preferable include policies where benefits in the early policy years are complicated, or where net annual premiums in the early policy years are not uniform year by year.

If published tables of net single premiums and life annuity factors are available, as is generally the case in practice, the terminal reserve can be calculated by the prospective method with less work.

To Illustrate—Calculate the 5th terminal reserve per $1,000 on an endowment-at-age-65 policy issued at age 20, given the following table:

Age	*Net Single Premium for $1,000 Endowment at Age 65*	*Present Value of a Temporary Life Annuity Due of 1 per Year to Age 65*
20	$304.75129	23.870206
21	312.66351	23.598552
22	320.80051	23.319182
23	329.17678	23.031596
24	337.80052	22.735515
25	346.68674	22.430421
26	355.84412	22.116018
27	365.27538	21.792211
28	374.98991	21.458679
29	384.99117	21.115303

(The values given in this table show several decimal places, in order to provide considerable accuracy in the answer.)

Solution—The first step is to calculate the net annual premium. The present value of the net premiums is a temporary life annuity due to age 65.

Basic equation

$$\begin{pmatrix}\text{Present Value of Future}\\ \text{Benefits at Time of Issue}\end{pmatrix} = \begin{pmatrix}\text{Present Value of Future Net}\\ \text{Premiums at Time of Issue}\end{pmatrix}$$

Expressing this equation in equivalent form

$$(\text{Net Single Premium}) = \begin{pmatrix}\text{Net Annual}\\ \text{Premium}\end{pmatrix}(\text{Annuity Factor})$$

Substituting values given

$$\$304.75129 = \begin{pmatrix}\text{Net Annual}\\ \text{Premium}\end{pmatrix}(23.870206)$$

$$\frac{\$304.75129}{23.870206} = \begin{pmatrix}\text{Net Annual}\\ \text{Premium}\end{pmatrix}$$

$$\$12.76702 = \begin{pmatrix}\text{Net Annual}\\ \text{Premium}\end{pmatrix}$$

The second step is to determine the attained age. If the 5th terminal reserve is to be calculated, the attained age is $20 + 5 = 25$.

In the equation for finding the terminal reserve, the "present value of future benefits" will then be the net single premium at attained age 25 for endowment-at-age-65 insurance. The "present value of future net premiums" will be the present value at attained age 25 of a temporary life annuity due of the remaining net annual premiums to age 65.

Basic equation

$$\begin{pmatrix}\text{Terminal}\\ \text{Reserve}\end{pmatrix} = \begin{pmatrix}\text{Present Value}\\ \text{of Future Benefits}\end{pmatrix} - \begin{pmatrix}\text{Present Value of}\\ \text{Future Net Premiums}\end{pmatrix}$$

Expressing this equation in equivalent form

$$= \begin{pmatrix}\text{Net Single Premium}\\ \text{at Attained Age 25}\end{pmatrix} - \begin{pmatrix}\text{Net Annual}\\ \text{Premium}\end{pmatrix}\begin{pmatrix}\text{Annuity Factor}\\ \text{at Attained Age 25}\end{pmatrix}$$

Substituting values given

$$= \$346.68674 - \$12.76702(22.430421)$$

$$= \$346.68674 - \$286.36963$$

$$= \$60.32$$

EXERCISES

1 Using the following information, calculate the 5th terminal reserve, using both the retrospective and prospective methods. Compare the answers obtained by the two methods:

Present value (at end of 5 years) of future net premiums	= $412.77
Accumulated cost of insurance (at end of 5 years)	= 181.33
Present value (at end of 5 years) of future benefits	= 816.04
Accumulated value (at end of 5 years) of net premiums received	= 584.60

2 The net annual premium on a certain policy issued at age 19 is $19.92. Calculate the 7th terminal reserve, using the following information:

Attained Age	*Present Value of Future Benefits*	*Present Value of Future Premiums (per $1)*
19	$406.17	$20.39
20	417.36	20.00
21	428.86	19.61
22	440.70	19.20
23	452.90	18.78
24	465.48	18.35
25	478.45	17.91
26	491.82	17.45
27	505.61	16.97
28	519.82	16.49
29	534.47	15.98

3 Using the following table, calculate the 38th terminal reserve on a $1,000 ordinary life policy issued at age 10:

Age	*Net Single Premium for $1,000 Whole Life Insurance*	*Present Value of Whole Life Annuity Due of 1 per year*
10	$351.30	33.083
11	357.06	32.790
12	362.99	32.488
.	.	.
.	.	.
.	.	.
47	634.69	18.631
48	643.86	18.163
49	653.04	17.695

4 Write expressions for the 2nd year terminal reserve for each of the following $1,000 policies, using both the retrospective and prospective methods. Calculate the value of each, using Table III and 3% interest. (Hint: Line diagrams should be helpful.)

a) A 5-year term insurance policy issued at age 60 (Net annual premium = $23.563)

b) An ordinary life policy issued at age 96 (Net annual premium = $479.992)

c) A 2-payment life policy issued at age 96 (Net annual premium = $595.950)

d) A 4-year endowment insurance policy issued at age 30 (Net annual premium = $232.896)

e) A 4-payment 5-year endowment insurance policy issued at age 25 (Net annual premium = $226.086)

11.4 COMMUTATION FUNCTIONS

The commutation functions explained in Chapters 8, 9, and 10 can be used to calculate terminal reserves. This device can be used for either the retrospective or prospective method, and will generally simplify the work.

As a first step in the calculation, regardless of which method is being used, commutation functions can be used to calculate the *net annual premium*. The procedure was described in Section 10.6.

In the equation for the *retrospective method*, namely,

$$\begin{pmatrix}\text{Terminal}\\\text{Reserve}\end{pmatrix}=\begin{pmatrix}\text{Accumulated Value}\\\text{of Net Premiums}\\\text{Received}\end{pmatrix}-\begin{pmatrix}\text{Accumulated}\\\text{Cost of}\\\text{Insurance}\end{pmatrix}$$

the items on the right side make use of principles previously presented. The "accumulated value of net premiums received" represents the accumulated value of a temporary life annuity due. Such a calculation, using commutation functions, was described in Section 8.7. The use of commutation functions to calculate "accumulated cost of insurance" was described in Section 9.8.

To Illustrate—Using Table IV, calculate the 4th terminal reserve for a $1,000 5-payment 10-year endowment policy issued at age 21. The net annual premium is $158.752.

Solution—This is the same problem presented in the illustrations in Sections 11.2 and 11.3. The solution will now be given using the retrospective method and commutation functions.

The "accumulated value of net premiums received" during the first 4 years may be written:

$$\begin{pmatrix}\text{Accumulated Value}\\\text{of Net Premiums}\\\text{Received}\end{pmatrix}=\$158.752\left(\frac{N_{21}-N_{25}}{D_{25}}\right)$$

This follows from the general statement made in Chapter 8 that the factor to use in evaluating a life annuity will be of the form $\frac{N-N}{D}$, where the subscript of the first N is the age when the first payment is due, the subscript of the second N is the first age when there are no more payments due, and the subscript of the D is the age at which the annuity is being evaluated.

Equation given above

$$\begin{pmatrix}\text{Accumulated Value}\\\text{of Net Premiums}\\\text{Received}\end{pmatrix}=\$158.752\left(\frac{N_{21}-N_{25}}{D_{25}}\right)$$

Substituting values from Table IV

$$= \$158.752\left(\frac{132{,}991{,}534 - 113{,}189{,}600}{4{,}573{,}377}\right)$$

$$= \$158.752\left(\frac{19{,}801{,}934}{4{,}573{,}377}\right)$$

$$= \$687.37$$

The "accumulated cost of insurance" for the first 4 years may be written

$$\begin{pmatrix}\text{Accumulated}\\ \text{Cost of}\\ \text{Insurance}\end{pmatrix} = \$1{,}000\left(\frac{M_{21} - M_{25}}{D_{25}}\right)$$

This follows from the general statement made in Chapter 9 that the factor to use in calculating an accumulated cost of insurance will be of the form $\frac{M - M + D}{D}$, where the subscript of the first M is the age when the insurance coverage begins, the subscript of the second M is the age at which the insurance coverage stops, the subscript of the D in the numerator is the age at which a pure endowment would be paid, and the subscript of the D in the denominator is the age at which this accumulated cost of insurance is evaluated. (In this particular case, the D in the numerator does not appear, because no pure endowment is involved in the first 4 years.)

Equation given above

$$\begin{pmatrix}\text{Accumulated}\\ \text{Cost of}\\ \text{Insurance}\end{pmatrix} = \$1{,}000\left(\frac{M_{21} - M_{25}}{D_{25}}\right)$$

Substituting values from Table IV

$$= \$1{,}000\left(\frac{1{,}312{,}569 - 1{,}276{,}590}{4{,}573{,}377}\right)$$

$$= \$1{,}000\left(\frac{35{,}979}{4{,}573{,}377}\right)$$

$$= \$7.87$$

Hence, as calculated by the retrospective method, the 4th terminal reserve is

Basic equation

$$\begin{pmatrix}\text{Terminal}\\ \text{Reserve}\end{pmatrix} = \begin{pmatrix}\text{Accumulated Value}\\ \text{of Net Premiums}\\ \text{Received}\end{pmatrix} - \begin{pmatrix}\text{Accumulated}\\ \text{Cost of}\\ \text{Insurance}\end{pmatrix}$$

Substituting values calculated above

$$= \$687.37 - \$7.87$$

$$= \$679.50$$

This answer agrees with that calculated in Sections 11.2 and 11.3.

In the equation for the *prospective* method, namely,

$$\begin{pmatrix}\text{Terminal}\\ \text{Reserve}\end{pmatrix} = \begin{pmatrix}\text{Present Value}\\ \text{of Future Benefits}\end{pmatrix} - \begin{pmatrix}\text{Present Value of}\\ \text{Future Net Premiums}\end{pmatrix}$$

the items on the right side make use of principles previously presented. The "present value of future benefits" is the *net single premium* at the attained age for those benefits then remaining. Such a calculation, using commutation functions, was described in Section 9.8. The "present value of future net premiums" represents the present value of a life annuity due. The use of commutation functions to calculate life annuities was described in Section 8.7.

To Illustrate—Using Table IV, calculate the 4th terminal reserve for a \$1,000 5-payment 10-year endowment policy issued at age 21. The net annual premium is \$158.752.

Solution—This is the same problem presented in the illustrations in Sections 11.2 and 11.3 and above in this section. The solution will now be given by using the prospective method and commutation functions.

The "present value of future benefits" (as of the end of the 4th year) may be written

$$\begin{pmatrix}\text{Present Value}\\ \text{of Future Benefits}\end{pmatrix} = \$1{,}000\left(\frac{M_{25} - M_{31} + D_{31}}{D_{25}}\right)$$

or

$$\begin{pmatrix}\text{Net Single Premium}\\ \text{at Attained Age}\end{pmatrix}$$

This follows from the general statement made in Chapter 9 that the factor to use in calculating a net single premium will be of the form $\frac{M - M + D}{D}$, where the subscript of the first M is the age when the insurance coverage begins, the subscript of the second M is the age at which the insurance coverage stops, the subscript of the D in the numerator is the age at which a pure endowment would be paid, and the subscript of the D in the denominator is the age at which this net single premium is evaluated.

Equation given above

$$\begin{pmatrix}\text{Present Value}\\ \text{of Future Benefits}\end{pmatrix} = \$1{,}000\left(\frac{M_{25} - M_{31} + D_{31}}{D_{25}}\right)$$

or

$$\begin{pmatrix}\text{Net Single Premium}\\ \text{at Attained Age}\end{pmatrix}$$

Substituting values from Table IV

$$= \$1{,}000\left(\frac{1{,}276{,}590 - 1{,}226{,}873 + 3{,}783{,}944}{4{,}573{,}377}\right)$$

$$= \$1{,}000\left(\frac{3{,}833{,}661}{4{,}573{,}377}\right)$$

$$= \$838.256$$

The "present value of future net premiums" (as of the end of the 4th year) may be written:

$$\begin{pmatrix}\text{Present Value of}\\ \text{Future Net Premiums}\end{pmatrix} = \$158.752\left(\frac{N_{25} - N_{26}}{D_{25}}\right)$$

This follows from the general statement in Chapter 8 that the factor to use in evaluating a life annuity will be of the form $\frac{N-N}{D}$, where the subscript of the first N is the age when the first payment is due, the subscript of the second N is the first age when there are no more payments due, and the subscript of the D is the age at which the annuity is being evaluated.

Equation given above

$$\begin{pmatrix}\text{Present Value of}\\ \text{Future Net Premiums}\end{pmatrix} = \$158.752\left(\frac{N_{25} - N_{26}}{D_{25}}\right)$$

Substituting values from Table IV

$$= \$158.752\left(\frac{113{,}189{,}600 - 108{,}616{,}223}{4{,}573{,}377}\right)$$

$$= \$158.752\left(\frac{4{,}573{,}377}{4{,}573{,}377}\right)$$

$$= \$158.752$$

Hence, as calculated by the prospective method, the 4th terminal reserve is

Basic equation

$$\begin{pmatrix}\text{Terminal}\\ \text{Reserve}\end{pmatrix} = \begin{pmatrix}\text{Present Value}\\ \text{of Future Benefits}\end{pmatrix} - \begin{pmatrix}\text{Present Value of}\\ \text{Future Net Premiums}\end{pmatrix}$$

Substituting values calculated above

$$= \$838.256 - \$158.752$$

$$= \$679.50$$

This answer agrees with that calculated in the previous illustrations.

EXERCISES

(Use Table IV for all of the following)

1 Write an expression (using commutation functions) for each of the following terminal reserves, using both the retrospective and prospective methods. (If the student wishes to practice, he can calculate the value of each reserve.)

a) Tenth terminal reserve on a $1,000 15-year term insurance policy issued at age 40 (Net annual premium = $6.308)

b) Terminal reserve at age 65 on a $1,000 ordinary life policy issued at age 25 (Net annual premium = $11.278)

c) Fifth terminal reserve on a $1,000 20-payment life policy issued at age 30 (Net annual premium = $21.145)

d) Eighth terminal reserve on a $1,000 20-year endowment insurance policy issued at age 0 (Net annual premium = $37.266)

2 Calculate the 10th terminal reserve for a $1,000 term-to-age-65 insurance policy issued at age 35.

3 The net annual premium per $1,000 for a 30-payment life insurance policy issued at age 25 is $14.32. Calculate the 15th terminal reserve per $1,000 using the prospective method.

4 Calculate the 5th terminal reserve for a $1,000 20-payment 35-year endowment policy issued at age 30. What would this reserve be for a $3,000 policy?

11.5 PATTERNS OF TERMINAL RESERVES

The reserve at any particular time for any particular policy is the amount the company must then have on hand for that policy. Some of the special instances of this, which have been described previously in this chapter, are:

1. *For any policy*, the terminal reserve at the end of *zero years* (at the time the policy is issued) equals zero.
2. *For term insurance policies*, the *final* terminal reserve (at the end of the term) equals zero. This is because all of the net premiums have been used to pay death claims. The company owes nothing further in benefits.
3. *For endowment insurance policies*, the *final* terminal reserve (on the date the pure endowment is payable) is equal to the amount of the pure endowment. This provides the exact amount which the company will have to pay on that date.
4. *For whole life insurance policies*, the *final* terminal reserve (at the end of the mortality table) equals zero. This is because, according

to the mortality table, none are then living; hence, the company should owe nothing further in benefits. However, the terminal reserve *one year prior* is nearly equal to the full amount of the death benefit. This helps to provide for payment of the full death benefit to *everybody* that final year (when all are presumed to die).

Typical patterns of terminal reserves, on the common types of policies, can be seen in the graphs that follow. The number of years since the policy was issued is shown along the bottom of the graphs. For each such year, the distance up to the line indicates the size of the reserve at the end of that year.

For a *term insurance policy,* the reserve rises up to a high-point near the middle of the term, and then decreases back to zero. The magnitude of the reserve never gets very large compared to the amount of insurance. (See Figure 11–1.)

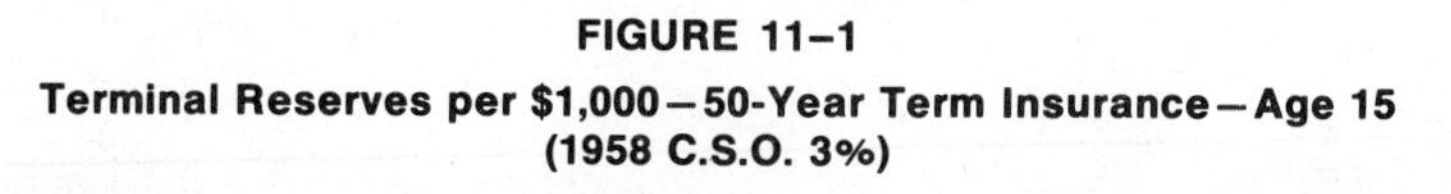

FIGURE 11–1

Terminal Reserves per $1,000—50-Year Term Insurance—Age 15 (1958 C.S.O. 3%)

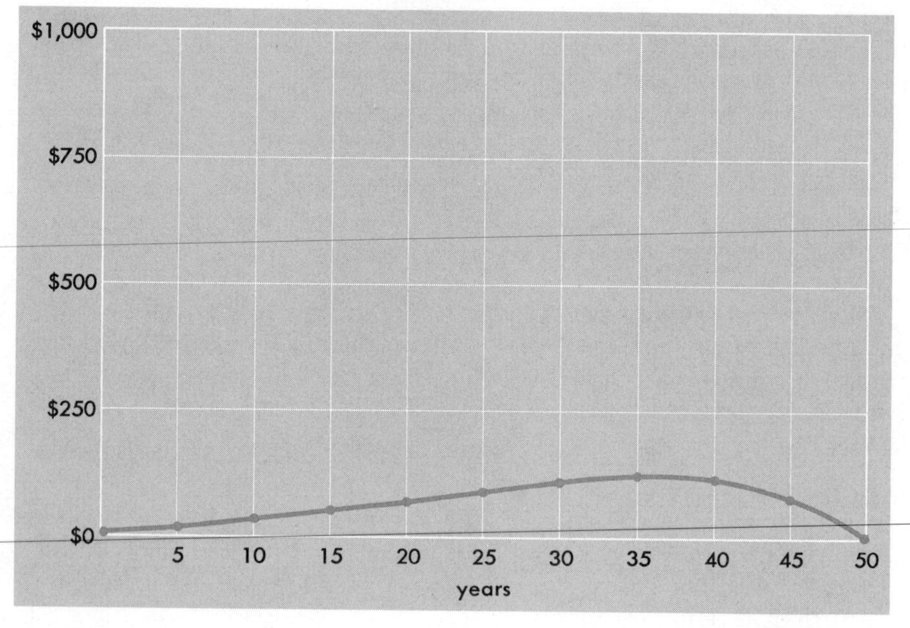

For an *endowment insurance policy,* the reserve rises up to equal the amount of the pure endowment on the date the pure endowment is payable. (See Figure 11–2.)

FIGURE 11–2
Terminal Reserves per $1,000—50-Year Endowment Insurance—Age 15 (1958 C.S.O. 3%)

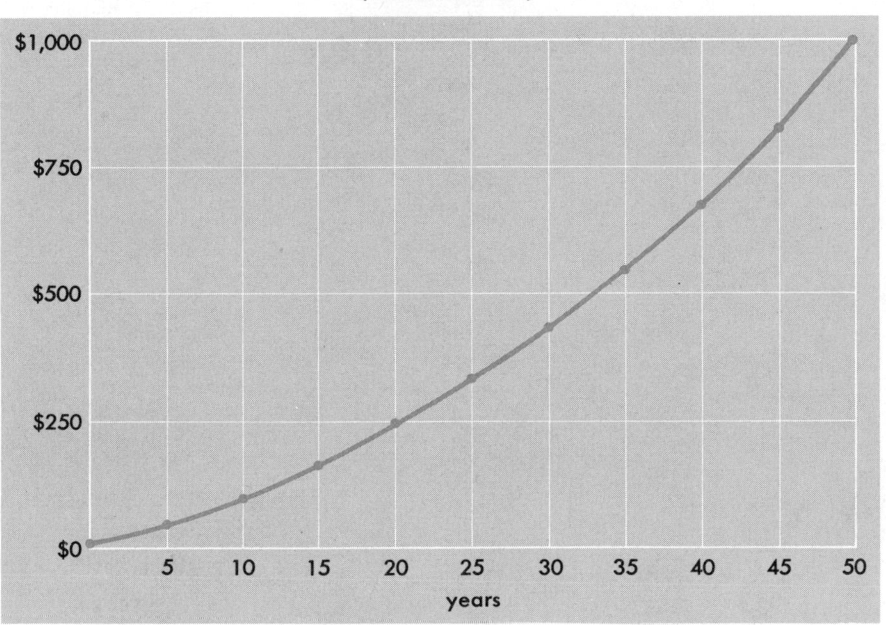

For a *whole life insurance policy,* the reserve rises up to nearly equal the amount of insurance one year prior to the end of the mortality table. One year later, at the end of the table, the reserve is zero. It was pointed out earlier that it is customary for the company to pay the amount of insurance to persons who actually are still alive at the end of the mortality table. For this reason, some published tables of terminal reserves per $1,000 show the final whole life reserve as being $1,000, instead of zero. (See Figure 11–3.)

Some life insurance policies have premiums payable for a shorter time than the period of insurance, such as 20-payment life policies. For such policies, the reserve will increase much faster during the time premiums are being paid than in later years. Another example would be the reserve for the 5-payment 10-year endowment policy used as an illustration in this chapter. The graph in Figure 11–4 shows this reserve, using the values from column (8) of the schedule in Section 11.1.

11.6 INITIAL AND MEAN RESERVES

The premiums for a life insurance policy are paid at the *beginning* of each year. The terminal reserves for a life insurance policy are

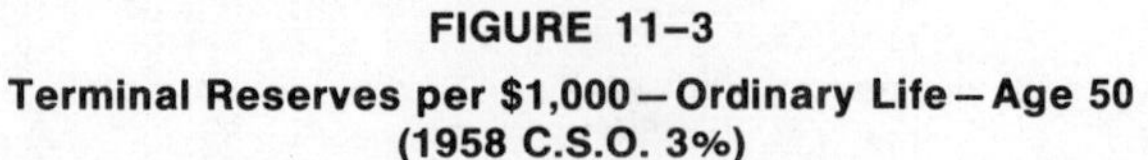

FIGURE 11–3
Terminal Reserves per $1,000 – Ordinary Life – Age 50
(1958 C.S.O. 3%)

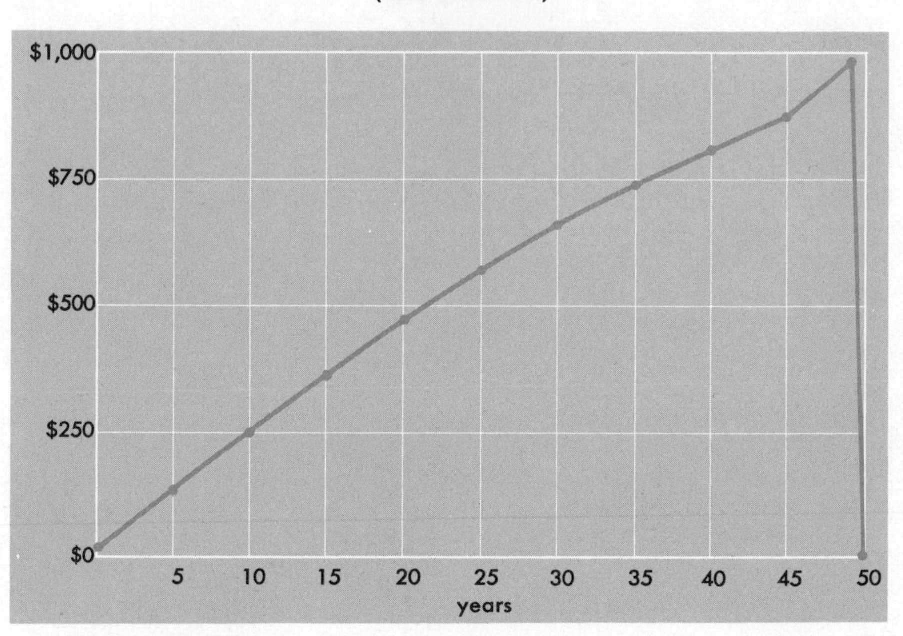

calculated as of the *end* of each year (after that year's death benefits are paid). It is assumed that the end of any year falls upon the same date as the beginning of the following year. For example, for a policy issued on August 17, 1971, the fifth terminal reserve would be the amount of liability the insurance company would have on August 17, 1976. Also, the premium for the sixth year would be due on August 17, 1976.

The *initial reserve* for a policy is the amount that the company has at the *beginning* of a given year. It equals the terminal reserve at the end of the previous year, plus the net premium collected at the beginning of the current year. In the example given in the above paragraph, the initial reserve for the sixth year would be the amount on August 17, 1976, after the collection of the net annual premium due on that date.

To Illustrate – Calculate the initial reserves per $1,000 for each year for a 5-payment 10-year endowment policy issued at age 21 (using the 1958 C.S.O. Table and 3% interest).

Solution – This is the same policy for which terminal reserves were calculated in Section 11.1. The net annual premium was given as $158.752, which will be rounded off to $158.75. The terminal re-

FIGURE 11–4
Terminal Reserves per $1,000—5-Pay 10-Year Endowment—Age 21
(1958 C.S.O. 3%)

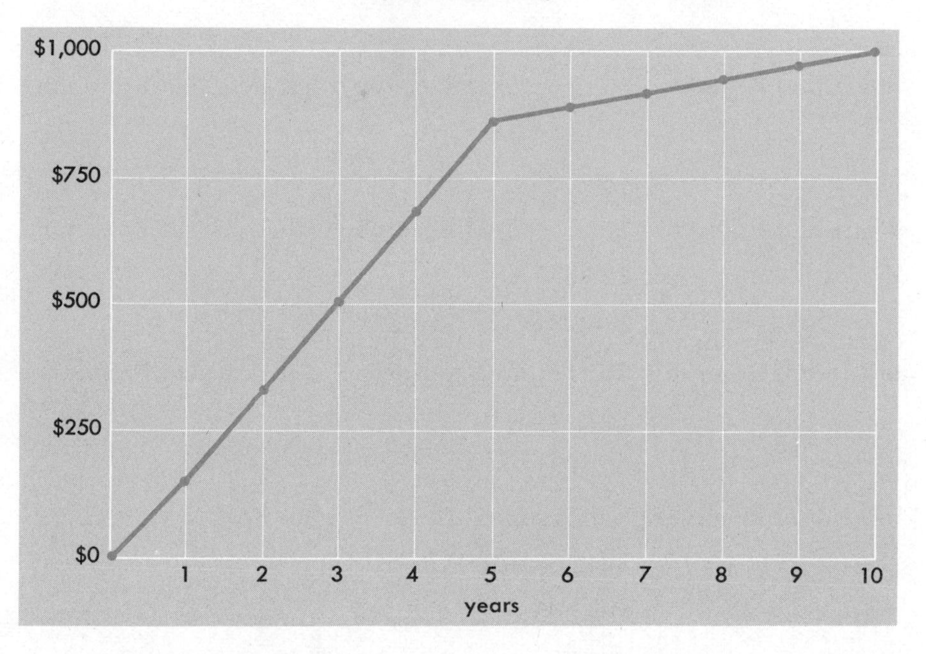

serves appear in column (8) of the schedule in Section 11.1. Each year's initial reserve equals the terminal reserve at the end of the previous year, plus the net premium for the current year:

1st Initial Reserve = 0 Terminal Reserve + 1st Year Net Premium
= 0 + $158.75
= $158.75

2nd Initial Reserve = 1st Terminal Reserve + 2nd Year Net Premium
= $161.98 + $158.75
= $320.73

3rd Initial Reserve = 2nd Terminal Reserve + 3rd Year Net Premium
= $329.11 + $158.75
= $487.86

4th Initial Reserve = 3rd Terminal Reserve + 4th Year Net Premium
= $501.55 + $158.75
= $660.30

5th Initial Reserve = 4th Terminal Reserve + 5th Year Net Premium
= $679.50 + $158.75
= $838.25

6th Initial Reserve = 5th Terminal Reserve + 6th Year Net Premium
= $863.14 + 0
= $863.14

7th Initial Reserve = 6th Terminal Reserve + 7th Year Net Premium
= $888.81 + 0
= $888.81

8th Initial Reserve = 7th Terminal Reserve + 8th Year Net Premium
= $915.31 + 0
= $915.31

9th Initial Reserve = 8th Terminal Reserve + 9th Year Net Premium
= $942.65 + 0
= $942.65

10th Initial Reserve = 9th Terminal Reserve + 10th Year Net Premium
= $970.87 + 0
= $970.87

The *first* initial reserve always equals the first year net premium, because there is no previous year's terminal reserve to add to it. It should also be observed that in a year in which no premiums are payable (after the 5th year in the above illustration), the initial reserve is equal to the previous year's terminal reserve.

In actual practice, life insurance companies are required by government regulatory authorities to determine the total reserves for all policies each December 31. To make this calculation, it is assumed that all policies are issued in the *middle of the calendar year.* For example, all policies issued in 1970 are assumed to be issued in the middle of 1970 (July 1, 1970). This assumption is reasonably accurate, the policies issued before July 1 each year counterbalancing those issued after July 1. Therefore, on December 31, all policies which were issued in the calendar year just ended are assumed to have been in effect for $\frac{1}{2}$ year. All policies issued in the calendar year *prior* to the calendar year just ended are assumed to have been in effect $1\frac{1}{2}$ years; and so forth.

For the December 31 reserve, *mean reserves* are used. The mean reserve for a policy is the amount that the company has on hand in the *middle* of a given policy year. It equals one half of the total of the initial and terminal reserves for that policy year:

$$\text{Mean Reserve} = \frac{\text{Initial Reserve} + \text{Terminal Reserve}}{2}$$

The answer is generally then rounded off to two decimal places. It should be noted that this calculation will often result in answers having a 5 in the third decimal place, such as \$148.725. The rule given in Section 1.4 would require that the 5 be dropped off and that 1 be added to the digit which is then in last place. That is, \$148.725 would be rounded off to \$148.73. However, published tables sometimes round off mean reserves to the nearest dollar.

To Illustrate—Calculate the mean reserves per \$1,000 for each year for a 5-payment 10-year endowment policy issued at age 21 (using the 1958 C.S.O. Table and 3% interest).

Solution—This is the same policy for which terminal reserves were calculated in Section 11.1 and initial reserves were calculated in the illustration above. For convenience, these figures are repeated here:

Policy Year	*Initial Reserve*	*Terminal Reserve*
1	\$158.75	\$ 161.98
2	320.73	329.11
3	487.86	501.55
4	660.30	679.50
5	838.25	863.14
6	863.14	888.81
7	888.81	915.31
8	915.31	942.65
9	942.65	970.87
10	970.87	1,000.00

Each year's mean reserve equals one half of the total of the initial and terminal reserves for that policy year:

$$\text{1st Mean Reserve} = \frac{\text{1st Initial Reserve} + \text{1st Terminal Reserve}}{2}$$

$$= \frac{\$158.75 + \$161.98}{2}$$

$$= \frac{\$320.73}{2}$$

$$= \$160.37$$

$$\text{2nd Mean Reserve} = \frac{\text{2nd Initial Reserve} + \text{2nd Terminal Reserve}}{2}$$

$$= \frac{\$320.73 + \$329.11}{2}$$

$$= \frac{\$649.84}{2}$$

$$= \$324.92$$

The remaining mean reserves, calculated in the same manner, are as follows:

3rd Mean Reserve = $494.71
4th Mean Reserve = 669.90
5th Mean Reserve = 850.70
6th Mean Reserve = 875.98
7th Mean Reserve = 902.06
8th Mean Reserve = 928.98
9th Mean Reserve = 956.76
10th Mean Reserve = 985.44

It should be noted that mean reserves can be calculated if the net premium and appropriate terminal reserves are known, because the "initial reserve" in the equation can be replaced by "net premium + previous terminal reserve":

$$\text{Mean Reserve} = \frac{\text{Initial Reserve} + \text{Terminal Reserve}}{2}$$

$$= \frac{\text{Net Premium} + \text{Previous Terminal Reserve} + \text{Terminal Reserve}}{2}$$

To Illustrate—Calculate the reserve used on December 31, 1975, for a policy issued in 1972. The following values are given:

Net level annual premium	$ 27.65
Terminal reserve	
1st year	22.42
2nd year	49.99
3rd year	78.67
4th year	108.30
5th year	138.92

Solution—If this policy is assumed to have been issued in the *middle* of 1972, then on December 31, 1975, it has been in effect for $3\frac{1}{2}$ years. That is, it completed 3 policy years in the middle of 1975, and is half-way through its 4th policy year. The 4th mean reserve is therefore required.

$$\text{4th Mean Reserve} = \frac{\text{Net Premium} + \text{3rd Terminal Reserve} + \text{4th Terminal Reserve}}{2}$$

$$= \frac{\$27.65 + \$78.67 + \$108.30}{2}$$

$$= \frac{\$214.62}{2}$$

$$= \$107.31$$

11.7 NET AMOUNT AT RISK

As explained before, each policy has its own reserve, which is the amount the company has on hand at any particular time for that policy. Therefore, for each death claim paid at the end of the year, a certain portion of the claim payment is available from that policy's terminal reserve. The remainder of the claim payment, known as the *net amount at risk,* is that portion which must be paid from the funds of the other policies. A policy's net amount at risk for any year is, therefore, the amount of insurance less the terminal reserve for that year:

$$\begin{pmatrix}\text{Net Amount}\\ \text{at Risk}\end{pmatrix} = \begin{pmatrix}\text{Amount of}\\ \text{Insurance}\end{pmatrix} - \begin{pmatrix}\text{Terminal}\\ \text{Reserve}\end{pmatrix}$$

To Illustrate—Calculate the net amount at risk each year for a \$1,000 5-payment 10-year endowment policy issued at age 21 (using the 1958 C.S.O. Table and 3% interest).

Solution—This is the same policy for which terminal reserves were previously calculated and tabulated (Section 11.6). Each year's net amount at risk equals \$1,000 less the terminal reserve for that year:

$$\text{1st Year Net Amount at Risk} = \$1{,}000 - \text{1st Terminal Reserve}$$

$$= \$1{,}000 - \$161.98$$

$$= \$838.02$$

$$\text{2nd Year Net Amount at Risk} = \$1{,}000 - \text{2nd Terminal Reserve}$$

$$= \$1{,}000 - \$329.11$$

$$= \$670.89$$

Continuing such calculations for the remaining years gives the following figures:

3rd Year Net Amount at Risk = $498.45

4th Year Net Amount at Risk = 320.50

5th Year Net Amount at Risk = 136.86

6th Year Net Amount at Risk = 111.19

7th Year Net Amount at Risk = 84.69

8th Year Net Amount at Risk = 57.35

9th Year Net Amount at Risk = 29.13

10th Year Net Amount at Risk = 0

For the final year of any endowment policy, such as this one, the net amount at risk is always zero. This is because the final year terminal reserve is the same as the amount of insurance. Accordingly, subtracting one from the other yields an answer of zero. This leads to the statement that, in the final year of an endowment insurance policy, it makes no difference financially to the company whether the person insured lives or dies. The full amount is paid at the end of the year in either instance.

11.8 TABULAR COST OF INSURANCE

The progress of the reserve for a policy, for any one-year period, can be described as follows: The initial reserve (at the beginning of the year) accumulates at interest for one year. At the end of the year, an amount necessary to help pay death claims is deducted. The remaining amount is the terminal reserve.

The amount so deducted is called the *tabular cost of insurance.* The word "tabular" means that this cost is calculated using the same mortality table and interest rate as used in the calculation of net premiums and reserves.

For all those policies where the persons insured die during this one-year period, the amount necessary to pay these total death claims is made up of the terminal reserves for those particular policies plus the tabular cost of insurance from *all* policies.

The progress of the reserve for one year, as described above, can be written in equation form:

$$\begin{pmatrix}\text{Initial}\\\text{Reserve}\end{pmatrix}(1+i)-\begin{pmatrix}\text{Tabular Cost}\\\text{of Insurance}\end{pmatrix}=\begin{pmatrix}\text{Terminal}\\\text{Reserve}\end{pmatrix}$$

When the above equation is solved for the tabular cost of insurance, the following equation results:

$$\begin{pmatrix}\text{Tabular Cost}\\ \text{of Insurance}\end{pmatrix} = \begin{pmatrix}\text{Initial}\\ \text{Reserve}\end{pmatrix}(1+i) - \begin{pmatrix}\text{Terminal}\\ \text{Reserve}\end{pmatrix}$$

This equation can be used to calculate tabular costs of insurance, provided initial and terminal reserves are known.

To Illustrate—Calculate the tabular cost of insurance each year for a $1,000 5-payment 10-year endowment policy issued at age 21 (using the 1958 C.S.O. Table and 3% interest).

Solution—This is the same policy for which terminal and initial reserves were previously calculated and tabulated (Section 11.6).

$$\begin{pmatrix}\text{1st Year}\\ \text{Tabular Cost}\\ \text{of Insurance}\end{pmatrix} = \begin{pmatrix}\text{1st Year}\\ \text{Initial}\\ \text{Reserve}\end{pmatrix}(1+i) - \begin{pmatrix}\text{1st Year}\\ \text{Terminal}\\ \text{Reserve}\end{pmatrix}$$

$$= \$158.75(1.03) - \$161.98$$

$$= \$163.51 - \$161.98$$

$$= \$1.53$$

$$\begin{pmatrix}\text{2nd Year}\\ \text{Tabular Cost}\\ \text{of Insurance}\end{pmatrix} = \begin{pmatrix}\text{2nd Year}\\ \text{Initial}\\ \text{Reserve}\end{pmatrix}(1+i) - \begin{pmatrix}\text{2nd Year}\\ \text{Terminal}\\ \text{Reserve}\end{pmatrix}$$

$$= \$320.73(1.03) - \$329.11$$

$$= \$330.35 - \$329.11$$

$$= \$1.24$$

If the calculations are continued in the same manner, the following results are obtained:

3rd Year Tabular Cost of Insurance = $0.95

4th Year Tabular Cost of Insurance = .61

5th Year Tabular Cost of Insurance = .26

6th Year Tabular Cost of Insurance = .22

7th Year Tabular Cost of Insurance = .16

8th Year Tabular Cost of Insurance = .12

9th Year Tabular Cost of Insurance = .06

10th Year Tabular Cost of Insurance = 0

For the final year of any endowment policy, such as this one, the tabular cost of insurance is always zero. This would be expected since, as mentioned in the previous section, it then makes no difference financially to the company whether the insured lives or dies. That is, for endowment policies the final year initial reserve accumulates at interest to the final year terminal reserve, without subtracting anything for tabular cost of insurance.

It should be noted that the above equation can be used when only the net premium and appropriate terminal reserves are given, because the "initial reserve" in the equation can be replaced by "net premium + previous terminal reserve":

$$\begin{pmatrix}\text{Tabular Cost}\\ \text{of Insurance}\end{pmatrix} = \begin{pmatrix}\text{Initial}\\ \text{Reserve}\end{pmatrix}(1+i) - \begin{pmatrix}\text{Terminal}\\ \text{Reserve}\end{pmatrix}$$

$$= \left[\begin{pmatrix}\text{Net}\\ \text{Premium}\end{pmatrix} + \begin{pmatrix}\text{Previous}\\ \text{Terminal Reserve}\end{pmatrix}\right](1+i) - \begin{pmatrix}\text{Terminal}\\ \text{Reserve}\end{pmatrix}$$

Tabular cost of insurance is sometimes referred to as the *tabular cost of insurance based on the net amount at risk.* This description refers to a second method of calculation for this cost, which is as follows: The tabular cost of insurance for a policy, for any one-year period, equals the net amount at risk multiplied by the rate of mortality for that year. In equation form, this may be written

$$\begin{pmatrix}\text{Tabular Cost}\\ \text{of Insurance}\end{pmatrix} = \begin{pmatrix}\text{Net Amount}\\ \text{at Risk}\end{pmatrix} q_x$$

where x is the attained age at the *beginning of the year.*

To Illustrate – Using the second method, verify the tabular cost of insurance calculated in the above illustration for the 1st, 2nd, and 10th years.

Solution – For the 1st year, the attained age is 21, and $q_{21} = .00183$ from Table III. The net amount at risk was calculated in Section 11.7 to be \$838.02:

$$\begin{pmatrix}\text{1st Year}\\ \text{Tabular Cost}\\ \text{of Insurance}\end{pmatrix} = \begin{pmatrix}\text{1st Year}\\ \text{Net Amount}\\ \text{at Risk}\end{pmatrix} q_x$$

$$= (\$838.02)(.00183)$$

$$= \$1.53$$

For the 2nd year, the attained age is 22, and $q_{22} = .00186$ from Table III. The net amount at risk was calculated in Section 11.7 to be \$670.89:

$$\begin{pmatrix}\text{2nd Year}\\\text{Tabular Cost}\\\text{of Insurance}\end{pmatrix} = \begin{pmatrix}\text{2nd Year}\\\text{Net Amount}\\\text{at Risk}\end{pmatrix} q_x$$

$$= (\$670.89)(.00186)$$

$$= \$1.25$$

For the 10th year, the attained age is 30, and $q_{30} = .00213$ from Table III. The net amount at risk was calculated in Section 11.7 to be zero:

$$\begin{pmatrix}\text{10th Year}\\\text{Tabular Cost}\\\text{of Insurance}\end{pmatrix} = \begin{pmatrix}\text{10th Year}\\\text{Net Amount}\\\text{at Risk}\end{pmatrix} q_x$$

$$= (\text{zero})(.00213)$$

$$= 0$$

These agree with the answers obtained in the first illustration in this section, except for a difference of 1 cent for the 2nd year. This is due to rounding off the reserves to two decimal places.

As mentioned above, the tabular cost is always zero for the final year of any endowment policy, such as this one. Here it is the result of the fact that the final year net amount at risk is always zero. Multiplying zero by any rate of mortality yields an answer of zero.

It should be noted that this second method can be used when only the appropriate terminal reserves are known. This is because the "net amount at risk" in the equation can be replaced by "amount of insurance – terminal reserve":

$$\begin{pmatrix}\text{Tabular Cost}\\\text{of Insurance}\end{pmatrix} = \begin{pmatrix}\text{Net Amount}\\\text{at Risk}\end{pmatrix} q_x$$

$$= \left[\begin{pmatrix}\text{Amount of}\\\text{Insurance}\end{pmatrix} - \begin{pmatrix}\text{Terminal}\\\text{Reserve}\end{pmatrix}\right] q_x$$

To Illustrate – Calculate the 6th year tabular cost of insurance on a \$5,000 policy issued at age 10, if the 6th terminal reserve is \$107.82 per \$1,000. Use the 1958 C.S.O. Table.

Solution – Since the amount of insurance is \$5,000, the total 6th terminal reserve is

$$(5)(\$107.82) = \$539.10$$

Since the policy was issued at age 10, the attained age at the *beginning* of the 6th year is 15.

$$\begin{pmatrix}\text{Tabular Cost}\\\text{of Insurance}\end{pmatrix} = \left[\begin{pmatrix}\text{Amount of}\\\text{Insurance}\end{pmatrix} - \begin{pmatrix}\text{Terminal}\\\text{Reserve}\end{pmatrix}\right] q_x$$

Substituting values calculated

$$= (\$5{,}000 - \$539.10)q_{15}$$

Substituting value from Table III

$$= (\$5{,}000 - \$539.10)(.00146)$$

$$= (\$4{,}460.90)(.00146)$$

$$= \$6.51$$

11.9 PREMIUM DEFICIENCY RESERVES

The mortality table and interest rate which are used to calculate the reserves for any particular policy are generally identified in the printed policy itself. In some circumstances it may happen that the *net* annual premium, calculated using this mortality table and interest rate, is larger than the *gross* annual premium for the policy, that is, there is a *negative loading*. This would generally happen only on nonparticipating policies where the mortality table used to calculate reserves exhibits mortality rates considerably larger than the company expects it will actually experience. This situation is most likely to occur when the mortality table is one which has been used for a considerable number of years. The existence of a number of policies being offered for sale with gross premiums less than the net premiums is usually regarded as evidence of the need to establish a new mortality table for calculating reserves.

The laws of all states require that, for such policies, a special reserve be added to the policy's regular reserve. This special reserve is known as a *premium deficiency reserve*. It must be calculated as the present value (with benefit of survivorship) of the future differences between the net premiums and gross premiums.

To Illustrate—Using the 1958 C.S.O. Table and 3% interest, calculate the premium deficiency reserve at the end of 17 years for a \$10,000 20-year term insurance policy issued at age 30, given the following:

Gross annual premium = \$34.20

Net annual premium = 35.30

Solution—The annual "premium deficiency" would be the difference between the two premiums:

$$\$35.30 - \$34.20 = \$1.10$$

At the end of 17 years, the attained age is 30 + 17 = 47. At that time, there are 3 premiums remaining. The premium deficiency reserve equals the present value of those 3 years' deficiencies. In line diagram form, they appear as follows:

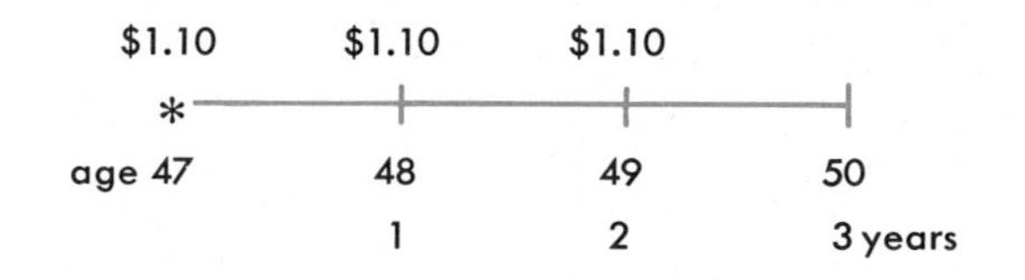

Basic equation

$$\begin{pmatrix}\text{Premium}\\ \text{Deficiency}\\ \text{Reserve}\end{pmatrix} = \$1.10\left[\frac{l_{47} + l_{48}v + l_{49}v^2}{l_{47}}\right]$$

Substituting values from the tables

$$= \$1.10\left[\frac{\begin{matrix}8{,}948{,}114\\ +8{,}891{,}204(.970874)\\ +8{,}829{,}410(.942596)\end{matrix}}{8{,}948{,}114}\right]$$

$$= \$1.10\left[\frac{8{,}948{,}114 + 8{,}632{,}239 + 8{,}322{,}567}{8{,}948{,}114}\right]$$

$$= \$3.18$$

For December 31 annual statement purposes, deficiency reserves are generally calculated for a point-in-time half-way between the policy's anniversaries, similar to the procedure for the regular mean reserve.

11.10 RESERVES FOR DECREASING TERM POLICIES

A popular type of life insurance policy is one wherein the death benefit decreases each year, although the annual premium stays the same. Normally, these are term-type policies, that is, the death benefit decreases to zero in a relatively few years. This type of policy has certain recognized advantages:

1. The death benefit is highest when the mortality rates are lowest (in the early years), and lowest when the mortality rates are highest (in the late years) resulting in a very low net level annual premium;
2. There are many situations where the insured person's need for insurance is a decreasing one, such as insurance to repay the balance of a mortgage loan; and
3. The reserves which the company needs to have are very small, and

the "nonforfeiture values" (to be presented in Chapter 13) are usually nonexistent.

In the calculation of the net annual premiums and reserves for decreasing term policies, the present value of future benefits will usually take the form

$$A\left(\frac{d_x v}{l_x}\right) + B\left(\frac{d_{x+1} v^2}{l_x}\right) + C\left(\frac{d_{x+2} v^3}{l_x}\right) + D\left(\frac{d_{x+3} v^4}{l_x}\right) + \cdots \text{ etc.}$$

where A, B, C, D, etc., are the respective death benefits in the first year, second year, third year, fourth year, etc. The present value of future net premiums will take the *usual form*

$$\begin{pmatrix}\text{Net Annual}\\ \text{Premium}\end{pmatrix}\left(\frac{l_x + l_{x+1}v + l_{x+2}v^2 + \cdots \text{ etc.}}{l_x}\right)$$

because the premiums do not change from year to year.

The unusual feature of the terminal reserves is that, in many instances, they are *negative*. That is, in the prospective calculation, the present value of future net premiums is sometimes greater than the present value of future benefits. In the retrospective calculation, the accumulated cost of insurance is sometimes greater than the accumulated value of net premiums received. The terminal reserve at the end of the term of the policy, however, is always zero.

Special attention must be directed to the calculation of *mean reserves* for such policies. In Section 11.6 the following equation was given:

$$\text{Mean Reserve} = \frac{\text{Net Premium} + \text{Previous Terminal Reserve} + \text{Terminal Reserve}}{2}$$

In the case of decreasing term insurance, either of the two terminal reserves (or both) may be negative. The usual rule followed is that if the total of Previous Terminal Reserve + Terminal Reserve is negative, this total is assumed to be zero. In the event that zero is so used, the equation can be written as

$$\text{Mean Reserve} = \frac{\text{Net Premium}}{2}$$

To Illustrate—Calculate the current mean reserve for a decreasing term policy, given the following information:

Net level annual premium = \$89.10
Previous terminal reserve = \$2.91
Terminal reserve = −\$5.12

Solution—The total of the terminal reserves is

$$\text{Previous Terminal Reserve} + \text{Terminal Reserve} = \$2.91 + (-\$5.12) = (-\$2.21)$$

Since this total is *negative*, the rule would require it to be used as zero. Hence, the equation becomes

$$\text{Mean Reserve} = \frac{\text{Net Premium}}{2} = \frac{\$89.10}{2} = \$44.55$$

It is a widely used practice to calculate the mean reserve on decreasing term policies as being equal to one-half the *gross* annual premium, instead of one-half the *net* annual premium. This is done for several reasons:

1. It is usually a simpler calculation, because gross premiums are always known exactly, whereas net premiums on these policies are often estimated or only calculated for a few sample ages;
2. This injects an element of conservatism into the company's financial statement by slightly overstating this liability; and
3. This helps offset the slight understatement in these reserves which the use of one-half the net premium would produce (because in a few instances the true mean reserve would exceed this).

11.11 RESERVES USING CONTINUOUS FUNCTIONS

In Section 8.6, "life annuities payable continuously" was presented. In Section 9.7, "insurance payable at the moment of death" was presented. The term *continuous functions* is used to describe the combination of the two concepts, that is, the assumptions of the death benefit payable immediately and the premiums payable continuously.

These assumptions came into wider use by insurance companies in calculating premiums and reserves at the time the 1958 C.S.O. Table was adopted. Use of the 1958 C.S.O. Table frequently produced lower reserves than the previously used table, a result which was unwelcome for some companies for a number of reasons. The use of continuous functions helped to increase the reserves to a more desired level.

It should be remembered that the equations given in Sections 8.6 and 9.7 are all *approximate* equalities. In actual practice, companies use more complicated equations which give the relationships exactly.

However, the approximations yield answers very close to the true figures.

To calculate the approximate present value of future benefits using continuous functions, the death benefit is multiplied by $(1 + \frac{1}{2}i)$, as explained in Section 9.7. In practice, this means that regular whole life net single premiums which are used to calculate net annual premiums and reserves (by the prospective method) may be multiplied by $(1 + \frac{1}{2}i)$.

To calculate the approximate present value of a whole life annuity due using continuous functions, one half of a year's payments must be subtracted from the regular present value, as explained in Section 8.6. In practice, this means that whole life annuity due factors which are used to calculate ordinary life net annual premiums and reserves (by the prospective method) may be diminished by $\frac{1}{2}$. For example, if the present value of a whole life annuity due of 1 per year were 22.7843, this factor would be diminished, as follows:

$$22.7843 - \tfrac{1}{2} = 22.7843 - .5000$$
$$= 22.2843$$

In the calculation of mean reserves by the usual equation:

$$\text{Mean Reserve} = \frac{\text{Net Premium} + \text{Previous Terminal Reserve} + \text{Terminal Reserve}}{2}$$

the year's net premium (if it is payable continuously) must be discounted to the beginning of the year. The methods used for doing this are complex and beyond the scope of this book.

EXERCISES

For Exercises 1 through 4, use the following information concerning a $10,000 policy.

Net annual premium	$1,107.65
Terminal reserve	
1st year	439.40
2nd year	870.60
3rd year	1,291.30
4th year	1,698.30
5th year	2,089.70

1 Calculate the 1st year initial reserve.

2 Calculate the 6th year initial reserve.

3 Calculate the 1st year mean reserve.

4 Calculate the net amount at risk for the 3rd year.

5 Calculate this year's tabular cost of insurance for a certain policy, given the following information:

Reserve basis = 1969 United Mortality Table at $3\frac{1}{2}\%$
This year's terminal reserve = \$8,401.40
This year's initial reserve = \$8,502.00

6 Using Table III, calculate the 1st year tabular cost of insurance for a policy issued at age 21. The 1st year net amount at risk is \$5,100.

7 Using Table III, calculate the 5th year tabular cost of insurance for a \$10,000 policy issued at age 32. The 5th year terminal reserve is \$112.40 per \$1,000.

8 Write an expression (using symbols) for the deficiency reserve at age 63 for a term-to-age-65 policy, given the following information:

Gross annual premium = \$207.80
Net annual premium = 209.95

Using Table III and 3% interest, calculate the value.

9 Calculate the mean reserves which a company should have for each policy year on a 5-year decreasing term policy, given the following information:

Net annual premium = \$10.36
Terminal reserves = \$.28, −\$1.79, −\$1.02, \$1.12, 0, respectively

10 Using the following table based on the 1958 C.S.O. Table and 3% interest, calculate the net annual premium (per \$1,000) and the 5th terminal reserve (per \$1,000) for an ordinary life policy issued at age 23. *Use continuous functions.*

Age	*Net Single Premium for \$1,000 Whole Life Insurance*	*Present Value of a Whole Life Annuity Due of 1 per Year*
23	\$265.75	25.209
24	272.34	24.983
25	279.14	24.750
26	286.13	24.509
27	293.33	24.262
28	300.74	24.008

11.12 SYMBOLS FOR TERMINAL RESERVES

Chart 11–3 displays certain internationally used symbols, each of which represents the terminal reserve at the end of t years for \$1 of life insurance issued at age x.

In general, the symbol is the capital letter "V." The subscripts at the lower right may be said to describe the benefits, and are identical to those shown in Section 9.9 which appear with "A" for the various types of net single premiums. The letters denoting the premium-paying period (if shorter than the benefit period) and the particular policy year to which the reserve applies both appears at the left side of the "V." For example, the symbol ${}^{m}_{t}V_{x:\overline{n|}}$ represents the tth-year terminal reserve for a \$1 m-payment n-year endowment policy issued at age x.

CHART 11–3

t^{th}-Year Terminal Reserves for \$1 of Life Insurance Issued at Age x

Type of Life Insurance	*Symbol for Terminal Reserve*
Ordinary Life	${}_{t}V_{x}$
m-Payment Life	${}^{m}_{t}V_{x}$
n-Year Term Insurance	${}_{t}V^{1}_{x:\overline{n|}}$
m-Payment n-Year Term Insurance	${}^{m}_{t}V^{1}_{x:\overline{n|}}$
n-Year Endowment Insurance	${}_{t}V_{x:\overline{n|}}$
m-Payment n-Year Endowment Insurance	${}^{m}_{t}V_{x:\overline{n|}}$

12. Modified Reserves

12.1 INTRODUCTION

The need for an addition to the net premium to provide for the expenses of operation was discussed in Section 10.7. This amount, called the loading, was shown as an amount added yearly to the net level premium. However, the actual expenses incurred by the insurance company are not the same each policy year, but are much heavier during the first year than in subsequent years.

The problem that heavy first-year expenses create for the insurance company can be shown by considering a typical 20-payment life policy issued at age 30. The following figures apply to each $1,000 of insurance provided by this policy. The net level annual premium is $21.15 (based upon the 1958 C.S.O. Table and 3% interest) and the gross annual premium is $30.04. Assume an agent's first-year commission is 45% of the gross annual premium, taxes are 2% of the gross annual premium, and expenses of issuing and administering a policy the first year are $10.00 per $1,000 of insurance. The total expenses the first year are

Agent's commission (45% of $30.04)	$13.52
Taxes (2% of $30.04)	.60
Issue and administration expenses	10.00
Total first-year expenses	$24.12

Since the entire *net* premium of $21.15 is needed to pay death claims and provide reserves, none of this net premium is available to help pay expenses. The available loading is the difference between the gross premium and the net premium:

$$\text{Gross Premium} - \text{Net Premium} = \$30.04 - \$21.15$$
$$= \$8.89$$

Therefore, the loading is *deficient* in the first year by

$$\text{Expenses} - \text{Loading} = \$24.12 - \$8.89$$
$$= \$15.23$$

If a life insurance company has considerable surplus funds, this first-year deficiency in the loading may be met by drawing upon such surplus funds. However, for companies with relatively small surplus funds, such as young companies or rapidly growing companies, this procedure may not be practical.

For this reason, another approach to alleviating the problem has been evolved which utilizes methods which require the establishment of little or no first-year reserve, and thus permit a larger portion of the first-year gross premium to be used for expenses. Briefly, such methods set a first-year net premium which is *smaller* than the net level premium, and consequently require net premiums for subsequent years which are *larger* than the net level premium. Methods which change or modify the net premiums and reserves to release more money for first-year expenses are known as *modified reserve methods.*

Several different modified reserve methods have been developed. In this book, the following will be presented:

1. Full Preliminary Term method
2. Illinois Standard method
3. Commissioners method
4. Canadian method

It is important to remember that the policyowner pays a *gross* premium each year throughout the policy's premium-paying period. He is generally unaware of the amount of the *net* premiums used by the company in calculating the reserves or of the methods of calculation which are employed.

12.2 FULL PRELIMINARY TERM METHOD

The net premium for one-year term insurance is exactly sufficient to pay the year's death claims, leaving nothing at the end of that year for any reserve. When a company uses the Full Preliminary Term method of calculating reserves, the modified *first-year* net premium is equal to this net premium for one-year term insurance, i.e., the natural premium. The first-year terminal reserve, therefore, is zero.

The modified net premiums for *all subsequent* years are the same as the net level annual premium for a policy with the same benefits, but issued *one age older* and with a premium-paying period which is *one year less.*

For example, the 20-payment life policy issued at age 30, which was discussed in the above section, has a net level annual premium of $21.15 (per $1,000). However, if the Full Preliminary Term method were being used to calculate modified reserves, then it would have a modified *first-year* net premium per $1,000 equal to the net premium for one-year term insurance at age 30, which is $2.07. The modified net premium for the remaining 19 years would then be the same as the net level annual premium for a 19-payment life policy issued at age 31, which is $22.51.

It is instructive to examine the amount of loading which is made available to pay expenses:

Net Level Method

For all 20 years,

$$\begin{aligned} \text{Loading} &= \text{Gross Premium} - \text{Net Premium} \\ &= \$30.04 - \$21.15 \\ &= \$8.89 \end{aligned}$$

Full Preliminary Term Method

For the first year,

$$\begin{aligned} \text{Loading} &= \text{Gross Premium} - \text{Net Premium} \\ &= \$30.04 - \$2.07 \\ &= \$27.97 \end{aligned}$$

For years 2 through 20,

$$\begin{aligned} \text{Loading} &= \text{Gross Premium} - \text{Net Premium} \\ &= \$30.04 - \$22.51 \\ &= \$7.53 \end{aligned}$$

Thus, the use of the Full Preliminary Term method makes available sufficient loading the first year ($27.97) to pay for the first-year expenses of $24.12 which were shown in the above section. (Any excess may be available to return to the policyowner as part of a dividend. Dividends will be discussed in Chapter 14.)

To Illustrate—Using the 1958 C.S.O. Table and 3% interest, calculate the modified net annual premium for the first year for a $1,000 ordinary life policy issued at age 22, using the Full Preliminary Term method. Describe the modified net annual premium for subsequent years.

Solution—Under this method, the modified *first year* net premium is equal to the net premium for 1-year term insurance:

Basic equation from Section 9.1

$$\text{1st Year Net Premium} = \$1{,}000\left(\frac{d_{22}v}{l_{22}}\right)$$

$$= \$1{,}000\left[\frac{(17{,}912)(.970874)}{9{,}630{,}039}\right]$$

$$= \$1.81$$

The modified net premium for *all subsequent years* is equal to the net premium for a policy issued one year later (at age 23), with premiums continuing to the end of the mortality table. This figure is $10.54.

Modified reserves are calculated by the methods for calculating reserves explained in Chapter 11, except that whenever net premiums are used, these are *modified* net premiums. This is true for any of the modified reserve methods explained in this chapter. For example, using the prospective method, the fifth-year terminal reserve for the ordinary life policy illustrated above (at attained age 27) would be:

$$\begin{pmatrix}\text{Terminal}\\\text{Reserve}\end{pmatrix} = \begin{pmatrix}\text{Present Value of}\\\text{Future Benefits}\end{pmatrix} - \begin{pmatrix}\text{Present Value of Future}\\\text{Modified Net Premiums}\end{pmatrix}$$

$$= \begin{pmatrix}\text{Net Single Premium}\\\text{at Age 27 for \$1,000}\\\text{Whole Life Insurance}\end{pmatrix}$$

$$- (\$10.54)\begin{pmatrix}\text{Annuity Factor for Present}\\\text{Value of Whole Life Annuity}\\\text{Due at Age 27}\end{pmatrix}$$

Using the first-year modified net premium, the initial reserve for the first year for the same policy would be:

$$\begin{pmatrix}\text{First}\\\text{Initial}\\\text{Reserve}\end{pmatrix} = \begin{pmatrix}\text{First-Year}\\\text{Modified}\\\text{Net Premium}\end{pmatrix}$$

$$= \$1.81$$

The initial reserve for the second year (remembering that the terminal reserve at the end of the first year is zero when using the Full Preliminary Term method) would be

$$\begin{pmatrix}\text{Second}\\\text{Initial}\\\text{Reserve}\end{pmatrix} = \begin{pmatrix}\text{First-Year}\\\text{Terminal Reserve}\end{pmatrix} + \begin{pmatrix}\text{Second-Year}\\\text{Modified}\\\text{Net Premium}\end{pmatrix}$$

$$= 0 + \$10.54$$

$$= \$10.54$$

The mean reserve for the first year (using the first year's modified net premium, and remembering that the first-year terminal reserve is zero) would be:

$$\begin{pmatrix}\text{Mean}\\\text{Reserve}\end{pmatrix} = \frac{\text{Modified Net Premium} + \text{Previous Terminal Reserve} + \text{Terminal Reserve}}{2}$$

$$= \frac{\$1.81 + 0 + 0}{2}$$

$$= \$.91$$

When the Full Preliminary Term method is used for policies having very high premiums per $1,000, an excessive amount is made available for expenses the first year. This occurs because the first-year modified net premium is just the one-year term insurance net premium, although the gross premium is very high. For example, the 5-payment 10-year endowment policy calculated in Section 11.1 has a net level annual premium of $158.75 per $1,000. The gross annual premium could conceivably be near $200 per $1,000. However, the first-year modified net premium using the Full Preliminary Term method is only $1.78, leaving the entire balance of the $200 for expenses. Because of this undesirable situation for high-premium policies, other modified reserve methods have been developed.

For certain higher premium policies, each of the other methods to be explained prevents the first-year modified net premium from being too small in relation to the gross premium (i.e., prevents the available loading from being too large). This is accomplished by setting forth a definite specified amount (for each age) for the *difference* between the first-year modified net premium and the modified net premium for subsequent years, or else for the *difference* between the first-year modified net premium and the net level annual premium. In each case, the result is a first-year modified net premium which is *smaller* than the net level premium, but not excessively smaller. The amount by which it is short of the net level premium for the first year is "repaid" during subsequent years by means of modified net premiums *higher* than the net level premium. The present value of these "repayments" equals the amount by which the first year's modified net premium was short. In other words, the present value of the entire series of *modified* net premiums (first-year and subsequent) is equal to the present value of the net *level* premiums.

To distinguish it from Full Preliminary Term, any other modified reserve method is called a *modified preliminary term* method. The three remaining methods to be explained are all modified preliminary term methods.

12.3 ILLINOIS STANDARD METHOD

Under the Illinois Standard method of modification, policies are divided into two classes:

Class A—policies with net level premiums *equal to or less than* the net level premium for a 20-payment life policy, at the same issue age.

Class B—policies with net level premiums *greater than* the net level premium for a 20-payment life policy, at the same issue age.

For all policies falling in Class A, modified net premiums and reserves are calculated by the Full Preliminary Term method explained in the preceding section.

Modified net premiums and reserves for all policies falling in Class B are calculated by the Illinois Standard method.

The Class B policies will have a special modified net premium for the first year, a different modified net premium for the next 19 years (if premiums are payable that long), and finally the regular net level premium thereafter.

The Illinois Standard method sets forth that the *difference* between the first-year modified net premium and the modified net premium for the next 19 years shall be equal to the amount of this difference on a 20-payment life policy which is being calculated by the Full Preliminary Term method. That is, it shall be equal to the amount of the difference between a one-year term net premium and the net level premium for a 19-payment life policy issued one age older.

For example, in the above section, it was shown that a $1,000 20-payment life policy issued at age 30 has the following modified net premiums when calculated by the Full Preliminary Term method:

First year	$ 2.07
Next 19 years.............................	22.51

The *difference* between the two is

$$\$22.51 - \$2.07 = \$20.44$$

Hence, under the Illinois Standard method, \$20.44 is *always the difference* between the first-year modified net premium and the modified net premium for the next 19 years (if premiums are payable that long) for all Class B policies issued at age 30. This is assuming the policy's reserves are based upon the 1958 C.S.O. Table and 3% interest.

Twenty-payment life policies would actually have the *same* net premiums and reserves calculated by either the Full Preliminary Term method or the Illinois Standard method. That is, it would make no difference whether they were classified as Class A or Class B (although the definition includes them in Class A).

For Class B policies, the actual Illinois Standard calculation first involves finding the amount of the modified net premium for the second through the 20th years. Secondly, the amount of the first-year modified net premium is found by use of the prescribed *difference* between the first-year modified net premium and the modified net premium for the next 19 years. If premiums are payable for more than 20 years, the net annual premiums beginning with the 21st year are then calculated by the *net level* method (as described in Chapter 10).

The above definition for the difference between the first year's modified net premium and the modified net premium for the next 19 years, plus the fact that the present value of the whole series of *modified* net premiums must equal the present value of net *level* premiums, leads to the following equations:

Illinois Standard Method

$$\begin{pmatrix}\text{Years 2–20}\\\text{Modified}\\\text{Net Premium}\end{pmatrix} = \begin{pmatrix}\text{Net Level}\\\text{Premium}\end{pmatrix} + \frac{\begin{pmatrix}\text{Net Level Premium}\\\text{for 19-Payment}\\\text{Life, One Age Older}\end{pmatrix} - \begin{pmatrix}\text{One-Year}\\\text{Term Net}\\\text{Premium}\end{pmatrix}}{\begin{pmatrix}\text{Present Value of Life Annuity Due}\\\text{of 1 for Premium-Period, but Not}\\\text{More Than 20 Years}\end{pmatrix}}$$

$$\begin{pmatrix}\text{First-Year}\\\text{Modified}\\\text{Net Premium}\end{pmatrix} = \begin{pmatrix}\text{Years 2–20}\\\text{Modified}\\\text{Net Premium}\end{pmatrix} - \left[\begin{pmatrix}\text{Net Level Premium}\\\text{for 19-Payment}\\\text{Life, One Age Older}\end{pmatrix} - \begin{pmatrix}\text{One-Year}\\\text{Term Net}\\\text{Premium}\end{pmatrix}\right]$$

Thus, if the following four items are known, the net premiums for all years for Class B policies can be calculated:

Net level premium (for the policy in question);
Net level premium for 19-payment life, one age older;
One-year term net premium;
Present value of life annuity due of 1 for premium period, but not more than 20 years.

It should be recognized that the equation given for the first-year modified net premium arises directly from the stipulation, set forth earlier in this section, that

> . . . the difference between the first-year modified net premium and the modified net premium for the next 19 years shall be equal to the amount of this difference on a 20-payment life policy which is being calculated by the Full Preliminary Term method.

A 20-payment life policy which is using the Full Preliminary Term method will have a first-year modified net premium equal to

$$\begin{pmatrix}\text{One-Year}\\ \text{Term Net}\\ \text{Premium}\end{pmatrix}$$

and a modified net premium for the subsequent years equal to

$$\begin{pmatrix}\text{Net Level Premium}\\ \text{for 19-payment}\\ \text{Life, One Age Older}\end{pmatrix}$$

To Illustrate—Calculate the modified net annual premiums for a $1,000 30-payment life policy issued at age 35, using the Illinois Standard method. The following information is given:

Net level premium, 30-payment life, age 35	$19.04
Net level premium, 20-payment life, age 35	24.23
1-year term net premium, age 35	2.44
Net level premium, 29-payment life, age 36	19.97

Solution—The policy's net level premium ($19.04) is *less than* the net level premium for a 20-payment life policy ($24.23). Hence, the policy falls into Class A. This means that, according to the Illinois Standard rules, its modified net premiums are calculated by the Full Preliminary Term method. Under this method, as presented in Section 12.2, the first year modified net premium is equal to the 1-year term insurance net premium. This is given above as $2.44.

The modified net premium for all subsequent years would be the same as the net level annual premium for a $1,000 29-payment life policy issued at age 36. This is given above as $19.97.

In the above illustration, it could have been reasoned that the 30-payment life policy would fall into Class A, without having been given the two actual net level annual premiums for comparison. This is because the policies being compared (30-payment life and 20-payment life) have the same benefits, but the benefits must be paid for over a shorter period of time in the case of the 20-payment life policy. Hence, its net level annual premium must be larger.

To Illustrate Again—Calculate the modified net annual premiums for a $1,000 25-year endowment policy issued at age 35, using the Illinois Standard method. The following information is given:

Net level premium, 25-year endowment, age 35	$29.48
Net level premium, 20-payment life, age 35	24.23
Net level premium, 19-payment life, age 36	25.80
1-year term net premium, age 35	2.44
Present value of life annuity due of 1 for 20 years, age 35	14.80519

Solution—The policy's net level premium ($29.48) is *greater than* the net level premium for a 20-payment life policy ($24.23). Hence, the policy falls into Class B. This means that, according to the Illinois Standard rules, its modified net premiums are calculated by the Illinois Standard method:

Basic equation

$$\begin{pmatrix}\text{Years 2–20}\\\text{Modified}\\\text{Net Premium}\end{pmatrix} = \begin{pmatrix}\text{Net Level}\\\text{Premium}\end{pmatrix} + \frac{\begin{pmatrix}\text{Net Level Premium}\\\text{for 19-Payment}\\\text{Life, 1 Age Older}\end{pmatrix} - \begin{pmatrix}\text{One-Year}\\\text{Term Net}\\\text{Premium}\end{pmatrix}}{\begin{pmatrix}\text{Present Value of Life Annuity Due}\\\text{of 1 for Premium-Period, but Not}\\\text{More Than 20 Years}\end{pmatrix}}$$

Substituting values given above

$$= \$29.48 + \left(\frac{\$25.80 - \$2.44}{14.80519}\right)$$

$$= \$29.48 + \left(\frac{\$23.36}{14.80519}\right)$$

$$= \$29.48 + \$1.58$$

$$= \$31.06$$

This result is then used in the equation for the first-year modified net premium:

Basic equation

$$\begin{pmatrix}\text{1st-Year}\\\text{Modified}\\\text{Net Premium}\end{pmatrix} = \begin{pmatrix}\text{Years 2–20}\\\text{Modified}\\\text{Net Premium}\end{pmatrix} - \left[\begin{pmatrix}\text{Net Level Premium}\\\text{for 19-Payment}\\\text{Life, 1 Age Older}\end{pmatrix} - \begin{pmatrix}\text{One-Year}\\\text{Term Net}\\\text{Premium}\end{pmatrix}\right]$$

Substituting values given above

$$= \$31.06 - [\$25.80 - \$2.44]$$

$$= \$31.06 - \$23.36$$

$$= \$7.70$$

The net premium beginning with the 21st year is equal to the regular net level annual premium ($29.48).

It is instructive to examine the amount of loading which is made available to pay expenses for the above 25-year endowment policy, if the gross premium is assumed to be $36.75:

For the first year,

$$\begin{aligned}\text{Loading} &= \text{Gross Premium} - \text{Net Premium}\\ &= \$36.75 - \$7.70\\ &= \$29.05\end{aligned}$$

Years 2–20,

$$\begin{aligned}\text{Loading} &= \text{Gross Premium} - \text{Net Premium}\\ &= \$36.75 - \$31.06\\ &= \$5.69\end{aligned}$$

Years 21–25,

$$\begin{aligned}\text{Loading} &= \text{Gross Premium} - \text{Net Premium}\\ &= \$36.75 - \$29.48\\ &= \$7.27\end{aligned}$$

It will be noted that the first-year loading available under the Illinois Standard method ($29.05) is considerably greater than under the net level premium method ($7.27). However, in years 2 through 20, it is slightly less than under the net level premium method.

A line diagram, showing the three different net premiums which would be collected for the above 25-year endowment, appears as follows:

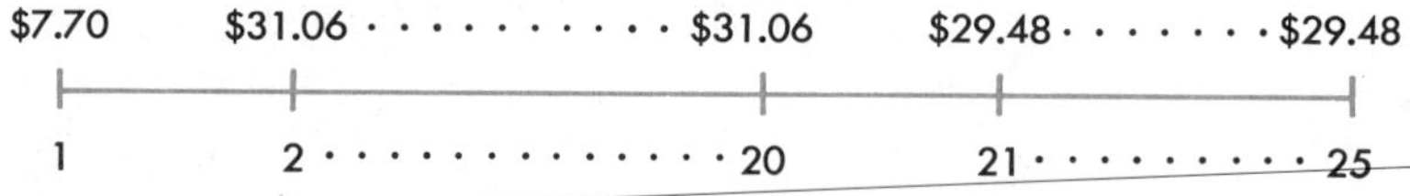

$7.70 $31.06 · · · · · · · · · · · $31.06 $29.48 · · · · · · · $29.48

1 2 · · · · · · · · · · · · · · 20 21 · · · · · · · · · · 25

If the net level method were being used instead, all 25 net premiums would be $29.48. The present value (with benefit of survivorship) of 25 net level premiums of $29.48 each is equal to the present value of the series of modified net premiums shown in the above line diagram.

In the case of a policy which has fewer than 20 premiums (such as a 10-year endowment), the Illinois Standard method would provide only two different modified net premiums, instead of three. These would be the first-year modified net premium and the modified net premium for the remainder of the years.

Since there are often three different modified net premiums over the life of a policy using the Illinois Standard method, the calculation of reserves becomes somewhat complicated. However, after 20 years the prospective method is identical with that for a policy using the net level method. This is because net annual premiums beginning with the 21st year are equal to *net level* premiums. For those years the prospective method of calculation is easier than the retrospective method, because the modified net premiums do not have to be used.

12.4 COMMISSIONERS METHOD

The Commissioners Reserve Valuation Method will be referred to by the shorter title, Commissioners method. This method differs in two important respects from the Illinois Standard method:

1. To determine whether a policy falls into Class A or Class B, the comparison is still made with a 20-payment life policy. However, the comparison is made using the Full Preliminary Term modified premiums (for years subsequent to the first) for the two policies, instead of their net level premiums.
2. The special modified net premiums for years subsequent to the first continue for the entire premium-paying period of the policy, instead of being limited to years 2 through 20.

Under the Commissioners method of modification, policies are divided into two classes:

Class A—policies with Full Preliminary Term modified net premiums (for years subsequent to the first) *equal to or less than* the Full Preliminary Term modified net premiums (for years subsequent to the first) for a 20-payment life policy, at the same issue age.

Class B—policies with Full Preliminary Term modified net premiums (for years subsequent to the first) *greater than* the Full Preliminary Term modified net premiums (for years subsequent to the first) for a 20-payment life policy, at the same issue age.

(This comparison is so nearly the same as the Illinois Standard comparison that, in practice, almost any policy that falls into Class A using one method will also fall into Class A using the other method.)

For all policies falling in Class A, modified net premiums and reserves are calculated by the Full Preliminary Term method.

Modified net premiums and reserves for all policies falling in Class B are calculated by the Commissioners method.

The Class B policies will have a special modified net premium for the first year, and a second modified net premium for *all subsequent* years.

The Commissioners method sets forth that the *difference* between the first-year modified net premium and the modified net premium for all subsequent years shall be equal to the amount of this difference on a 20-payment life policy which is being calculated by the Full Preliminary Term method. (This is the same as set forth in the Illinois Standard method, except that this difference does not apply after the 20th year under the Illinois Standard method.)

For example, it was shown in Section 12.2 that a $1,000 20-payment life policy issued at age 30 has the following modified net premiums calculated by the Full Preliminary Term method:

First year ....$ 2.07
Next 19 years 22.51

The *difference* between the two is

$$\$22.51 - \$2.07 = \$20.44$$

Hence, under the Commissioners method, $20.44 is *always the difference* between the first year's modified net premium and all subsequent modified net premiums for all Class B policies issued at age 30. This is assuming the policy's reserves are based upon the 1958 C.S.O. Table and 3% interest.

Twenty-payment life policies would actually have the *same* modified net premiums and reserves calculated by any of the methods introduced so far: Full Preliminary Term, Illinois Standard, or Commissioners.

Any Class B policy which has *20 or fewer* premiums will have the *same* modified net premiums and reserves calculated by either the Illinois Standard or Commissioners method. Class B policies having *more than 20* premiums, however, will have completely different modified net premiums and reserves under one method than under the other (although the *difference* between the first year's modified net premium and the modified net premium for the next 19 years will be the same for the two methods).

The above definition for the difference between the first-year modified net premium and the modified net premium for all subsequent years, plus the fact that the present value of the whole series of *modified* net premiums must equal the present value of the net *level* premiums, leads to the following equations:

Commissioners Method

$$\begin{pmatrix}\text{Modified}\\ \text{Net Premium}\end{pmatrix} = \begin{pmatrix}\text{Net Level}\\ \text{Premium}\end{pmatrix} + \frac{\begin{pmatrix}\text{Net Level Premium}\\ \text{for 19-Payment}\\ \text{Life, One Age Older}\end{pmatrix} - \begin{pmatrix}\text{One-Year}\\ \text{Term Net}\\ \text{Premium}\end{pmatrix}}{\begin{pmatrix}\text{Present Value of Life Annuity}\\ \text{Due of 1 for Premium Period}\end{pmatrix}}$$

This is exactly the same as the equation for the modified net premium (years 2–20) under the Illinois Standard method, except that here the life annuity due referred to in the denominator extends for the entire premium-paying period, regardless of its length.

The equation for the first-year modified net premium is essentially the same as the equation for the first-year modified net premium under the Illinois Standard method:

$$\begin{pmatrix}\text{First-Year}\\ \text{Modified}\\ \text{Net Premium}\end{pmatrix} = \begin{pmatrix}\text{Subsequent}\\ \text{Years' Modified}\\ \text{Net Premium}\end{pmatrix} - \left[\begin{pmatrix}\text{Net Level Premium}\\ \text{for 19-Payment}\\ \text{Life, One Age Older}\end{pmatrix} - \begin{pmatrix}\text{One-Year}\\ \text{Term Net}\\ \text{Premium}\end{pmatrix}\right]$$

Thus, if the following four items are known, the two modified net premiums for Class B policies can be obtained:

Net level premium (for the policy in question);
Net level premium for 19-payment life, one age older;
One-year term net premium;
Present value of life annuity due of 1 for premium period.

To Illustrate—Calculate the modified net annual premiums for a $1,000 30-year endowment policy issued at age 20, using the Commissioners method. The following information is given:

Full preliminary term modified net premium, 30-year endowment, age 20	$22.89
Full preliminary term modified net premium, 20-payment life, age 20	17.44
Net level premium, 30-year endowment, age 20	21.82
1-year term net premium, age 20	1.74
Present value of life annuity due of 1 for 30 years, age 20	19.63044

Solution—The policy's Full Preliminary Term modified net premium for years subsequent to the first ($22.89) is *greater than* that for a 20-payment life policy ($17.44). Therefore, the policy falls into Class B. This means that, according to the Commissioners rules, its modified net premiums are calculated by the Commissioners method. It should be noted that the Full Preliminary Term modified net premium for 20-payment life given above is the same as the net level premium for 19-payment life, 1 age older needed in the equations:

Basic equation

$$\begin{pmatrix}\text{Modified}\\ \text{Net Premium}\end{pmatrix} = \begin{pmatrix}\text{Net Level}\\ \text{Premium}\end{pmatrix} + \frac{\begin{pmatrix}\text{Net Level Premium}\\ \text{for 19-Payment}\\ \text{Life, 1 Age Older}\end{pmatrix} - \begin{pmatrix}\text{One-Year}\\ \text{Term Net}\\ \text{Premium}\end{pmatrix}}{\begin{pmatrix}\text{Present Value of Life Annuity}\\ \text{Due of 1 for Premium Period}\end{pmatrix}}$$

Substituting the values given above

$$= \$21.82 + \left(\frac{\$17.44 - \$1.74}{19.63044}\right)$$

$$= \$21.82 + \left(\frac{\$15.70}{19.63044}\right)$$

$$= \$21.82 + \$.80$$

$$= \$22.62$$

This result is then used in the equation for the first-year modified net premium:

Basic equation

$$\begin{pmatrix}\text{1st-Year}\\ \text{Modified}\\ \text{Net Premium}\end{pmatrix} = \begin{pmatrix}\text{Subsequent}\\ \text{Years' Modified}\\ \text{Net Premium}\end{pmatrix} - \left[\begin{pmatrix}\text{Net Level Premium}\\ \text{for 19-Payment}\\ \text{Life, 1 Age Older}\end{pmatrix} - \begin{pmatrix}\text{One-Year}\\ \text{Term Net}\\ \text{Premium}\end{pmatrix}\right]$$

Substituting the values given above

$$= \$22.62 - [\$17.44 - \$1.74]$$

$$= \$22.62 - \$15.70$$

$$= \$6.92$$

12.5 CANADIAN METHOD

Under the Canadian method of modification, policies are divided into two classes:

Class A – policies with net level premiums *equal to or less than* the net level premium for an ordinary life policy, at the same issue age.

Class B – Policies with net level premiums *greater than* the net level premium for an ordinary life policy, at the same issue age.

For all policies falling into Class A, modified net premiums and reserves are calculated by the Full Preliminary Term method.

Modified net premiums and reserves for all policies falling into Class B are calculated by the Canadian method.

The Class B policies will have a special modified net premium for the first year, and a second modified net premium for *all subsequent* years.

The Canadian method sets forth that the *difference* between the first-year modified net premium and the net level premium shall be equal to the amount of this difference on an ordinary life policy which is being calculated by the Full Preliminary Term method. That is, it shall be equal to the amount of the difference between a one-year term net premium and the net *level* premium for an ordinary life policy.

It should be noted that this *difference* is between a first-year modified net premium and a net *level* premium, whereas the previous methods described set forth this difference as being between a first-year modified net premium and subsequent years' *modified* net premiums.

For example, a $1,000 ordinary life policy issued at age 20 has a net level premium as follows:

Net Level Premium..................$9.56

The one-year term net premium (per $1,000) at age 20 is as follows:

One-Year Term Net Premium..................$1.74

The *difference* between the two is

$$\$9.56 - \$1.74 = \$7.82$$

Hence, under the Canadian method, $7.82 is *always the difference* between the first-year modified net premium and the policy's net *level* premium for all Class B policies issued at age 20. This is assuming the policy's reserves are based upon the 1958 C.S.O. Table and 3% interest.

Ordinary life policies, therefore, would actually have the *same* modified net premiums and reserves calculated by either the Full Preliminary Term method or the Canadian method. That is, it would make no difference whether they were classified as Class A or Class B (although the definition includes them in Class A).

The above definition for the difference between the first-year modified net premium and the net *level* premium, plus the fact that the present value of the whole series of *modified* net premiums must equal the present value of net *level* premiums, leads to the following equations:

Canadian Method

$$\begin{pmatrix}\text{Modified}\\\text{Net Premium}\end{pmatrix} = \begin{pmatrix}\text{Net Level}\\\text{Premium}\end{pmatrix} + \frac{\begin{pmatrix}\text{Net Level Premium}\\\text{for Ordinary Life}\end{pmatrix} - \begin{pmatrix}\text{One-Year}\\\text{Term Net}\\\text{Premium}\end{pmatrix}}{\begin{pmatrix}\text{Present Value of Life Annuity}\\\text{Immediate of 1 for One Year Less}\\\text{Than Premium Period}\end{pmatrix}}$$

This equation differs in two important respects from the Illinois Standard and the Commissioners equations:

1. The net level premium specified in the *numerator* is for the same age, not one age older.
2. The annuity in the *denominator* is an annuity immediate, not an annuity due.

The modified net premium which applies to the first year is defined by the equation:

$$\begin{pmatrix}\text{First-Year}\\\text{Modified}\\\text{Net Premium}\end{pmatrix} = \begin{pmatrix}\text{Net Level}\\\text{Premium}\end{pmatrix} - \left[\begin{pmatrix}\text{Net Level Premium}\\\text{for Ordinary Life}\end{pmatrix} - \begin{pmatrix}\text{One-Year}\\\text{Term Net}\\\text{Premium}\end{pmatrix}\right]$$

It should be realized that this equation permits the calculation of the *first-year* modified net premium independently of that for subsequent years. The subsequent years' modified net premium does not appear in this equation, as it does in the first-year equation for the other methods presented.

Thus, if the following four items are known, the two modified net premiums for Class B policies can be calculated:

Net level premium (for the policy in question);
Net level premium for ordinary life policy;
One-year term net premium;
Present value of life annuity immediate of 1 for one year less than the premium period.

It should be recognized that the above equation for the first-year modified net premium arises directly from the stipulation, set forth earlier in this section, that

> . . . the *difference* between the first-year modified net premium and the net level premium shall be equal to the amount of this difference on an ordinary life policy which is being calculated by the Full Preliminary Term method.

To Illustrate—Calculate the modified net annual premiums for a $1,000 25-payment life insurance policy issued at age 30, using the Canadian method. The following information is given:

Net level premium, 25-payment life, age 30	$18.25
Net level premium, ordinary life, age 30	13.47
1-year term net premium, age 30	2.07
Present value of life annuity immediate of 1 for 24 years, age 30	16.32464

Solution—This policy's net level premium ($18.25) is *greater than* the net level premium for an ordinary life policy ($13.47). (This could be expected, because the two policies have the same benefits, but these benefits must be paid for over a shorter period of time in the case of the 25-payment life policy.) Therefore, the policy falls into Class B. This means that, according to the Canadian rules, its modified net premiums are calculated by the Canadian method. In the Canadian method, either modified net premium may be calculated first, as mentioned before:

Basic equation

$$\begin{pmatrix}\text{1st-Year}\\\text{Modified}\\\text{Net Premium}\end{pmatrix} = \begin{pmatrix}\text{Net Level}\\\text{Premium}\end{pmatrix} - \left[\begin{pmatrix}\text{Net Level Premium}\\\text{for Ordinary Life}\end{pmatrix} - \begin{pmatrix}\text{One-Year}\\\text{Term Net}\\\text{Premium}\end{pmatrix}\right]$$

Substituting values given above

$$= \$18.25 - [\$13.47 - \$2.07]$$

$$= \$18.25 - \$11.40$$

$$= \$6.85$$

Basic equation

$$\begin{pmatrix}\text{Modified}\\\text{Net Premium}\end{pmatrix} = \begin{pmatrix}\text{Net Level}\\\text{Premium}\end{pmatrix} + \frac{\begin{pmatrix}\text{Net Level Premium}\\\text{for Ordinary Life}\end{pmatrix} - \begin{pmatrix}\text{One-Year}\\\text{Term Net}\\\text{Premium}\end{pmatrix}}{\begin{pmatrix}\text{Present Value of Life Annuity Immediate}\\\text{of 1 for One Year Less Than Premium Period}\end{pmatrix}}$$

Substituting values given above

$$= \$18.25 + \left(\frac{\$13.47 - \$2.07}{16.32464}\right)$$

$$= \$18.25 + \left(\frac{\$11.40}{16.32464}\right)$$

$$= \$18.25 + \$.70$$

$$= \$18.95$$

12.6 COMPARISON OF METHODS

Chart 12–1 summarizes some of the important stipulations of the modified reserve methods presented in this chapter.

It is instructive to compare the modified net premiums and the reserves which are produced by the four methods which have been presented. For this purpose, a 25-year endowment policy issued at age 25 will be used. This particular policy will fall into Class B in every instance. Accordingly, modified net premiums will be different for every method.

Chart 12–2 shows the various modified net premiums, as well as premiums calculated by the net level premium method (Page 296).

The present value, at time of issue, of these modified net premiums is the same for all five methods shown. This present value must be equal to the present value, at time of issue, of the policy's benefits. Also, the following points about Class B policies should be noted:

1. The Net Level method has the same net premium throughout, the Illinois Standard method has three different net premiums, and the other methods each have two.
2. Of the four modified methods, the Full Preliminary Term method releases the largest loading for the first year, and the Canadian method releases the smallest.
3. The Illinois Standard method has net premiums beginning in the 21st year which are equal to the net level premiums.
4. The *difference* between the first-year modified net premium and the modified net premium for the next 19 years will be the *same* ($17.89) for both the Illinois Standard and the Commissioners methods. It was pointed out in Section 12.4 that this is true for all Class B policies.

Chart 12–3 shows the modified terminal reserves for this policy produced by each of the methods (Page 297).

The following points should be noted:

1. All methods produce a final terminal reserve of $1,000. This is the amount of the pure endowment which the company must pay at that time.
2. The smaller the first-year modified net premium, the smaller the first-year modified reserve will be. The Full Preliminary Term first-year modified net premium equals the one-year term net premium, and hence its terminal reserve is zero.
3. The modified reserves by the Illinois Standard, Commissioners, and Canadian methods will be intermediate between the Full Preliminary Term and the Net Level reserves. However, after 20 years, the Illinois Standard and the Net Level reserves are equal.

CHART 12–1

Comparison of Modified Reserve Methods

Method	*Comparison Made (to Determine Class A or B)*	*Method for Class A Policies*	*Method for Class B Policies*		*Period of Modification for Class B Net Premiums*
			Difference between. . .	*Will Be Equal for. . .*	
Illinois Standard	*Net Level Premium* This Policy and 20-Pay Life	Full Preliminary Term	First-Year Net Premium and Next 19 Net Premiums	This Policy and 20-Pay Life on Full Preliminary Term Basis	Premium Period, but Not More Than 20 Years
Commissioners	*Full Prelim. Term Net Premium* This Policy and 20-Pay Life	Full Preliminary Term	First-Year Net Premium and Subsequent Net Premiums	This Policy and 20-Pay Life on Full Preliminary Term Basis	Entire Premium Period
Canadian	*Net Level Premium* This Policy and Ordinary Life	Full Preliminary Term	First-Year Net Premium and Net Level Premium	This Policy and Ordinary Life on Full Preliminary Term Basis	Entire Premium Period

CHART 12–2

Modified Net Annual Premiums, $1,000 25-Year Endowment, Age 25 (1958 C.S.O. 3%)

Policy Year	*Net Level Method*	*Full Preliminary Term Method*	*Illinois Standard Method*	*Commissioners Method*	*Canadian Method*
1	$28.12	$ 1.87	$11.42	$11.25	$18.71
2	28.12	29.71	29.31	29.14	28.69
.	.	.	.	.	.
.	.	.	.	.	.
.	.	.	.	.	.
20	28.12	29.71	29.31	29.14	28.69
21	28.12	29.71	28.12	29.14	28.69
.	.	.	.	.	.
.	.	.	.	.	.
.	.	.	.	.	.
25	28.12	29.71	28.12	29.14	28.69

The National Association of Insurance Commissioners, composed of the Insurance Commissioners of each of the states, has been instrumental in preparing model legislation prescribing minimum reserve standards. Their model Standard Valuation Law has been enacted into law, with few modifications, in all of the states. The Standard Valuation Law prescribes a minimum standard for reserves (for policies currently being issued) of the 1958 C.S.O. Table, $3\frac{1}{2}\%$ interest, and the Commissioners method. For females, a "setback" in the age may be used (not exceeding three years). Since these are minimum standards, a company is free to use other bases for calculating its reserves, provided higher reserves are produced.

In Canada, the Canadian method is prescribed as a minimum standard for reserves. This applies to companies which are registered with the Dominion of Canada Insurance Department.

EXERCISES

1 Using Table III and 3% interest, calculate the 1st-year modified net premium for a $5,000 17-year endowment policy issued at age 40, using the Full Preliminary Term method.

2 Using Table III and 3% interest, calculate the modified net premium for years subsequent to the 1st year for a $1,000 3-year term insurance policy issued at age 60, using the Full Preliminary Term method.

3 Calculate the modified net premiums for the following policy, assuming it uses the Illinois Standard method and falls in Class B:

Net level premium	= $41.70
Net level premium for 19-payment life, 1 age older	= $28.73
1-year term net premium	= $ 4.91
Present value of 20-year life annuity due of 1	= 14.917

CHART 12–3

Modified Terminal Reserves, $1,000 25-Year Endowment, Age 25 (1958 C.S.O. 3%)

Policy Year	*Net Level Method*	*Full Preliminary Term Method*	*Illinois Standard Method*	*Commissioners Method*	*Canadian Method*
1	$ 27.08	$ 0	$ 9.85	$ 9.68	$ 17.38
2	55.00	28.70	38.45	38.10	45.58
3	83.79	58.29	67.93	67.40	74.65
4	113.46	88.79	98.32	97.60	104.62
5	144.05	120.22	129.65	128.73	135.51
6	175.57	152.62	161.94	160.82	167.35
7	208.06	186.02	195.22	193.90	200.16
8	241.56	220.45	229.53	227.99	233.99
9	276.09	255.94	264.90	263.14	268.87
10	311.68	292.52	301.35	299.36	304.81
11	348.35	330.21	338.92	336.69	341.85
12	386.14	369.05	377.63	375.16	380.02
13	425.08	409.07	417.51	414.79	419.34
14	465.18	450.29	458.59	455.61	459.84
15	506.49	492.75	500.92	497.66	501.57
16	549.05	536.50	544.52	540.99	544.55
17	592.92	581.59	589.47	585.64	588.86
18	638.16	628.09	635.82	631.69	634.55
19	684.84	676.06	683.65	679.20	681.69
20	733.03	725.60	733.03	728.25	730.36
21	782.82	776.77	782.82	778.93	780.65
22	834.29	829.68	834.29	831.33	832.64
23	887.57	884.44	887.57	885.56	886.45
24	942.76	941.16	942.76	941.73	942.19
25	1000.00	1000.00	1000.00	1000.00	1000.00

4 Calculate the modified net premiums for the following policy, assuming it uses the Commissioners method and falls in Class B:

1-year term net premium	= $145.20
Net level premium for 19-payment life, 1 age older	= $412.67
Present value of life annuity due of 1 for premium period	= 25.722
Net level premium	= $577.87

5 Calculate the modified net premiums for the following policy, assuming it uses the Canadian method and falls in Class B:

1-year term net premium	= $ 54.86
Net level premium	= $406.60
Net level premium for ordinary life policy	= $257.15
Present value of life annuity immediate of 1 for 1 year less than premium period	= 12.778

6 What amount, in addition to the regular loading, is made available for first-year expenses for the policies in Exercises 3, 4 and 5?

13. Nonforfeiture Values

13.1 INTRODUCTION

Life insurance policies are required by law to contain a provision which guarantees that certain values will be available if the policyowner decides to stop paying the premiums. These values are known as *nonforfeiture values.* The amounts of the guaranteed values for various policy years are printed in a policy when it is issued, and cannot be changed subsequently.

A provision is also required giving the policyowner the right to borrow money from the insurance company. Such a *policy loan* can be made at any time, but cannot exceed the guaranteed value which the policyowner could then receive if he stopped paying premiums. If premium payments are stopped after a loan is made (and before it is repaid), the amount of the loan still unpaid is generally *deducted from* the guaranteed nonforfeiture value stipulated in the policy.

At the time premium payments are stopped, the policyowner may also be entitled to receive certain additional values if he has been credited with policy *dividends* from the company. The subject of policy dividends will be presented in Chapter 14. It will be sufficient here to state that the *total* value available when premium payments are stopped is generally:

Guaranteed Nonforfeiture Value + Value of Dividend Credits (If any)
− Loan (If any)

This *total* value can generally be used by the policyowner in any one of these ways:

1. Received in a lump sum (such a lump sum could also be used under the settlement option provisions);
2. Used to continue the policy in force as "reduced paid-up" insurance; or
3. Used to continue the policy in force as "extended term" insurance.

The *guaranteed* nonforfeiture value is often referred to as the "cash value." Section 13.2 will present methods of calculating this cash value. Sections 13.3 and 13.4 will describe the calculation of "reduced paid-up" and "extended term" insurance, which can be provided by the *total* value.

13.2 CASH VALUE

The *reserve* is the amount a company is legally required to have on hand for a policy. The *cash value* is the amount a company guarantees to pay if the policy is terminated. State laws specify minimums for both, but companies are free to have reserves and cash values higher than the minimums. The minimum cash value specified for any policy at any time is less than the minimum reserve. In actual practice, guaranteed cash values are generally less than the reserve actually held during the early years of a policy. After the early years, however, the cash value is often equal to the reserve. It cannot legally exceed the reserve since the company cannot, in effect, promise that a policyowner could receive more money than the company has set up as its liability for that policy.

SURRENDER CHARGE METHOD. Prior to 1948, state laws generally required that, beginning at the end of the third year, a policy must provide a guaranteed cash value at least equal to the terminal reserve *minus* $25 per $1,000 of insurance. This deduction was known as a *surrender charge*. It was customary in practice, however, for the surrender charge to be higher for the earlier policy years and progressively reduced by policy duration, with the surrender charge eliminated after a period of time, such as 10 years. Thus, the cash value actually guaranteed at the expiration of such period was equal to the full terminal reserve.

The surrender charge method is still used by a number of companies in their currently issued policies, although the state laws were changed to specify a different method for policies issued beginning in 1948. A company using the surrender charge method for policies being issued today must check to make certain that all cash values are equal to or greater than the minimums specified in today's laws.

To Illustrate—Calculate all of the cash values for a $1,000 5-payment 10-year endowment policy issued at age 21, using a surrender charge of $27 for the first year, decreasing to 0 at the end of 10 years (using the 1958 C.S.O. Table and 3% interest).

Solution—This is the same policy for which terminal reserves were calculated in Section 11.1. They are repeated in the tabulation below. The surrender charge to be deducted from the reserve was given as $27 at the end of the first year:

$$\begin{pmatrix}\text{1st Year}\\\text{Cash Value}\end{pmatrix}=\begin{pmatrix}\text{1st Year}\\\text{Terminal Reserve}\end{pmatrix}-\begin{pmatrix}\text{1st Year}\\\text{Surrender Charge}\end{pmatrix}$$

$$= \$161.98 - \$27.00$$

$$= \$134.98$$

After the end of the first year, the surrender charge will decrease by 9 equal reductions, down to 0 at the end of 10 years. Hence, each year's reduction will equal

$$\$27 \div 9 = \$3$$

At the end of the second year, therefore, the surrender charge will be $\$27 - \$3 = \$24$

$$\begin{pmatrix}\text{2nd Year}\\\text{Cash Value}\end{pmatrix}=\begin{pmatrix}\text{2nd Year}\\\text{Terminal Reserve}\end{pmatrix}-\begin{pmatrix}\text{2nd Year}\\\text{Surrender Charge}\end{pmatrix}$$

$$= \$329.11 - \$24.00$$

$$= \$305.11$$

Chart 13–1 shows the calculation for all years.

CHART 13–1

(1) *Year*	(2) *Terminal Reserve*	(3) *Surrender Charge*	(4) *Cash Value* *(Col. 2 – Col. 3)*
1	$ 161.98	$27.00	$ 134.98
2	329.11	24.00	305.11
3	501.55	21.00	480.55
4	679.50	18.00	661.50
5	863.14	15.00	848.14
6	888.81	12.00	876.81
7	915.31	9.00	906.31
8	942.65	6.00	936.65
9	970.87	3.00	967.87
10	1,000.00	0	1,000.00

STANDARD NONFORFEITURE LAW. The Standard Nonforfeiture Law, originally drafted by the National Association of Insurance Commissioners, has been enacted into law, with few modifications, in all of the states. According to this law, the *minimum cash value* at any time is defined to be the present value of future benefits, minus the present value of future special premiums called *adjusted premiums*. These adjusted premiums are precisely defined in the law. In general, the present value of the adjusted premiums (at time of issue) is meant to be equal to the present value of the policy's net level premiums, *plus* the *excess* of the first-year expenses over the annual expenses for subsequent years. To achieve this aim, the law specifies that this *excess* shall be calculated (for each $1,000 of insurance) as

40% of the adjusted premium (to a maximum of $16)
+ 25% of the adjusted premium for an ordinary life policy (to a maximum of $10)
+ $20

The first two parts of the calculation are intended to take account of those excess first-year expenses which vary by the amount of the premium. The $20 is intended to take account of those excess first-year expenses which are constant for each policy or vary with the amount of insurance.

Since the adjusted premiums are greater than the net level premiums, their present value is greater than the present value of the policy's net level premiums. This, in turn, produces minimum cash values which are *less than* the net level terminal reserve during the entire premium-paying period of a policy. This can be seen by examining the two equations:

$$\begin{pmatrix}\text{Terminal}\\ \text{Reserve}\end{pmatrix} = \begin{pmatrix}\text{Present Value of}\\ \text{Future Benefits}\end{pmatrix} - \begin{pmatrix}\text{Present Value of}\\ \text{Future Net Premiums}\end{pmatrix}$$

$$\begin{pmatrix}\text{Minimum}\\ \text{Cash Value}\end{pmatrix} = \begin{pmatrix}\text{Present Value of}\\ \text{Future Benefits}\end{pmatrix} - \begin{pmatrix}\text{Present Value of}\\ \text{Future Adjusted Premiums}\end{pmatrix}$$

The item subtracted on the right-hand side of the "minimum cash value" equation is *larger* than the item so subtracted in the terminal reserve equation. Therefore, the value of the "minimum cash value" is *less* than the value of the terminal reserve.

The Standard Nonforfeiture Law generally became effective in 1948. It has subsequently been amended, and today provides that the minimum cash values for policies now being issued shall be calculated by the method described above and by using the 1958 C.S.O. Table. For females, a "setback" in the age may be used, not exceeding three years. The interest rate used is that rate which the company chooses to use in calculating its own cash values, but cannot exceed $3\frac{1}{2}\%$.

To Illustrate—Using an interest rate of 3%, calculate the minimum cash value at the end of 10 years for a $1,000 30-payment life policy issued to a male age 25. The following information is given (based upon the 1958 C.S.O. Table and 3% interest):

Net single premium at age 35 for $1,000 whole life insurance	$358.66
Present value at age 35 of 20-year life annuity due of 1	14.80519
Adjusted premium for this policy	$ 15.83

Solution—Under the law, the minimum cash value for this policy would be calculated using the 1958 C.S.O. Table at 3% interest. The *adjusted premiums* run for 30 years under this policy (to age 55). At any time, their present value is calculated as a temporary life annuity due to age 55. The attained age at the end of 10 years is $25 + 10 = 35$; the temporary life annuity then runs for 20 more years:

Basic equation

$$\begin{pmatrix}\text{Minimum}\\ \text{Cash}\\ \text{Value}\end{pmatrix} = \begin{pmatrix}\text{Present Value}\\ \text{of Future}\\ \text{Benefits}\end{pmatrix} - \begin{pmatrix}\text{Present Value}\\ \text{of Future}\\ \text{Adjusted Premiums}\end{pmatrix}$$

Expressing this equation in equivalent form

$$= \begin{pmatrix}\text{Net Single Premium}\\ \text{at Age 35}\end{pmatrix} - \begin{pmatrix}\text{Adjusted}\\ \text{Premium}\end{pmatrix}\begin{pmatrix}\text{20-Year Annuity}\\ \text{Factor at Age 35}\end{pmatrix}$$

Substituting values given above

$$= \$358.66 - \$15.83\ (14.80519)$$

$$= \$358.66 - \$234.37$$

$$= \$124.29$$

In actual practice, many companies would guarantee a cash value for the above policy equal to the full terminal reserve at the end of 10 years. If the net level method were used, this terminal reserve would be $146.68. However, it has been shown that the law does allow a cash value which is *less than* this terminal reserve by as much as

$$\text{Terminal Reserve} - \text{Minimum Cash Value} = \$146.68 - \$124.29$$
$$= \$22.39$$

In a sense, this $22.39 may be thought of as a surrender charge available at that time. Similarly, if the Commissioners modified reserve method were used, the terminal reserve would be $136.71. In that event, the law allows a cash value which is *less than* this modified terminal reserve by as much as

$$\text{Terminal Reserve} - \text{Minimum Cash Value} = \$136.71 - \$124.29$$
$$= \$12.42$$

NONFORFEITURE FACTORS. Many companies now calculate their policies' cash values in a manner similar to that set forth in the law for the calculation of the legal minimums. That is, the cash values are calculated to be the present value of future benefits minus the present value of future *special premiums.* These *special premiums* are not greater than the legally prescribed adjusted premiums, and are usually called *nonforfeiture factors.* Each company calculates its own nonforfeiture factors. Since they are not greater than the adjusted premiums, their present value is not greater than the present value of the adjusted premiums. This, in turn, produces actual *cash values* which are at least as great as the legal minimums (as they must be).

One widely used method is to specify a certain nonforfeiture factor applicable to the first several years the policy will be in effect, and a second factor applicable to the remaining years.

To Illustrate—Calculate the cash value which a certain company would specify at the end of 10 years for a $1,000 ordinary life policy issued at age 35. This company specifies that its nonforfeiture factor on this policy is $17.50 for the first 30 years, and $16.29 thereafter. The following information is given:

Present value at age 45 of 20-year life annuity due of 1	14.14529
Present value at age 45 of whole life annuity due of 1, deferred for 20 years	4.43261
Net single premium at age 45 for $1,000 whole life insurance	$458.89

Solution—The cash value at any time is calculated as the present value of future benefits, minus the present value of future nonforfeiture factors. At the end of 10 years, the attained age is $35 + 10 = 45$. The remaining nonforfeiture factors at that time are as shown in the following line diagram:

$17.50 $17.50 $17.50 · · · · · · · $17.50 $16.29 $16.29 · · · · $16.29

*

attained age 45   46   47 · · · · · · · · · 64   65   66 · · · · end of the mortality table

At age 45, there are 20 remaining factors of $17.50 each (due at ages 45 to 64, inclusive), plus $16.29 thereafter each year for the remainder of life (beginning at age 65). The present value of all of them can be looked upon as the present value of a temporary life annuity due ($17.50 per year for 20 years), plus the present value of a deferred whole life annuity due ($16.29 per year deferred 20 years):

Basic equation

$$\begin{pmatrix}\text{Cash}\\\text{Value}\end{pmatrix} = \begin{pmatrix}\text{Present Value}\\\text{of Future}\\\text{Benefits}\end{pmatrix} - \begin{pmatrix}\text{Present Value}\\\text{of Future}\\\text{Nonforfeiture Factors}\end{pmatrix}$$

Expressing this equation in equivalent form

$$= \begin{pmatrix}\text{Net Single}\\ \text{Premium}\\ \text{at Age 45}\end{pmatrix} - \left[\begin{pmatrix}\text{First}\\ \text{Nonforfeiture}\\ \text{Factor}\end{pmatrix}\begin{pmatrix}\text{20-Year Life}\\ \text{Annuity Factor}\\ \text{at Age 45}\end{pmatrix} + \begin{pmatrix}\text{Second}\\ \text{Nonforfeiture}\\ \text{Factor}\end{pmatrix}\begin{pmatrix}\text{Whole Life Annuity}\\ \text{Factor deferred}\\ \text{20 Years at Age 45}\end{pmatrix}\right]$$

Substituting values given above

$$= \$458.89 - [(\$17.50)(14.14529) + (\$16.29)(4.43261)]$$

$$= \$458.89 - [\$247.54 + \$72.21]$$

$$= \$458.89 - \$319.75$$

$$= \$139.14$$

It is interesting to note that the policy in this illustration has a net level annual premium equal to \$16.29 and that its *adjusted premium* under the Standard Nonforfeiture Law is \$17.72. Therefore, the particular nonforfeiture factors used (\$17.50 and \$16.29) are *not less than* the policy's net premium. This is imperative; otherwise, cash values would be produced which exceed the policy's terminal reserve (an illegal situation). Also, the particular nonforfeiture factors used are *not greater than* the policy's *adjusted premium* under the Standard Nonforfeiture Law. This is also imperative, as mentioned earlier; otherwise, cash values would be produced which would be less than the policy's minimum cash value (an illegal situation).

It is also interesting to note that the second nonforfeiture factor (\$16.29) used in the above illustration is exactly equal to the policy's net level annual premium. The effect of so specifying is that after the period of the first nonforfeiture factor (30 years in this illustration), all of the cash values will then be equal to the full terminal reserve. This can be seen by examining the two equations:

$$\begin{pmatrix}\text{Terminal}\\ \text{Reserve}\end{pmatrix} = \begin{pmatrix}\text{Present Value}\\ \text{of Future Benefits}\end{pmatrix} - \begin{pmatrix}\text{Present Value of}\\ \text{Future Net Premiums}\end{pmatrix}$$

$$\begin{pmatrix}\text{Cash}\\ \text{Value}\end{pmatrix} = \begin{pmatrix}\text{Present Value}\\ \text{of Future Benefits}\end{pmatrix} - \begin{pmatrix}\text{Present Value of}\\ \text{Future Nonforfeiture Factors}\end{pmatrix}$$

If the net premium is equal to the nonforfeiture factor, then the right-hand sides of both equations are the same.

13.3 REDUCED PAID-UP INSURANCE

It was pointed out in Section 13.1 that the policyowner can stop paying premiums at any time and use the policy's *total value* in various ways, one of which is to continue the policy in force as "reduced paid-up" insurance. In such a case, the insurance continues in effect, but it is for a smaller amount. The nature of the benefit will be the same (whole life, endowment, etc.), but no more premiums will be payable. The basis for the calculation is the principle that the policy's *total value* is used as if it were a *net single premium* for the paid-up benefits.

For example, an ordinary life policy issued at age 20 might have the following values at the end of 12 years:

Cash value	$227.04
Value of dividend credits	41.80
Total	$268.84
Less loan	−97.60
Total value	$171.24

At the end of 12 years, the attained age is $20+12=32$. Hence, $171.24 will be used as the net single premium at age 32 for a certain amount of whole life insurance. If the 1958 C.S.O. Table and 3% interest are used, the amount of the reduced paid-up insurance will be $515, since the net single premium for $515 of whole life insurance at age 32 equals the $171.24 which is available.

If the amount of the total value is known, and it is desired to calculate the amount of the reduced paid-up insurance which this total value will purchase, the equation is

$$\begin{pmatrix}\text{Amount of Reduced}\\ \text{Paid-Up Insurance}\end{pmatrix} = \frac{(\text{Total Value})}{\begin{pmatrix}\text{Net Single Premium}\\ \text{for \$1 of Insurance}\end{pmatrix}}$$

The net single premium for $1,000 whole life insurance at age 32 is $332.50. The net single premium for $1 of such insurance would be $\frac{1}{1000}$ of $332.50, or $.33250 (by moving the decimal point three places to the left). Applying the equation to the above example, the amount of reduced paid-up insurance would be calculated as follows:

$$\begin{pmatrix}\text{Amount of Reduced}\\ \text{Paid-Up Insurance}\end{pmatrix} = \frac{(\text{Total Value})}{\begin{pmatrix}\text{Net Single Premium}\\ \text{for \$1 of Insurance}\end{pmatrix}}$$

$$= \frac{\$171.24}{.33250}$$

$$= \$515$$

This procedure is simple in actual practice because published tables of net single premiums are usually available.

Amounts of life insurance are always established in whole dollars, without any cents. Therefore, when the amount of reduced paid-up insurance is calculated, the answer is expressed in the form of whole dollars only. In this particular calculation, however, the usual rules for "rounding off" the answer are not followed. It is customary instead to drop off any cents from the answer and to add 1 to the number of dollars. For example, if the amount of reduced paid-up insurance were calculated to be $2,017.12, the company would actually establish $2,018 of such insurance. This is called "rounding up to the next higher dollar." This is a case of maintaining goodwill by never giving the policyowner less than he is entitled to.

To Illustrate—Calculate the amount of reduced paid-up insurance which is available at the end of 15 years for a $1,000 20-year endowment policy issued at age 25. Assume the cash value is $676.29, and there are no other credits and no loan. The net single premium at age 40 for $1,000 of 5-year endowment insurance is $863.63.

Solution—At the end of 15 years, there are 5 years still remaining of the original 20-year period. The attained age is $25+15=40$. Hence, the net single premium needed will be for $1 of 5-year endowment insurance at age 40. This can easily be obtained, because it will be $\frac{1}{1000}$ of the premium given above (the premium above being for $1,000 of such insurance). By moving the decimal point 3 places to the left, the net single premium for $1 of such insurance is obtained:

$$\frac{1}{1000} \text{ of } \$863.63 = \$.86363$$

As stated above, the amount of reduced paid-up insurance is found by dividing the policy's available value by the net single premium for $1 of insurance:

Basic equation

$$\begin{pmatrix}\text{Amount of Reduced}\\ \text{Paid-Up Insurance}\end{pmatrix} = \frac{(\text{Total Value})}{\begin{pmatrix}\text{Net Single Premium}\\ \text{for \$1 of Insurance}\end{pmatrix}}$$

$$= \frac{\$676.29}{.86363}$$

$$= \$783.08$$

Rounding to next higher dollar

$$= \$784$$

This endowment policy will now provide a death benefit of $784 if death occurs between ages 40 and 45. A pure endowment of $784 will be payable if the insured is alive at age 45. There are no more premiums due, because the policyowner has elected to stop paying premiums and use the policy's nonforfeiture value to provide reduced paid-up insurance.

In calculating reduced paid-up insurance, it should always be remembered that the form of the benefit will be determined only by the policy's original benefit and that the premium-paying period will not affect the net single premium to be used. For example, this net single premium will be a *whole life* net single premium whether the policy is a 20-payment life policy, a whole life policy with premiums to age 65, or an ordinary life policy.

After the end of the regular premium-paying period of any policy (such as after 20 years on a 20-payment life policy), a calculation of reduced paid-up insurance would, in effect, be meaningless. Such a policy is already "paid-up" for its full amount of insurance. Therefore, no reduced paid-up insurance is available in such an instance. However, the policyowner may still voluntarily terminate his policy and be entitled to receive its cash value.

13.4 EXTENDED TERM INSURANCE

The third nonforfeiture option is "extended term" insurance. Under this option, the insurance continues in effect, but for a *shorter period of time;* and with no more premiums payable. Two basic calculations are necessary for most extended term insurance cases: first, the *amount* of such insurance, and second, the *period of time* for which such insurance will continue.

AMOUNT OF EXTENDED TERM INSURANCE. The principle underlying the determination of the *amount* of such insurance is that the death benefit shall be the same as the death benefit available at the time the policyowner elects to stop paying premiums. This amount is generally calculated as

Regular death benefit of the policy
+ Additional insurance purchased previously by dividends (if any)
− Loan (if any)

The additional insurance purchased by dividends will be discussed in Chapter 14. It will be sufficient here to state that the amount of any such additional insurance is payable at the time of death, just like the policy's regular death benefit. At the time of death, any policy loan still unpaid is deducted from the policy's regular death benefit. This accounts for its deduction in calculating the amount of extended term insurance.

PERIOD OF TIME OF EXTENDED TERM INSURANCE. The basis for determining the *period of time* for which the insurance will continue is the principle that the policy's *total value* shall be used as if it were a *net single premium* for such insurance. The insurance will continue for a limited period of time, that is, it will become *term insurance* (with no further premiums payable), but it would be only by coincidence that the total value would provide this extended term insurance for an *exact* number of years. It is customary, therefore to calculate the number of *years and days* that it will continue. Any fractional part of a day in the answer is used as if it added an entire extra day. For example, if the answer were 5 years and 21.247 days, the insurance would actually be granted for a term of 5 years and 22 days.

To Illustrate—Calculate the extended term insurance (amount and period of time) which may be provided 10 years after the date of issue of a $10,000 ordinary life policy issued at age 20, given the following information:

Cash value, end of 10 years	$674.40
Dividend additions (additional insurance purchased previously by dividends)	47.00
Cash value of the dividend additions	14.86
Policy loan	100.00
Net single premium per $1,000 at age 30 for 21 years' term insurance	56.87
Net single premium per $1,000 at age 30 for 22 years' term insurance	61.22

Solution—The total value which is available to provide extended term insurance is

Cash value	$ 674.40
Value of dividend credits	14.86
Total	$ 689.26
Less loan	−100.00
Total value	$ 589.26

The amount of extended term insurance is

Regular death benefit	$10,000
Additional insurance purchased previously by dividends	47
Total	$10,047
Less loan	−100
Total amount	$ 9,947

Therefore, the total value which is available *per $1 of insurance* is $\frac{\$589.26}{9{,}947} = \$.05924$ and the total value available *per $1,000 of insurance* is $\$.05924 \times 1{,}000 = \$59.24$. It is given that a net single premium of $56.87 will pay for $1,000 of 21-year term insurance, and a net single premium of $61.22 will pay for $1,000 of 22-year term insurance. Therefore, the total value per $1,000 which is actually available ($59.24) will pay for 21 years, and there will be an amount *left over* of $\$59.24 - \$56.87 = \$2.37$.

This $2.37 left over will pay for part of a year. The difference between the two given net single premiums equals the cost of insurance for *1 year* beyond the 21-year period:

Cost for 22 years	$ 61.22
Less cost for 21 years	−56.87
Cost for 1 year beyond 21 years	$ 4.35

The $2.37 left over will pay for $\frac{\$2.37}{\$4.35}$ of a year beyond 21 years. This fraction may be multiplied by 365 to determine the number of days:

$$\left(\frac{\$2.37}{\$4.35}\right)(365) = 198.862 \text{ days}$$

The extended term insurance actually granted, therefore, will be $9,947 of insurance for a period of 21 years and 199 days.

AMOUNT OF PURE ENDOWMENT. If the extended term insurance nonforfeiture option is selected for an endowment policy, the total value available may be more than sufficient to carry the policy as term insurance for the number of years remaining in the original endowment period. Under these circumstances, any portion of the total value not needed to pay for the term insurance is used as a net single premium, at the attained age, to provide a pure endowment payable at the end of the original endowment period. It is customary to "round up to the next higher dollar" the amount of this pure endowment. (In calculating extended term insurance where there is a pure endowment involved, there is no need to first find the amount of total value available per $1,000 of insurance, as the following illustration will show.)

To Illustrate—At the end of the 15th year, the cash value of a $5,000 20-year endowment policy, which was issued at age 40, is $3,422.75. Assuming there are no dividend values and no loan, calculate the extended term insurance benefit, given the following information:

Net single premium per $1,000 at age 55 for 5-year term insurance	$ 69.25
Net single premium per $1,000 at age 55 for pure endowment due in 5 years	797.11

Solution—At the end of the 15th year, there are 5 years remaining in the original 20-year endowment period. The attained age is 40 + 15 = 55. The net single premium necessary at age 55 to provide the full $5,000 of term insurance for the remaining years is

$$(5)(\$69.25) = \$346.25$$

The policy's cash value of $3,422.75 is sufficient to pay this amount, and there will be an amount left over of

$$\$3{,}422.75 - \$346.25 = \$3{,}076.50$$

This $3,076.50 left over will pay for a certain amount of pure endowment (due in 5 years). It is given that $797.11 will pay for $1,000 of such pure endowment. Therefore, the $3,076.50 left over will pay for $\frac{\$3{,}076.50}{\$797.11}$ times $1,000:

$$\text{Pure Endowment} = \left(\frac{\$3{,}076.50}{\$797.11}\right)(\$1{,}000)$$

$$= \$3{,}859.57$$

The entire benefit under the extended term insurance option, therefore, consists of 5-year term insurance for $5,000, plus a pure endowment due in 5 years of $3,860.

After the end of the regular premium-paying period of any policy, a calculation of extended term insurance would, in effect, be meaningless. Such a policy is already in force for its full amount of benefits, and for its full period of time, with no more premiums payable. Therefore, no extended term insurance is available in such an instance. However, the policyowner may still voluntarily terminate his policy and receive its cash value.

A part of the Standard Nonforfeiture Law states that, in calculating the extended term insurance benefit for policies currently being issued, the rates of mortality assumed may be not more than those shown in the Commissioners 1958 Extended Term Insurance Table. This refers to a mortality table which was published at the same time as the 1958 C.S.O. Table. It exhibits mortality rates generally higher than those of the 1958 C.S.O. Table, and is intended to reflect the generally higher mortality which is observed for persons who have elected this particular nonforfeiture option.

This higher-than-normal mortality observed for policies in force as extended term insurance might be expected because this option is attractive to persons who find cause to anticipate an early death. Their full death benefit remains in force (temporarily), and it does so without the necessity of further premium payments.

13.5 INSURANCE PAID-UP OR MATURED BY DIVIDENDS

PAID-UP BY DIVIDENDS. Generally, life insurance policies contain a provision which states that the company will declare the policy to be fully paid-up (the full benefits will continue in effect, but no more premiums need be paid), if the policyowner so desires, whenever the cash value, plus the value of dividend credits, equals or exceeds the *net single premium* at the attained age for the future benefits. Any loan against the policy generally remains in effect.

For example, assume a $1,000 endowment-at-age-65 policy issued at age 30 has a cash value of $775.47 at the end of 30 years. It also has dividend credits valued at $131.18. The total of these values is

$$\$775.47 + \$131.18 = \$906.65$$

In order for this policy to be declared fully paid up, this total value must equal or exceed the net single premium at the attained age. The attained age is $30 + 30 = 60$. The net single premium at age 60 for the future benefits (endowment-at-age-65) is $868.42, using the 1958 C.S.O. Table and 3% interest. The cash value plus dividend credits ($906.65) does exceed the net single premium ($868.42). Hence, if the policyowner so desires, the company will declare this policy to be fully paid up. In this instance, there is more value than is needed, amounting to

$$\$906.65 - \$868.42 = \$38.23$$

Generally, this extra $38.23 will either be paid to the policyowner at the time the policy is declared to be paid up or else it will remain in the form of a dividend credit for the policy.

To Illustrate—A $5,000 20-payment life policy issued at age 15 has a cash value at the end of 17 years of $1,451.90. How much dividend credit must the policy have at that time in order to be declared as fully paid up? The net single premium at age 32 for $1,000 of whole life insurance is $332.50.

Solution—The smallest amount of dividend credits necessary is that which will make the following equation true:

$$\begin{pmatrix}\text{Cash}\\ \text{Value}\end{pmatrix} + \begin{pmatrix}\text{Value of}\\ \text{Dividend Credits}\end{pmatrix} = \begin{pmatrix}\text{Net Single}\\ \text{Premium}\end{pmatrix}$$

If this equation is solved for the value of dividend credits, it appears as follows:

$$\begin{pmatrix}\text{Value of}\\ \text{Dividend Credits}\end{pmatrix} = \begin{pmatrix}\text{Net Single}\\ \text{Premium}\end{pmatrix} - \begin{pmatrix}\text{Cash}\\ \text{Value}\end{pmatrix}$$

The attained age is $15 + 17 = 32$. The net single premium for the future benefits ($5,000 of whole life insurance) at the attained age is 5 times the net single premium given for $1,000 of such insurance.

$$\begin{pmatrix}\text{Net Single}\\ \text{Premium}\end{pmatrix} = 5(\$332.50)$$

$$= \$1,662.50$$

Hence, the amount of dividend credits necessary is

$$\begin{pmatrix}\text{Value of}\\ \text{Dividend Credits}\end{pmatrix} = \begin{pmatrix}\text{Net Single}\\ \text{Premium}\end{pmatrix} - \begin{pmatrix}\text{Cash}\\ \text{Value}\end{pmatrix}$$

$$= \$1{,}662.50 - \$1{,}451.90$$

$$= \$210.60$$

MATURED BY DIVIDENDS. Generally, life insurance policies also contain a provision which states that the company will mature the policy as an endowment (will pay out the amount of insurance), if the policyowner so desires, whenever the cash value, plus the value of dividend credits, equals or exceeds the *amount of insurance.* Any loan against the policy is deducted from the amount so payable, and any *excess* dividend credits would be added.

It should be recognized, however, that the policyowner would have this right even if there were no such special provision, because he always has the right to terminate the policy and receive the cash value plus the value of dividend credits, less any loan.

For example, it may be desired to find the number of years after issue when a certain $1,000 policy can be so "matured by dividends." Assume the following table (Chart 13–2) shows the policy's guaranteed cash values, and the dividend credits which it is expected that the policy will have:

CHART 13–2

End of Year	*Cash Value*	*Expected Dividend Credits*
1	$ 52.20	$ 18.11
2	145.09	40.06
3	240.85	65.84
4	339.58	95.66
5	441.36	129.33
6	546.30	167.25
7	654.51	209.44
8	766.11	256.10
9	881.23	307.02
10	1,000.00	362.63

At the end of the seventh year, the cash value, plus value of dividend credits, is

$$\$654.51 + \$209.44 = \$863.95$$

At the end of the eighth year, the cash value, plus value of dividend credits, is

$$\$766.11 + \$256.10 = \$1{,}022.21$$

Since the amount of insurance is $1,000, the end of the eighth year is the earliest time when it may be expected that the cash value, plus value of dividend credits, will equal or exceed the amount of insurance. In actual practice, if the policyowner chose to exercise the special option and have the company mature his policy at that time, the company would pay $1,000 plus the $22.21 extra value (excess dividend credits) which the policy would have.

EXERCISES

1 Calculate the amount of money the policyowner will be entitled to receive in a lump sum if he terminates his policy at a time when it has a $250 loan and the following values:

Cash value	$4,817.12
Value of dividend credits	304.04

2 A company defines its cash values as being equal to the terminal reserve, minus a surrender charge. Calculate the 5th-year cash value, if the 5th-year reserve is $412.13 per $1,000, and the surrender charge is $24.92 at the end of the 1st year, decreasing by equal reductions to 0 at the end of 15 years.

3 Calculate the 10th-year minimum cash value for a $1,000 endowment-at-age-65 policy issued to a male age 30, given the following information:

Net single premium at age 40 for $1,000 25-year endowment	$515.63
Present value at age 40 of 25-year life annuity due of 1	16.6299
Adjusted premium for this policy	$ 20.58

4 Using the following table (1958 C.S.O. 3%), calculate the 4th-year minimum cash value for a $1,000 ordinary life policy issued to a male age 25. The adjusted premium is $12.41.

Age	*Net Single Premium for $1,000 Whole Life Insurance*	*Present Value of Whole Life Annuity Due of 1*
25	$279.14	24.7497
26	286.13	24.5095
27	293.33	24.2623
28	300.74	24.0080
29	308.36	23.7464
30	316.19	23.4776
31	324.23	23.2014
32	332.50	22.9176
33	340.99	22.6260
34	349.71	22.3266
35	358.66	22.0193

5 Using the table given in Exercise 4, calculate the minimum cash value at attained age 30 for a $1,000 20-payment life policy issued to a male age 5. The adjusted premium is $13.10.

6 A company calculates its cash values as being equal to the present value of future benefits, minus the present value of future nonforfeiture factors. Using the following figures, calculate the 10th-year cash value for a $1,000 ordinary life policy issued at age 22.

Nonforfeiture factor for this policy ....$ 10.40
Net single premium at age 32 for $1,000 whole life insurance..... 332.50
Present value at age 32 of whole life annuity due of 1 .... 22.9176

7 Calculate the 5th-year cash value for a $1,000 20-payment life policy issued at age 30. Assume the company specifies a nonforfeiture factor of $23.00 for the first 10 years, and $21.15 for the remainder of the premium-paying period. The following information is given:

Net single premium at age 35 for $1,000 whole life insurance...$358.66
Present value at age 35 of 5-year life annuity due of 1............. 4.69286
Present value at age 35 of 10-year life annuity due of 1, deferred 5 years 7.33180

8 Calculate the amount of reduced paid-up insurance which is available at the end of 20 years for a 30-year endowment policy issued at age 18, based on the following information:

Net single premium at age 38 for $1 10-year endowment..........$ 0.74817
Cash value at end of 20 years for this policy........................... 553.80
There is no loan, and no dividend credit.

9 Using the table in Exercise 4, calculate the amount of reduced paid-up insurance which is available at the end of 15 years for an ordinary life policy issued at age 20, assuming the policy's total value is $12,853.50.

10 Calculate the extended term insurance benefit which is available 12 years after the date of issue for a 20-payment life policy issued at age 40, given the following information:

Regular death benefit of the policy $5,000.00
Additional insurance purchased previously by dividends 845.00
Loan 200.00
Cash value, end of 12 years 1,655.65
Value of the above dividend credits.. 454.53
Net single premium per $1,000 at age 52 for 22 years term insurance.. 327.70
Net single premium per $1,000 at age 52 for 23 years term insurance.. 345.47

11 Assuming there are no dividend values and no loan, calculate the extended term insurance benefit which is available 20 years after the date of issue for a $10,000 endowment-at-age-70 policy issued at age 45, having given the following:

Cash value, end of 20 years $7,127.40
Net single premium per $1,000 at age 65 for 5 years' term insurance.. 162.26
Net single premium per $1,000 at age 65 for pure endowment due in 5 years 709.32

12 May the following policy be declared to be fully paid up at the present time?

Net single premium, at attained age, for future benefits $5,412.70
Value of dividend credits... 418.99
Cash value 4,988.18

14.

Dividends

14.1 INTRODUCTION

In calculating gross premiums for participating life insurance policies, the company makes *conservative* assumptions as to interest, mortality, and expenses. These conservative assumptions result in gross premiums which are generally more than adequate to cover operating conditions as they currently exist or are anticipated. Therefore, unless the actual interest, mortality, or expenses become extremely unfavorable, there are *savings from operations*. These savings can be returned to the policyowners in the form of dividends. Such policy dividends are generally paid annually, on the anniversary date of each policy. They are meant to reflect savings which have been realized in the policy year just past. They are payable at the *end* of each policy year, and represent a return of part of the premium which was paid at the beginning of that same year.

(The dividends paid to policyowners on participating policies must not be confused with dividends paid to shareholders of corporations. Policy dividends are, in effect, refunds of part of the gross premiums. Dividends to stockholders represent a share of the corporation's income derived from invested funds.)

A common method for calculating annual policy dividends is known as the *three-factor contribution method*. Under this method, a contribution is made toward the dividend each year from the areas of interest, mortality, and expenses. The contribution which each factor makes may fluctuate from year to year, and may even be negative under unfavorable circumstances.

14.2 CONTRIBUTION FROM INTEREST

For each policy, the contribution from interest to the dividend for any policy year is usually based upon the year's initial reserve. This reserve at the beginning of the policy year is used because it represents an amount which is invested during the policy year. In general, the contribution from interest to the dividend for a specific policy year is shown by the equation:

$$\begin{pmatrix}\text{Contribution}\\ \text{from Interest}\end{pmatrix} = \begin{pmatrix}\text{Initial}\\ \text{Reserve}\end{pmatrix}\left[\begin{pmatrix}\text{Dividend}\\ \text{Interest}\\ \text{Rate}\end{pmatrix} - \begin{pmatrix}\text{Tabular}\\ \text{Interest}\\ \text{Rate}\end{pmatrix}\right]$$

The "dividend interest rate" is that interest rate which the company chooses to use for dividend purposes. It approximates the rate actually being earned on the company's present investments. The "tabular interest rate" is the rate used in calculating the policy's reserves. To find the contribution from interest, the initial reserve is multiplied by the difference between these two rates.

To Illustrate—Calculate the contribution from interest to the dividend at the end of the 6th year on a $1,000 30-year endowment policy issued at age 30, given the following information:

5th terminal reserve	$113.62
Net annual premium	22.82
Dividend interest rate	$4\frac{1}{2}\%$
Tabular interest rate	3%

Solution—The initial reserve for the 6th year is the 5th-year terminal reserve plus the net annual premium:

$$\begin{aligned}\text{6th Initial Reserve} &= \text{5th Terminal Reserve} + \text{Net Annual Premium}\\ &= \$113.62 + \$22.82\\ &= \$136.44\end{aligned}$$

The 6th year's contribution from interest may be calculated by using the equation given above:

$$\begin{aligned}\begin{pmatrix}\text{Contribution}\\ \text{from Interest}\end{pmatrix} &= \begin{pmatrix}\text{Initial}\\ \text{Reserve}\end{pmatrix}\left[\begin{pmatrix}\text{Dividend}\\ \text{Interest}\\ \text{Rate}\end{pmatrix} - \begin{pmatrix}\text{Tabular}\\ \text{Interest}\\ \text{Rate}\end{pmatrix}\right]\\ &= \$136.44\,[.045 - .03]\\ &= \$136.44\,[.015]\\ &= \$2.05\end{aligned}$$

The contribution from interest may be positive, zero, or negative, depending on whether the dividend interest rate is greater than, equal to, or less than the tabular interest rate. Note that the contribution varies directly with the amount of the initial reserve.

14.3 CONTRIBUTION FROM MORTALITY

For each policy, the contribution from mortality to the dividend is usually based upon the year's net amount at risk. In general, this contribution is shown by the equation:

$$\begin{pmatrix}\text{Contribution}\\ \text{from Mortality}\end{pmatrix} = \begin{pmatrix}\text{Net Amount}\\ \text{at Risk}\end{pmatrix}\left[\begin{pmatrix}\text{Tabular}\\ \text{Rate of}\\ \text{Mortality}\end{pmatrix} - \begin{pmatrix}\text{Dividend}\\ \text{Rate of}\\ \text{Mortality}\end{pmatrix}\right]$$

The "tabular rate of mortality" is the value of q_x as shown in the mortality table which is used in calculating the policy's reserves. The "dividend rate of mortality" for each age is that mortality rate which the company chooses to use for dividend purposes. It approximates the mortality rate currently being experienced on the company's own insurance. The age at which these rates apply is the insured's age at the *beginning* of the particular policy year. To find the contribution from mortality, the net amount at risk is multiplied by the difference between these two rates.

To Illustrate—Calculate the contribution from mortality to the dividend at the end of the 6th year on a $1,000 30-year endowment policy issued at age 30, given the following information:

6th terminal reserve	$138.38
Tabular rate of mortality, age 35	.00251
Dividend rate of mortality, age 35	.00124

Solution—For the 6th policy year, the age used is the age at the *beginning* of the year, which is the same as the end of 5 years ($30 + 5 = 35$). Hence, the rates of mortality are used for age 35. The net amount at risk for the 6th year is the amount of insurance minus the terminal reserve at the *end* of the year (the 6th terminal reserve):

$$\begin{aligned}\text{6th-Year Net Amount at Risk} &= \text{Amount of Insurance} - \text{6th Terminal Reserve}\\ &= \$1{,}000 - \$138.38\\ &= \$861.62\end{aligned}$$

The 6th year's contribution from mortality may be calculated by using the equation given above:

$$\begin{aligned}\begin{pmatrix}\text{Contribution}\\ \text{from Mortality}\end{pmatrix} &= \begin{pmatrix}\text{Net Amount}\\ \text{at Risk}\end{pmatrix}\left[\begin{pmatrix}\text{Tabular}\\ \text{Rate of}\\ \text{Mortality}\end{pmatrix} - \begin{pmatrix}\text{Dividend}\\ \text{Rate of}\\ \text{Mortality}\end{pmatrix}\right]\\ &= \$861.62\,[.00251 - .00124]\\ &= \$861.62\,[.00127]\\ &= \$1.09\end{aligned}$$

If the dividend rate of mortality is lower than the tabular rate of mortality, there will be a gain from mortality. Conversely, if the dividend rate of mortality is greater than the tabular rate of mortality, there will be a loss from mortality, and the dividend contribution from this source will be negative.

It should be observed that, for policies with reserves which increase with the age of the policy, the net amount at risk progressively decreases. The contribution from mortality would therefore be expected to decrease with increasing age. However, an increase in the difference between the tabular and dividend mortality rates may more than offset the rate of decrease of the net amount at risk. On the other hand, since the contribution from interest varies directly with the initial reserve, the contribution from interest usually increases for policies with increasing reserves. When opposing factors are combined, it may be that the decreases offset the increases, or the increases offset the decreases.

14.4 CONTRIBUTION FROM EXPENSES

The excess of the gross premium over the net annual premium, called loading, is the principal source to which the company looks for funds to pay its expenses in connection with the policy. If the policy reserves are being calculated by the net level premium method, this loading will be the same for each year during the premium-paying period. If the policy reserves are being calculated by one of the modified reserve methods described in Chapter 12, the loading in the first year will be greater than in subsequent years. If the policy is past its premium-paying period, the loading each year will be zero, indicating that expenses must be paid for from other sources. These other sources might include a portion of the year's contribution from interest and mortality.

In general, the contribution from expenses to the policy dividend for a specific policy year is shown by the equation:

$$\begin{pmatrix}\text{Contribution}\\ \text{from Expenses}\end{pmatrix} = \begin{pmatrix}\text{Loading}\end{pmatrix} - \begin{pmatrix}\text{Dividend}\\ \text{Expenses}\end{pmatrix}$$

The "dividend expenses" are those expenses which the company chooses to use for dividend purposes. They are determined by careful studies of *actual expenses* with consideration given to allocation of expenses to the appropriate policies by kind, age, duration, and size of policy. Consideration is also given to the general *trend* of expenses. The contribution to the dividend from expenses is the difference between the loading and the "dividend expenses."

To Illustrate—Calculate the contribution from expenses to the dividend at the end of the 6th year on a $1,000 30-year endowment policy issued at age 30, given the following data:

Gross annual premium	$28.40
Net annual premium	22.82
6th year dividend expenses	4.99

Solution—The loading is the gross annual premium minus the net annual premium:

$$\text{Loading} = \text{Gross Annual Premium} - \text{Net Annual Premium}$$
$$= \$28.40 - \$22.82$$
$$= \$5.58$$

The 6th year's contribution from expenses may be calculated by using the equation given above:

$$\begin{pmatrix}\text{Contribution}\\ \text{from Expenses}\end{pmatrix} = \left(\text{Loading}\right) - \begin{pmatrix}\text{Dividend}\\ \text{Expenses}\end{pmatrix}$$
$$= \$5.58 - \$4.99$$
$$= \$.59$$

SUMMARY OF THREE-FACTOR CONTRIBUTION METHOD

Under the three-factor contribution method, the policy dividend is equal to the total of the contributions from the three sources. For example, the dividend for the 6th policy year for the 30-year endowment policy in the above illustrations would be

Contribution from interest	$2.05
Contribution from mortality	1.09
Contribution from expenses	.59
Total dividend	$3.73

This amount would be payable to the policyowner at the *end* of the 6th policy year.

To Illustrate—Given the following data pertaining to a particular $1,000 policy, calculate the dividend for the 8th policy year, for a company using the three-factor contribution method for distributing dividends:

Basis for calculating reserves	1958 C.S.O. Table, 3%
Issue age	65
Gross annual premium	$ 74.10
Net annual premium	$ 64.75
7th terminal reserve	$237.69
8th terminal reserve	$268.61
Dividend interest rate	$2\frac{1}{2}\%$
Dividend rate of mortality	80% of tabular rate
Dividend expenses	70% of loading

Solution—The contribution from *interest* depends upon the initial reserve, dividend interest rate, and tabular interest rate. The initial reserve for the 8th year is the 7th-year terminal reserve plus the net annual premium:

$$\begin{aligned}\text{8th Initial Reserve} &= \text{7th Terminal Reserve} + \text{Net Annual Premium}\\ &= \$237.69 + \$64.75\\ &= \$302.44\end{aligned}$$

The dividend interest rate is given as $2\frac{1}{2}\%$. The tabular interest rate is 3%, as given above.

$$\begin{aligned}\begin{pmatrix}\text{Contribution}\\ \text{from Interest}\end{pmatrix} &= \begin{pmatrix}\text{Initial}\\ \text{Reserve}\end{pmatrix}\left[\begin{pmatrix}\text{Dividend}\\ \text{Interest}\\ \text{Rate}\end{pmatrix} - \begin{pmatrix}\text{Tabular}\\ \text{Interest}\\ \text{Rate}\end{pmatrix}\right]\\ &= \$302.44\,[.025 - .03]\\ &= \$302.44\,[-.005]\\ &= -\$1.51\end{aligned}$$

The answer indicates a negative contribution from interest, arising because the dividend interest rate is lower than the tabular interest rate.

The contribution from *mortality* depends upon the net amount at risk, tabular rate of mortality, and dividend rate of mortality. The net amount at risk for the 8th year is the amount of insurance minus the 8th terminal reserve:

$$\begin{aligned}\text{8th-Year Net Amount at Risk} &= \text{Amount of Insurance} - \text{8th Terminal Reserve}\\ &= \$1{,}000 - \$268.61\\ &= \$731.39\end{aligned}$$

For the 8th policy year, the age at the *beginning* of the year is $65 + 7 = 72$. Hence, the rates of mortality are used for age 72. Using Table III, this tabular rate is found to be .05865. It is given that the dividend rate of mortality is 80% of this tabular rate (80% of .05865 = .04692).

$$\begin{aligned}\begin{pmatrix}\text{Contribution}\\ \text{from Mortality}\end{pmatrix} &= \begin{pmatrix}\text{Net Amount}\\ \text{at Risk}\end{pmatrix}\left[\begin{pmatrix}\text{Tabular}\\ \text{Rate of}\\ \text{Mortality}\end{pmatrix} - \begin{pmatrix}\text{Dividend}\\ \text{Rate of}\\ \text{Mortality}\end{pmatrix}\right]\\ &= \$731.39\,[.05865 - .04692]\\ &= \$731.39\,[.01173]\\ &= \$8.58\end{aligned}$$

The contribution from *expenses* depends upon the loading and the dividend expenses. The loading is the gross annual premium minus the net annual premium:

$$\text{Loading} = \text{Gross Annual Premium} - \text{Net Annual Premium}$$

$$= \$74.10 - \$64.75$$

$$= \$9.35$$

It is given that the dividend expenses are 70% of the loading (70% of $9.35 = $6.55).

$$\begin{pmatrix}\text{Contribution} \\ \text{from Expenses}\end{pmatrix} = \left(\text{Loading}\right) - \begin{pmatrix}\text{Dividend} \\ \text{Expenses}\end{pmatrix}$$

$$= \$9.35 - \$6.55$$

$$= \$2.80$$

In this case, the contribution from expenses could also have been calculated as simply 30% of the loading (100% − 70% = 30%).

The policy dividend is equal to the total of the contributions from the three sources, in this instance taking account of the fact that one number is *negative:*

Contribution from interest	$−1.51 (negative)
Contribution from mortality	8.58
Contribution from expenses	2.80
Total dividend	$ 9.87

(The total $9.87 is found by adding $8.58 and $2.80, and subtracting the $1.51 which is negative.)

It should be noted that it would be uncommon for the contributions from interest and mortality to be negative, but it may not be unusual to find a negative contribution from expenses.

14.5 EXPERIENCE-PREMIUM METHOD

It often happens that the use of the three-factor contribution method results in dividends which do not increase smoothly from year to year for a particular policy. One reason for this is that some of the expenses, such as the agent's commission, may change considerably from one year to the next for a particular policy. In general, policyowners expect their dividends to increase each year, and to do so fairly smoothly. The *experience-premium method* is intended to achieve this.

The experience-premium method involves a two-step calculation. The first step of this method is to calculate level "experience premiums" for all policies. These experience premiums are calculated by using dividend rates of mortality and dividend expenses, but using the tabular interest rate. The basis for that calculation is the principle that, at the date the policy is issued, the present value of these level experience premiums must be equal to the present value of the benefits plus the present value of the dividend expenses to be incurred.

Experience premiums are lower than the actual gross premiums received. The *difference* represents the first part of the policy dividend which can be paid each year. For example, if a policy's gross premium were \$112.82 and the experience premium \$94.99, then

$$\$112.82 - \$94.99 = \$17.83$$

could be paid each year as part of the dividend.

The second step in calculating the dividend consists of adding the "contribution from interest." This is calculated exactly as described in Section 14.2. It is then added to the difference between the gross premium and the experience premium to find the policy dividend for the year.

The dividend rates of mortality, the dividend interest rate, and the dividend expenses used in the experience-premium method are generally analogous to their respective counterparts used in the three-factor contribution method.

To Illustrate—Using the experience-premium method, calculate all of the dividends for a \$1,000 10-year endowment policy issued at age 20, given the following data:

Reserve Basis	1958 C.S.O. 3%
Gross annual premium	\$ 94.85
Experience premium (calculated using 3%)	91.17
Dividend interest rate	4%
Initial reserve	
1st year	\$ 85.60
2nd year	172.13
3rd year	261.39
4th year	353.46
5th year	448.46
6th year	546.49
7th year	647.63
8th year	752.01
9th year	859.72
10th year	970.88

Solution—The difference between the gross annual premium and the experience premium represents the first part of the dividend which can be paid each year:

$$\text{Gross Annual Premium} - \text{Experience Premium} = \$94.85 - \$91.17$$
$$= \$3.68$$

The second part of the dividend is the contribution from interest. The basic equation, as given in Section 14.2, is

$$\begin{pmatrix}\text{Contribution}\\\text{from Interest}\end{pmatrix} = \begin{pmatrix}\text{Initial}\\\text{Reserve}\end{pmatrix}\left[\begin{pmatrix}\text{Dividend}\\\text{Interest}\\\text{Rate}\end{pmatrix} - \begin{pmatrix}\text{Tabular}\\\text{Interest}\\\text{Rate}\end{pmatrix}\right]$$

In this illustration, the dividend interest rate is given as 4%. The tabular interest rate is given as 3%. Hence, the contribution from interest is

$$\begin{pmatrix}\text{Contribution}\\\text{from Interest}\end{pmatrix} = \begin{pmatrix}\text{Initial}\\\text{Reserve}\end{pmatrix}[.04 - .03]$$

$$= \begin{pmatrix}\text{Initial}\\\text{Reserve}\end{pmatrix}[.01]$$

Each year's total dividend is therefore calculated as \$3.68 (the difference between the gross premium and the experience premium), *plus* the initial reserve times .01 (the contribution from interest):

$$\text{First Dividend} = \$3.68 + \begin{pmatrix}\text{First}\\\text{Initial}\\\text{Reserve}\end{pmatrix}(.01)$$

$$= \$3.68 + (\$85.60)(.01)$$

$$= \$3.68 + \$.86$$

$$= \$4.54$$

$$\text{Second Dividend} = \$3.68 + \begin{pmatrix}\text{Second}\\\text{Initial}\\\text{Reserve}\end{pmatrix}(.01)$$

$$= \$3.68 + (\$172.13)(.01)$$

$$= \$3.68 + \$1.72$$

$$= \$5.40$$

The remaining dividends, calculated in the same manner, are as follows:

Third Dividend = \$ 6.29
Fourth Dividend = 7.21
Fifth Dividend = 8.16
Sixth Dividend = 9.14
Seventh Dividend = 10.16
Eighth Dividend = 11.20
Ninth Dividend = 12.28
Tenth Dividend = 13.39

It should be observed that these dividends increase each year, and also that they exhibit a fairly smooth sequence.

In all types of dividend calculations it is important that strict *equity* (fairness) be maintained. Careful consideration must be given to the sources of gain, so that policies which make the greatest contribution to the gain receive proportionately greater dividends. To achieve this end, extensive studies are regularly made in the areas of actual mortality and expenses (and even interest). Most insurance companies make individual studies, as well as studies based on the "pooled," or combined, actual experience of several companies.

14.6 DIVIDEND OPTIONS

A dividend apportioned to a particular policy may generally be used by the policyowner in any one of the following ways, called *dividend options:*

1. Withdrawn in cash;
2. Applied toward any premium payment then due;
3. Left as a deposit with the company to accumulate at interest (but withdrawable at any time); or
4. Used to purchase paid-up insurance.

The first three options require no further explanation. The fourth option above is referred to as *paid-up additions.* Paid-up additions represent additional insurance payable in the same manner as the basic policy itself. The amount of such additional insurance is calculated by using the *dividend* as if it were a *net single premium* for the paid-up benefits. This is analogous to the calculation of reduced paid-up insurance, described in Section 13.3. There it was stated that the amount of paid-up insurance purchased by the cash value was found by dividing the cash value by the net single premium for $1 of insurance. Similarly, the amount of paid-up additions is found by dividing the dividend by the net single premium for $1 of insurance. The answer is usually rounded to the nearest dollar, not necessarily up to the next higher dollar as is customary for reduced paid-up insurance. (However, some companies do round to the next higher dollar as good public relations.)

To Illustrate—The dividend at the end of the 10th year on an ordinary life policy, issued at age 30, is $45. Calculate the amount of paid-up additions which this dividend will purchase. It is given that the net single premium at age 40 for $1,000 of whole life insurance is $406.58.

Solution—At the end of the 10th year, the attained age is $30 + 10 = 40$. Hence, the net single premium needed will be for $1 of whole life insurance at age 40. This can easily be obtained; it will be $\frac{1}{1000}$ of the net single premium given above (the value above being for $1,000 of such insurance). By moving the decimal point 3 places to the left, the net single premium for $1 of such insurance is obtained:

$$\frac{1}{1000} \text{ of } \$406.58 = \$.40658$$

As stated above, the amount of paid-up additions is found by dividing the dividend by the net single premium for $1 of insurance:

Basic equation

$$\begin{pmatrix}\text{Amount of Paid-Up}\\ \text{Additions}\end{pmatrix} = \frac{\text{Dividend}}{\text{Net Single Premium}}$$

Substituting the given amount for the dividend and the calculated amount for the net single premium

$$= \frac{\$45.00}{.40658}$$

$$= \$110.68$$

Rounding to nearest dollar

$$= \$111$$

To Illustrate Again—The dividend at the end of the 5th year on a 20-year endowment policy issued at age 40 is $92.70. Calculate the amount of paid-up additions which this dividend will purchase if the net single premium at age 45 for $1 of 15-year endowment insurance at age 45 is $.65985.

Solution—At the end of the 5th year, the attained age is $40 + 5 = 45$. There are $20 - 5 = 15$ years remaining of the original 20-year endowment period. Hence, the net single premium needed will be for $1 of 15-year endowment insurance at age 45. The amount of paid-up additions is found by dividing the dividend by the net single premium for $1 of insurance:

$$\begin{pmatrix}\text{Amount of Paid-Up}\\ \text{Additions}\end{pmatrix} = \frac{\text{Dividend}}{\text{Net Single Premium}}$$

$$= \frac{\$92.70}{.65985}$$

$$= \$140.49$$

$$= \$140$$

The paid-up additions purchased by dividends are, in many ways, like a separate paid-up policy. They have reserves and cash values which are equal to the present value of the future benefits. The paid-up additions may also provide gains to the company in the form of savings in mortality and interest, and those gains are often returned to the policyowner in the form of a dividend in addition to the regular dividend on the basic policy.

If the policyowner should later elect to surrender the basic policy and receive its cash value, then the paid-up additions must be similarly terminated in exchange for their cash value. On the other hand, the paid-up additions may be terminated by the policyowner, without terminating the basic policy.

14.7 "FIFTH DIVIDEND OPTION"

Some policies contain a provision stipulating that the dividend apportioned each year may be used to purchase one-year term insurance. This is often referred to as the "fifth dividend option." In a sense, this is not a true option comparable to the four basic options listed in Section 14.6, because generally only a *portion* of each dividend is so applied. The remainder of the dividend is then used for one of the basic options.

The usual purpose of the "fifth dividend option" is to provide one-year term insurance with a death benefit equal to the next cash value. This would allow the policyowner to borrow the full next cash value without impairing the total amount of insurance which would be paid upon death.

The net single premium for such one-year term insurance acquired by dividend option is

$$\begin{pmatrix} \text{Next} \\ \text{Cash Value} \end{pmatrix} \begin{pmatrix} \text{One-Year Term} \\ \text{Net Premium} \\ \text{Per \$1} \end{pmatrix}$$

where the one-year term net premium is calculated at the attained age on this particular policy anniversary. In practice, *gross* single premiums per $1,000 are computed for each attained age. The interest and mortality rates are chosen to reflect *experienced* conditions, and a loading is added for expenses. The company is then free to change these gross rates at any time. This is in contrast to the practice used to calculate paid-up additions and reduced paid-up insurance (under the nonforfeiture options). In the latter instances, net single premiums, based upon the same interest and mortality rates assumed in the calculation of the basic policy's reserves, are always used.

To Illustrate—The dividend at the end of the 10th policy year on a policy issued at age 35 is $24.07. The cash value of the policy at the end of 11 years is $865. Calculate the amount of the current dividend which will be used to buy 1-year term insurance, if the policyowner is using the "5th dividend option" and the gross premium rate at age 45 for this option currently is $5.03 per $1,000.

Solution—The attained age on this policy is 35 + 10 = 45. The amount of 1-year term insurance to be purchased is equal to the next cash value, $865. Since $1,000 of 1-year term insurance costs $5.03 at this age, $865 of 1-year term insurance will cost

$$\$5.03\left(\frac{865}{1{,}000}\right) = \$4.35$$

The remainder of the $24.07 dividend is

$$\$24.07 - \$4.35 = \$19.72$$

This remainder may be used for any one of the basic dividend options which the policyowner elects.

It sometimes happens that the amount of the year's dividend is not enough to buy one-year term insurance equal to the full cash value. In that case, the extra amount needed to purchase such insurance may be withdrawn from any dividend credits the policy may have from previous dividend distributions. If the total available from both these sources is insufficient, the amount of one-year term insurance will be that amount (smaller than the cash value) which can be purchased.

EXERCISES

1 Given the following data for a $1,000 life insurance policy, calculate the dividend for the 10th policy year according to the three-factor contribution method:

Gross annual premium	$ 42.68
Net annual premium	33.90
9th-year terminal reserve	228.98
10th-year terminal reserve	254.18
Tabular rate of interest	3%
Dividend rate of interest	$3\frac{3}{4}$%
Tabular mortality rate	.02224
Dividend mortality rate	.01793
Dividend expenses incurred	$ 5.12

2 Using the 1958 C.S.O. Table (3%) and the three-factor contribution method, calculate the dividend to be paid at the *end* of the year on a $1,000 paid-up life policy if the insured is age 60 at the *beginning* of that year, and the *dividend* interest and mortality rates and expenses are as given in Exercise 1. Whole life net single premiums per $1,000 are

Age 60	$632.00
Age 61	643.71

3 Using the 1958 C.S.O. Table (3%) and the three-factor contribution method, calculate the dividend to be paid at the end of the year on a

$1,000 1-year term insurance policy issued at age 62 for a premium of $30, ignoring the small contribution from interest. Actual expenses and mortality are as given in Exercise 1.

4 Calculate the amount of paid-up whole life additions which a dividend of $15.12 will purchase at attained age 22. It is given that the net single premium at age 22 for $1,000 of whole life insurance is $259.33.

5 Rework Exercise 4, assuming the dividend is used to purchase paid-up endowment-at-age-65 additions. It is given that the net single premium at age 22 for $1,000 of endowment-at-age-65 insurance is $320.80.

6 Calculate the amount of paid-up additions purchased by the dividend in Exercise 1, assuming the policy is an ordinary life policy issued at age 52. It is given that the net single premium at age 62 for $1,000 of whole life insurance is $655.36.

7 The net single premium for a $1,000, 8-year endowment policy, issued at age 62, is $808.83. The dividend for the 12th policy year on a $5,000, 20-year endowment policy, issued at age 50, is $42.30. Calculate the amount of paid-up endowment additions which the dividend will purchase.

8 How much of the dividend which is due at the end of the 10th policy year on a $5,000 insurance policy issued at age 35 will be used to buy 1-year term insurance under the "5th dividend option," given the following:

11th-year cash value per $1,000	$351.95
Premium for 1-year term insurance at age 45, per $1,000	$ 5.08

9 If the actual dividend paid on the policy in Exercise 8 were only $8, and the *entire* dividend were used to buy 1-year term insurance under the "fifth dividend option," how much such insurance would it purchase?

10 Using the experience-premium method, calculate the 10th-year dividend on a $1,000 ordinary life policy issued at age 30, given the following data:

Basis for calculating reserves	1958 C.S.O. 3%
Experience premium (using 3%)	$ 14.07
Gross premium	15.10
Dividend rate of interest	4%
10th-year initial reserve	$131.09

15. Additional Topics

15.1 PREMIUMS AND RESERVES FOR SPECIAL BENEFITS

Many of the principles which have been presented for calculating life insurance premiums and reserves are applicable to other insurance benefits which are commonly sold as riders attached to a life insurance policy, and to certain other types of insurance with which life companies are often involved.

ACCIDENTAL DEATH BENEFIT. A popular type of insurance is one which covers the risk of dying by *accident*. It may be sold either as a policy by itself or as a rider to a regular life insurance policy. (State supervisory authorities regard such a policy by itself as being "health insurance.")

A large body of data regarding the rates of occurrence of death by accident has been compiled both from insurance company statistics and general population statistics. At the present time, the 1959 Accidental Death Benefits Table is widely used to calculate premiums for this benefit. This table is also specified in the Standard Valuation Law for computation of reserves for this benefit on policies issued after January 1, 1966.

Chart 15–1 shows rates of mortality at certain ages. The left-hand column shows the probability of dying by *accident*, according to the 1959 Accidental Death Benefits Table. For comparison, the right-hand column shows overall death rates (from all causes) at these ages, according to the 1958 C.S.O. Table. The accidental death rates do not vary greatly from age to age under age 60, with the exception of the

CHART 15–1
Mortality Rates

Age	*1959 Accidental Death Benefits Table*	*From All Causes 1958 C.S.O. Table*
10	.000303	.001210
20	.000748	.001790
30	.000394	.002130
40	.000395	.003530
50	.000465	.008320
60	.000624	.020340
70	.001065	.049790
80	.003277	.109980
90	.008022	.228140

late teens and early twenties when the rates rise to a point approaching half of all deaths.

Since accidental death rates rise rapidly after age 60 (even though they decrease as a percentage of total deaths), most insurance companies terminate the accidental death benefit at age 60, 65, or 70. This has a marked effect in keeping the premium for this insurance at a low level.

In the calculation of accidental death benefit premiums and reserves, an accidental death benefits table must be *combined* with a regular mortality table. In this way, the number dying at each age can be looked upon as the number dying from accident plus those dying from all other causes.

In Chapter 10, it was explained that the basis for the calculation of net annual premiums is the principle that, at the date the policy is issued, the present value of the net premiums must be equal to the present value of the benefits. In calculating premiums for the accidental death benefit, the same principle is used, except that the present value of the *benefits* is calculated by referring *only* to the deaths from accident. The present value of the net *premiums*, however, is calculated from the regular mortality table, because the net annual premiums are payable each year only if the insured lives, and will cease because of death from any cause.

Premiums for this benefit never extend beyond the age at which the benefit itself is terminated, even though the benefit may be attached to a life insurance policy having premiums payable longer. On the other hand, if the premiums on the basic life insurance policy terminate *earlier* (such as on a 20-payment life policy), the accidental death benefit premiums terminate at the same time and *prior* to the time such insurance terminates.

Reserves are calculated by either the retrospective or prospective method, in a manner analogous to those for regular life insurance. The only difference is that mentioned above in connection with calculation of the premium: the values of benefits are calculated by referring *only* to the deaths from accident.

DISABILITY BENEFITS. Another popular type of supplemental benefit is the *disability benefit*. The usual disability benefit provides that if the insured becomes disabled (as defined by his policy), the company will waive the payment of future premiums on the life insurance policy. To the company, waiving premiums is the same as granting a series of payments (a life annuity) to the insured when he becomes disabled.

Another (less common) type of disability benefit provides that if the insured becomes disabled (as defined by his policy), the company will pay him a monthly income (a life annuity).

Two kinds of "disability tables" are necessary in calculating premiums and reserves for these benefits. The first such table shows rates of disability, i.e., the probability of becoming disabled, at each age. It has been difficult to compile such tables for widespread use by insurance companies, partly because there are great variations among companies in their definitions of "disability." Policies generally stipulate that a person must remain disabled for a certain period of time, called the *waiting period*, before he is considered eligible to receive benefits. The rates of disability shown in the tables represent the probability of *becoming disabled and remaining so throughout the waiting period*. Another source of difficulty has been the large changes which take place in actual disability experience as economic conditions change.

The Standard Valuation Law prescribes that minimum reserves for disability benefits shall use the "1952 Disability Study—Period 2" for policies issued after January 1, 1966. For policies issued prior to January 1, 1961, the "1926 Class(3) Disability Table" is prescribed. Between the two dates either table may be used. Chart 15–2 shows rates of disability for certain ages, according to these two widely used tables. As explained above, these rates are directly affected by the

CHART 15–2
Disability Rates

Age	*1952 Disab. Study-Period 2 6 Months Waiting Period*	*1926 Class(3) Disab. Table 3 Months Waiting Period*
10	.00052	.00470
20	.00076	.00435
30	.00112	.00405
40	.00164	.00473
50	.00347	.00760
59	.01144	.01413

waiting period used therein. In actual use, these tables must be *combined* with a regular mortality table, as was the case for accidental death benefits.

The second kind of "disability table" necessary in calculating premiums and reserves involves the "life annuities" granted when a person becomes disabled. These "annuities" are unique in that in order to receive each periodic payment, the insured must not only be *alive,* but also must be *still disabled.* The annuity stops upon either death or recovery. Therefore, special tables are constructed which show the number of persons still *alive and disabled* at each age. Such tables are similar to the select and ultimate tables discussed in Section 7.7, because they involve the age at which *disability began,* as well as the actual attained age.

In life insurance, the net single premium for $1,000 of insurance covering a one-year period can be calculated from the expression (given in Section 9.1)

$$\$1{,}000\left(\frac{d_x v}{l_x}\right)$$

In calculating disability premiums, the same approach is used, except that the values in the numerator are calculated by referring *only* to those persons in the table who are assumed to become *disabled* (instead of those who die). In the above expression, $1,000 represents the benefit to be granted upon death. In the case of disability, the benefit is a *life annuity,* as mentioned before. Therefore, the present value of this life annuity at age x must be multiplied by the $\frac{d_x v}{l_x}$ factor for each age.

Generally in life insurance, the death benefit is the *same* regardless of the age at which death occurs. Hence, the present value of the benefits may be expressed with this common multiplier factored out, such as

$$\$1{,}000\left(\frac{d_x v + d_{x+1}v^2 + d_{x+2}v^3 + \cdots \text{ etc.}}{l_x}\right)$$

From this, it is expedient to create commutation functions for calculating the value inside the parentheses. In disability insurance, since the benefit is *different* for each age at which disability may occur, no such common multiplier can be factored out. This gives rise to commutation functions which are more complicated than those used in life insurance. That is, the details of the benefit itself (the period of time for which the annuity benefit will run) become an integral part of the definition of the various commutation functions.

The calculation of reserves on disability benefits follows the same logic as for life insurance. At the end of any policy year, the terminal reserve equals the present value of future benefits minus the present value of future net premiums.

GUARANTEED INSURABILITY BENEFITS. This type of insurance covers the risk that the insured may be unable to qualify for life insurance in the future. The inability might arise because of his health becoming impaired. The common type of *guaranteed insurability benefit* is attached as a rider to a regular life insurance policy. It guarantees the right to purchase *specified amounts of additional insurance* upon *specified dates* in the future. No examination of the insured's health is made when such new insurance is purchased, and the premiums are guaranteed to be the same as those charged to persons whose good health is established.

A small premium is paid for this rider. The calculation of the premium and reserves for this rider can become quite complicated. Many factors are involved, such as the probability that the insured will actually have impaired health when each of the various specified dates arrive, the probability that the insured will actually choose to buy the new policy on each of the dates, and the amount of expense which the company will save on the new policies by virtue of not examining the insured's health.

In practice, a wide variety of sophisticated formulas are used, but usually the following basic concepts are involved. The "extra mortality" which can be expected to be experienced in a new policy (to be purchased at a future date) is evaluated. This involves calculating the tabular cost of insurance for each policy year on two different bases. In Section 11.8, the tabular cost of insurance was defined by the equation:

$$\begin{pmatrix}\text{Tabular Cost}\\ \text{of Insurance}\end{pmatrix} = \begin{pmatrix}\text{Net Amount}\\ \text{at Risk}\end{pmatrix} q_x$$

The two different bases involve the use of select and ultimate mortality rates, as described in Section 7.7. For example, assume that a man purchases a guaranteed insurability benefit at age 20 giving him the right to purchase a new policy at age 30 (10 years later). At age 20, his good health has just been established. A new policy taken out at age 30 in accordance with this guarantee will exhibit a rate of mortality the first year of

$$q_{[20]+10}$$

Without the guaranteed insurability benefit, the fact of *current* good health would have to be established when the new policy was purchased. Thus, normally policies purchased at age 30 will exhibit a rate of mortality the first year of

$$q_{[30]}$$

The *difference* between the tabular cost of mortality on these two bases is calculated for each policy year:

$$\text{First year:} \quad \begin{pmatrix}\text{Net Amount}\\ \text{at Risk}\end{pmatrix}(q_{[20]+10} - q_{[30]})$$

$$\text{Second year:} \quad \begin{pmatrix}\text{Net Amount}\\ \text{at Risk}\end{pmatrix}(q_{[20]+11} - q_{[30]+1})$$

$$\text{Third year:} \quad \begin{pmatrix}\text{Net Amount}\\ \text{at Risk}\end{pmatrix}(q_{[20]+12} - q_{[30]+2})$$

The *present value,* with benefit of survivorship, of these *differences* represents the "extra mortality" which can be expected to be experienced on a new policy purchased at age 30. This represents a *benefit* for which the insured is paying a premium. This benefit will be available at age 30, and hence can be treated like a pure endowment available at age 30. Net annual premiums are calculated which will provide for these pure endowments at the various specified dates. To these net annual premiums, *loading* is added to cover whatever expenses are expected in connection with this guaranteed insurability benefit.

GROUP INSURANCE. This life insurance is granted to members of a group with no evidence being required as to the good health of any of the members so insured. No such evidence is required because it is assumed at the outset that a "normal proportion" of persons with impaired health will be included.

In order to be certain that the overall death rates of the group will be that which is normal for groups generally, certain rules are established. These rules typically require that the group has been formed for a purpose other than to obtain insurance, that a large percentage of the persons in the group shall be included in the insurance, and that no individual person in the group shall say how much insurance he personally will have. In fact, these rules are generally required by law before any group insurance can be effected.

Most insured groups are made up of employees of a common employer. Normally, the amount of insurance which each employee in the group will have is geared to his salary or job classification. For example, all employees earning between $5,000 and $7,500 per year may receive $10,000 of group insurance.

Members who leave the group are guaranteed the right to convert their group coverage to regular individual life insurance policies (other than term policies) without any medical examination. This is an extremely valuable privilege. It represents an opportunity for those in poor health to "get a bargain." Group premium rates must include a large factor for this privilege.

The premiums for group insurance may be paid entirely by the employees, entirely by the employer, or partly by each. The insurance company bases its premiums on the age of each person in the group, but normally any contribution toward the premium which each person in the group actually makes himself is set up to be independent of his age.

Group insurance is usually written on the one-year renewable term plan and each year's premium pays for just that year's coverage. However, level-premium permanent group insurance does exist, and provides nonforfeiture values on termination. The one-year term premium rates are usually guaranteed for only one year. New premium rates may be calculated each year, depending on the experience of the group. Theoretically, each group should be considered separately when calculating premiums each year for that group, but many groups are too small to consider their mortality experience for any one year as meaningful. The company may, therefore, pool the experience of several groups.

There may be little latitude for first-year premiums because some states prescribe "minimum initial premium rates" for group insurance. This is done to protect the public from inadequate rates or discrimination, since one-year renewable term coverage does not afford the states the usual control they have via reserve requirements. Generally, a minimum schedule of rates (by age) for the first year is set by New York, and because a New York-licensed company must comply with the New York requirements in all states, the result is that the New York schedule is generally applicable. Companies are free to reduce the rates for years subsequent to the first year.

Premiums are usually paid monthly. At each yearly anniversary, an age distribution of insurance-in-force in the group is prepared, and the appropriate premium rate multiplied by the amount in force at each age. The total premium thus produced is divided by the total insurance in force, and the resulting *average* premium rate is applied to the new total of insurance-in-force at each monthly premium-paying date throughout the year.

Participating companies pay policy dividends on group insurance, just as they do on individual insurance. Generally, state laws provide that if these dividends exceed the employer's contribution, the excess must be applied to the benefit of the insured individuals.

Nonparticipating companies accomplish the same thing as dividends by means of premium refunds, called "experience refunds" or "retroactive rate reductions."

The process of calculating either dividends or premium refunds is the same and generally involves the annual determination of the "surplus since issue" that the particular group has built up. The "surplus since issue" is equal to the premiums collected to date plus interest, minus actual death claims, expenses, contribution to reserve for unforeseen contingencies, and all previous years' refunds and dividends. The amount by which this exceeds the surplus necessary to retain is equal to the current year's dividend.

It should be noted that since one-year renewable term insurance accumulates little in the way of funds available for investment, the interest element in group dividends is very small. It can also be said that expenses are comparatively small on group insurance, since there are no medical examinations, and agents' commissions are low. This leaves death claims as the principal factor affecting the size of both premiums and dividends.

The reserve liability which companies must establish each December 31 for group insurance is equal to the portion of the last premium paid which is not yet "used up." (This is known as an "unearned premium reserve.") In other words, if an annual premium was paid on October 1, then $\frac{3}{12}$ of it has been "used up" by December 31, and the other $\frac{9}{12}$ of the premium equals the reserve liability. Just as with individual insurance, it is the *net* premium which is considered in calculating reserves. The net premiums must be calculated from mortality tables which are prescribed by (or approved by) the state authorities. In the case of level-premium permanent group insurance, calculation of reserves is identical with individual insurance as described in Chapters 11 and 12.

It should be noted that some companies use the more conservative approach of considering *gross* premiums instead of net premiums when calculating reserves on the one-year renewable term cases.

An additional reserve is almost always calculated for the *individual* policies which are issued from exercise of the conversion privilege in group insurance (over and above the regular required reserve on the individual policy). This is because death rates on such policies are generally very high, and the "present value of future benefits" in the reserve calculation is quite inadequate when using the 1958 C.S.O. Table. Typically, a simple approximation may be used. For example, this additional reserve may be figured to be $70 per $1,000 of insurance the first year, decreasing by $7 per year for 10 years.

HEALTH INSURANCE. The mathematical theory for health insurance is very similar to that for life insurance. Very often, the two types of insurance are sold by the same company.

Health insurance includes reimbursement to cover the two principal areas of monetary loss when health is impaired:

1. Loss of income (through inability to work), and
2. Expense of medical treatment.

In the first area, much of the principles and mathematics of *income replacement* are the same as described above for "Disability Benefits." A few of the areas of differences which must be reckoned with in actual practice, however, are

1. The waiting periods (after disablement, before benefits are paid) are generally very short, being from 7 days to 30 days in most cases;
2. The payments are generally made for short periods of time, such as two years;
3. Disability caused by impairments which existed prior to the issuance of the insurance is not covered in the insurance;
4. Policies may contain a "nonduplication" provision, which prevents the insured from collecting full benefits if he has similar insurance in other companies. This is to keep *total* benefits reasonable in relation to the insured's actual loss.

The second area of health insurance includes the following four distinct breakdowns:

1. *Hospital Insurance,* which pays a daily benefit towards the daily room charges, and also pays all other hospital charges (up to a limit);
2. *Surgical Insurance,* which pays a benefit towards the doctor's fee for performing operations (different amounts of benefit are paid for different types of operations);
3. *Medical Expense Insurance,* which pays benefits towards doctors' bills other than for performing operations (the benefit is usually quite small and many restrictions are put on it); and
4. *Major Medical Insurance,* which recognizes that the first three breakdowns fail to compensate adequately for very large medical bills. It therefore pays a benefit equal to 75% or 80% of all the medical bills (after first deducting a sum such as $200 or $1,000). There is considerable variation in the exact terms of this coverage, but there is always a limit on the payment, such as $2,000 or $15,000.

Health insurance payments are subject to a situation quite unlike life insurance in that the loss insured against may occur again and again for any one person. This possibility must be dealt with in premium calculation.

In general, health insurance policies are either: renewable each year only at the company's option (subject to certain legal restrictions), or guaranteed to be renewable but with the company retaining the right to change the premiums (for broad classes as a whole), or else "noncancellable and guaranteed renewable" just like life insurance policies.

The calculation of premiums for health insurance is not fundamentally different from life insurance. However, the primary figures underlying the calculation involve *morbidity* assumptions, rather than *mortality*, i.e., sickness rather than death. Morbidity is much more difficult to measure than mortality, because the experience changes as economic conditions change and as medical practices change. There is also a marked scarcity of morbidity data available.

Tables showing the number living (to pay premiums) are calculated, but the lives leaving the table include terminations of all kinds (lapse, death, disability, etc.), instead of just deaths, as in a mortality table. These tables are calculated on a select basis similar to that described in Section 7.7.

Rates of claim are shown in the tables, and represent the probability of submitting a health claim between age x and age $(x + 1)$. In addition, the average *amount* of each claim must be known. Where the benefit is a single-sum payment, this is the average such single sum. Where the benefit is a series of payments (like daily hospital room benefit), it is the average *present value* thereof at the date payments begin. From these rates and average claims, certain commutation functions are calculated.

In actual practice, because of the complexity of the formulas, premiums are figured for only a few issue-ages and the others closely estimated. Unlike life insurance, different premiums are quoted for various categories other than age and sex. These include breakdowns by occupation, geographical location, and sometimes even by income level.

Since health insurance is most commonly sold with level premiums, which increase with the issue-age, *reserves* naturally emerge, as in life insurance. These reserves are calculated by the same methods and theories as in life insurance. The legal requirements regarding the calculation of health insurance reserves are less specific than for life insurance, but they do include specific disability, hospital, and surgical tables.

Theoretically, nonforfeiture benefits could be granted from these reserves when a health policy is surrendered. However, reduced paid-up insurance would provide benefits too small to be worthwhile, and extended term insurance would only be for brief periods. The effect of lapses is taken into account in calculating premiums. The resulting premiums are lower than they would be if a nonforfeiture value were allowed.

15.2 SUBSTANDARD LIVES

A very large percentage of the applicants for life insurance policies come under the category of *standard risks*. However, some applicants, because of poor health, occupation, habits, or environment, can be expected to exhibit higher than normal rates of mortality. This class of risks is referred to as *substandard.*

Fortunately, extensive studies of mortality rates applicable to substandard lives are available so that premiums for this class of risks can be calculated which are both fair and adequate. Most impairments lead to rates of mortality which can be expressed as a percentage of the standard rates. For example, a recent study showed that persons who are approximately 50 pounds overweight will exhibit a rate of mortality approximately 150% of normal rates. There is some variation in this percentage at different ages and durations since the date of issue, but the *total* deaths for this group was approximately 150% of the number expected for a standard group.

This being true, it is possible to construct a mortality table in which each value of q_x is 150% of the corresponding q_x in a standard table. This table can be used to calculate the higher premiums applicable to those persons who are 50 pounds overweight. Such a table would also produce reserves, nonforfeiture values, and dividends which would be different from the standard values. In actual practice, however, it is customary for policies on substandard lives to use the *standard* terminal reserves, nonforfeiture values, and dividends. Standard values are utilized because the assumption is made that the *extra premium* is exactly "used up" each year in payment of "extra death claims," leaving nothing to increase or decrease the standard terminal reserves. A major exception is that extended term insurance is generally not made available.

After calculation of such mortality tables (one table for each of the several percentages to be used), net annual premiums for substandard risks are calculated. The *excess* of these net premiums over those calculated from a *standard* mortality table forms the basis for the annual extra premiums to be charged. Loading is added to cover the extra taxes, commissions, and expenses.

Chart 15–3 shows some typical net and gross premiums for standard and substandard lives:

CHART 15–3

Premiums for Standard and Substandard Lives
$1,000 Endowment at Age 65, Age 30
(1958 C.S.O. 2½%)

Mortality Classification	*Net Annual Premium*	*Gross Annual Premium*
Standard	$20.69	$26.35
200% of Standard	23.59	30.57
300% of Standard	26.45	34.33
400% of Standard	29.26	38.05
500% of Standard	32.03	41.73

Sometimes the policy will stipulate that the higher premium is to be charged for only a limited number of years, and the regular standard premium will be charged thereafter. This is often true in the case of certain impairments which cause mortality rates to be only temporarily higher than normal, such as certain types of surgery. The higher premium may be later reduced by the insurance company if the insured submits evidence that his health or occupation is more favorable than it was at the time the policy was issued. However, the insurance company cannot *increase* the premium for any reason after the policy is issued.

It was mentioned above that, by practice, the *standard* terminal reserves are customarily used for substandard policies. In the calculation of the *mean reserves* for December 31 statement purposes, however, some account must be taken of the extra premium which was received. As mentioned above, the customary assumption is made that this extra premium is "used up" each year in payment of "extra death claims." In other words, it is similar to a one-year term insurance premium each year. Therefore, for December 31 statement purposes, the standard mean reserve is *increased* by the "unearned" half of the *extra* net annual premium.

In practice, companies often compute this extra mean reserve as one half of the extra *gross* annual premium because the exact gross extra premiums are readily available, whereas the net extra premiums are often estimated or calculated for a few sample ages. Furthermore, this practice injects an element of conservatism into the company's financial statement by slightly overstating the legally required liability.

Other methods are occasionally used to calculate premiums for substandard lives, besides the use of percentages of q_x as described above:

1. Very large companies with their own experience data on the effect of various impairments may subdivide substandard lives into special premium classifications wherein the premiums are calculated from their own observed mortality rates.
2. A policy may be issued to a substandard life with an "age rate-up." This means that the policy is issued at the regular premium (based on a standard table) with an advance in age. Although this method causes an increase in the premium and is easy to calculate as well as to administer, it is open to the objection that the extra mortality it provides does not bear a logical relationship to standard mortality year by year. Chart 15–4 demonstrates this fact for the case of a five-year "age rate-up":

CHART 15–4
Rates of Mortality with Age Rate-up
(1958 C.S.O. Table)

True Age	Assumed Age	Rate of Mortality per 1,000: At True Age	Rate of Mortality per 1,000: At Assumed Age	Extra Deaths per 1,000	Relative Increase (%)
20	25	1.79	1.93	.14	7.8
25	30	1.93	2.13	.20	10.4
30	35	2.13	2.51	.38	17.8
35	40	2.51	3.53	1.02	40.6
40	45	3.53	5.35	1.82	51.6
45	50	5.35	8.32	2.97	55.5

It should be observed that the last column would be constant if the usual method described earlier were employed.

3. A policy may be issued to a substandard life with standard premiums and reserves, but with *varying death benefits* to account for the higher anticipated mortality.

15.3 ASSET SHARES

The *asset share* technique is a useful tool in life insurance mathematics. By means of asset share calculations, the company can test the general adequacy and appropriateness of gross premiums, cash values, and dividends year by year during the future for any policy. An asset share may be defined as the *actual* amount which it is forecast the company will have accumulated at any given time from a policy (including profit).

The calculation is begun by assuming that a large number of such policies (all alike) are issued all at once. The amount of funds which the company will have on hand for this hypothetical group is carried forward year by year. This is based on reasonable assumptions regarding future rates of interest earned, mortality, voluntary terminations of policies, and expenses to be paid.

It should be noted that this process is somewhat similar to carrying forward *reserves* year by year, such as was demonstrated in Section 11.1. However, in calculating reserves the interest and mortality rates are those specified by law, and no provision is made for expenses, dividends, or voluntary terminations of policies. The resulting reserves per $1,000 each year represent the amounts required by law to be established as *liabilities*. Asset shares, on the other hand, represent the amount of *assets* which, it is forecast, a specific policy will actually accumulate. It is important and instructive to compare a policy's asset share with its reserves each year.

The following is a simplified example of an asset share calculation. It assumes that $10,000,000 of 20-payment life insurance is sold at one time to a group of persons all age 25:

First Year

1. In force beginning of year = $10,000,000
2. Amount of death claims during year = $5,000 (from experience values of $q_{[25]}$)
3. Amount surrendered end of year = $1,500,000 (from experience rates of surrender)
4. In force end of year = $8,495,000 (1 – 2 – 3)
5. Premium income = $285,500 ($10,000,000 in force at $28.55 per $1,000)
6. Expenses = $65,000 (from forecast of first-year expenses)
7. Premium taxes = $5,710 (2% of 5)
8. Commissions = $214,125 (75% of 5)
9. Surrender values paid = none (first-year cash value is zero)
10. Interest earned on the fund this year = $27 (4% of 5 – 6 – 7 – 8)
11. Dividends paid = $31,184 ($3.12 per $1,000, multiplied by 1 – 2)
12. Total fund end of year = –$35,492 (5 – 6 – 7 – 8 – 9 + 10 – 11 – 2)

According to this calculation, the company will pay out more money during the first policy year than it takes in during that year. Actually, this often happens in the first year of a policy because first-year expenses and commissions are higher than in subsequent years.

The total fund at the end of the year is divided by the number of thousands of insurance then in force to derive the asset share:

$$-\$35{,}492 \div 8{,}495 = -\$4.18$$

That is, the asset share at the end of the first policy year is *negative* $4.18 per $1,000 of insurance. This is why the company would establish a cash value of "zero" for the first year.

The asset share calculation for the second policy year might appear as follows:

Second Year

1. In force beginning of year = $8,495,000 (same as 4 above)
2. Amount of death claims during year = $6,000 (from experience values of $q_{[25]+1}$)
3. Amount surrendered end of year = $500,000 (from experience rates of surrender)
4. In force end of year = $7,989,000 (1 – 2 – 3)

5. Premium income = $242,532 ($8,495,000 in force at $28.55 per $1,000)
6. Expense = $22,000 (from forecast of second-year expenses)
7. Premium taxes = $4,851 (2% of 5)
8. Commissions = $24,253 (10% of 5)
9. Surrender values paid = $7,800 ($15.60 cash value per $1,000 × 3)
10. Interest earned on the fund this year = $6,237 (4% of 12 above + 5 − 6 − 7 − 8)
11. Dividends paid = $45,586 ($5.37 per $1,000, multiplied by 1 − 2)
12. Total fund end of year = $102,787 (12 above + 5 − 6 − 7 − 8 − 9 + 10 − 11 − 2)

The total fund at the end of the second year is divided by the number of thousands of insurance then in force to derive the second asset share:

$$\$102{,}787 \div 7{,}989 = \$12.87$$

That is, the asset share at the end of the second policy year is $12.87 per $1,000 of insurance.

The cash value at the end of two years, in the above illustration, is shown as $15.60 per $1,000. Since the asset share is only $12.87 per $1,000, the company would not have accumulated sufficient funds from this particular group of policies to pay the cash value which is promised if very large numbers of them were to terminate.

The *reserve* figured by the Commissioners method (using the 1958 C.S.O. Table, 3%) at the end of two years is $18.43 per $1,000. Since the asset share is only $12.87 per $1,000, the company will realize no profit from this group by the end of two years. Typical calculations in actual practice will show, however, that asset shares will exceed the reserves and the cash values after a certain number of years.

Thus, by using asset share calculations, it is possible for a company to observe the effects upon its future financial condition which would be caused by variations in premium rates, dividends, interest rates earned, nonforfeiture values guaranteed, commission rates, etc.

15.4 ELECTRONIC DATA PROCESSING

In the mid-1950's electronic data processing machines (called "computers" or "E.D.P. equipment") became available to perform calculations. Their speed and capacity make these machines ideally suited to jobs involving a large number of calculations or very complex calculations, as frequently found in insurance operations.

Such machines combine the following major advantages:

1. *Stored Programs.* This refers to the ability of the machine to store a series of instructions on how to perform its calculations;

2. *Branching Operations.* This refers to the ability of the machine to choose among different sets of instructions under different circumstances;
3. *Speed.* The speed with which calculations are performed far surpasses anything previously available. Only a few millionths of a second are required to perform each instruction.

The calculation of asset shares would become very tedious if done by hand or even by electric "desk calculators." With E.D.P. equipment, such calculations can be done in large volume fairly easily. Once the series of instructions has been given to the machine, it will automatically perform all the calculations. It is also easy to change the assumptions as to death rates, number of voluntary terminations, size of premiums, dividends, cash values, or rates of interest earned. The machine will show how these changes will affect the size of the asset shares.

There are many other areas described in this book to which E.D.P. equipment is ideally suited, such as calculation of reserves, cash values, nonforfeiture benefits, and dividends. Another interesting example is the calculation of the "Life Income Option with Refund" (described in Section 8.5), which is quite complex. The answers can best be found by a *trial and error method.* This is very burdensome and time-consuming when using a desk calculator. However, an E.D.P. machine can try hundreds of possible answers in just a few seconds of time, until the right one is found.

It is common practice in life insurance companies to prepare a set of instructions for an E.D.P. machine to calculate commutation functions when it is given all the values of q_x and an interest rate. This set of instructions is then always available. When new mortality or interest assumptions are made, the E.D.P. machine will automatically produce the columns of l_x, d_x, D_x, N_x, C_x, and M_x.

E.D.P. equipment also makes feasible certain calculations wherein each policy in force is handled separately. This is particularly important when preparing the company's December 31 financial statement. In large companies, it was customary formerly to group similar policies together when calculating such items as the mean reserves. E.D.P. machines can now calculate the totals just as quickly by calculating each policy separately. Another example would be the calculation of the number exposed to the risk of dying at each age, when calculating mortality rates as described in Section 7.2.

E.D.P. equipment has even been used to calculate net premiums and gross premiums by trial and error methods. Terminal reserves may be carried forward by a year-by-year process as follows: the previous year's terminal reserve, plus the current year's net premium, accumulates at interest for one year. At the end of the year, the tabular cost of insurance is deducted. For example, a net premium of 1 cent may be tried by the machine, then 2 cents, etc., until the correct net premium is found which will produce a final reserve of $1,000 (for an endowment policy) or zero (for a term policy). Some companies calculate their gross premiums by instructing the E.D.P. machine to use a trial and error method until it finds a gross premium which will produce a desired asset share at a certain duration.

The jobs which E.D.P. equipment can perform for a life insurance company are almost endless. However, it should be remembered that the time and effort needed to prepare the set of instructions for the machine must be justified by the fact that the particular calculation will then be mechanically performed many times. Such equipment is not suitable for short "one-time" calculations.

15.5 SUBMISSION OF STATISTICS TO GOVERNMENTAL AUTHORITIES

The principal financial statement which life insurance companies must prepare is the annual statement which is required by law to be filed with the state governmental authorities (of those states in which the company does business). The form of this annual statement is prescribed by the National Association of Insurance Commissioners. Hence, it is virtually uniform for all states.

While this book has been concerned with the calculation of premiums and reserves for *individual* insurance policies and annuities, the emphasis in the annual statement is on *aggregate* totals for all policies in force.

The principal liability shown in a life insurance company's annual statement is the *reserve* item. This is the aggregate total of the reserves on December 31 of all policies and annuity contracts then in force. It was pointed out in Section 11.6 that *mean reserves* are universally used in calculating this December 31 figure.

All life insurance policies are grouped by calendar year of issue and assumed to be issued July 1 of the calendar year, producing durations of $\frac{1}{2}$ year, $1\frac{1}{2}$ year, $2\frac{1}{2}$ years, etc.

Reserves must also be calculated as of December 31 for annuity contracts of all kinds, as well as for policy proceeds left under the settlement options. Here the practices vary considerably between companies.

For life insurance policies, the use of mean reserves implies that an annual premium was paid on the previous July 1 anniversary. That is, the equation

$$\text{Mean Reserve} = \frac{\text{Net Premium} + \text{Previous Terminal Reserve} + \text{Terminal Reserve}}{2}$$

contains a full year's net premium in the numerator. In actual practice, on December 31 many policies do not have a full year's premium paid for the current policy year. This may occur because the policyholder is paying *fractional premiums* instead of annual premiums. It may also occur because a premium is *past due* on December 31 (due to the grace period allowed for payment of premiums). On the other hand, by December 31 some premiums may be paid in *advance* of their due date. However, the annual statement prescribes that net premiums past due, as well as net fractional premiums still due to complete the current policy year, be set up as an asset. Net premiums (plus loading thereon) received in advance of their due date must be set up as a liability. The net effect of these requirements is that exactly one year's premium enters the annual statement as income. The usual mean reserve can, therefore, correctly be used for all policies.

The N.A.I.C. annual statement requires that an "Analysis of Increase in Reserves During the Year" be reported. In this particular report, the year's increase in aggregate reserves must be accounted for by showing the year's aggregate net annual premiums, interest, and tabular cost of insurance. These three items must be calculated on the same bases as used in calculating the reserves. The general outline of this part of the report is

Previous Year's Reserve + Net Premiums + Interest
− Tabular Cost of Insurance = This Year's Reserve

Thus, companies must either actually keep track of net premiums as they are collected, or apply carefully developed ratios to the amount of gross premiums collected.

The tabular cost of insurance would be the most difficult item to calculate. However, the instructions specify that it be calculated as the "balancing item." In other words, since all other items are known, companies are instructed to fill in whatever amount will make the "Net Premiums + Interest − Tabular Cost of Insurance" exactly equal to the year's increase in reserves.

15.6 A LOOK TO THE FUTURE

The amount of life insurance in force in the United States has been doubling approximately every 10 years. It now stands considerably in excess of a trillion dollars (a thousand billion dollars). The life insurance business today is characterized by a mood of innovation. New types of coverage and marketing methods are being explored constantly. This points the way toward a significant need for technically trained personnel.

Even the fundamental mathematics of life insurance keeps expanding and changing. This is demonstrated by the inclusion in this book of many topics which were not discussed in most such previous texts, such as guaranteed insurability benefits, "fifth dividend option," and E.D.P. developments. One can only speculate as to the new topics which might be included in future texts.

Even today we see emerging such new ideas as specially calculated premiums for persons who do not smoke cigarettes, and contracts wherein benefit payments depend upon a combination of mortality rates and the performance of the stock market. These two topics will undoubtedly be included in tomorrow's textbooks on life insurance mathematics.

Many more things can be done in the future than in the past because of the existence of electronic data processing equipment. Tomorrow's life insurance mathematicians will be obliged to become very familiar with such equipment.

Certain areas in the life insurance field are in a relatively young stage. Their popularity and rapid growth indicate that much will need to be done in the years ahead to handle and guide this growth. This includes, for example: *pension plans,* the details of which are changing and continually becoming more complicated; *health insurance,* which has been described as "wide open" for the introduction of new concepts; and *social insurance,* which includes government-provided insurance against medical expenses, disability, unemployment, etc.

The life insurance mathematician of the future will need to make extensive studies and analyses of data. The scarcity of data involved in health insurance has already been mentioned. There also exists a significant need to know more concerning the effect of various health impairments upon mortality rates. Studies are also needed of the ways in which the calculation of premiums, reserves, and dividends will affect the company's tax burden.

The future seems full of interesting opportunities for technically trained personnel to explore this important and challenging environment.

Glossary

These words and phrases are described in the way they are used in this text. *Many of them have other meanings in other contexts.*

Accidental Death Benefit—Insurance which promises to pay money when death occurs because of an accident (as defined by the policy).

Accruing the Discount (of a Bond)—The periodic increase in the book value of a bond bought at a price below par, so that the book value will equal par at maturity.

Accumulated Cost of Insurance—The amount which would have to be paid at the end of the term of coverage (by the survivors) to provide the death benefits for those who had died during the term.

Accumulated Value—The total of the amount of money originally invested plus the interest.

Accumulation Factor—The number to be multiplied by the amount of money paid now, to derive the accumulated value of that money. (May be calculated with interest only or with benefit of survivorship.)

Adjusted Premiums—Special premiums (greater than net premiums) which are defined in the Standard Nonforfeiture Law and are used in calculating the legal minimum cash values.

Age Rate-Up—Issuing a policy at the premium rate which would regularly be charged to a person who is an older age (as a means of charging a higher premium to a person who is a substandard risk).

Agent—A person who represents a life insurance company for the purpose of selling the company's contracts.

Amortize—To repay a debt by means of regular periodic payments.

Amortization Payments—Regular periodic payments made for the purpose of repaying a debt.

Amortizing a Bond Premium—The periodic reduction of the book value of a bond bought at a price above par, so that the book value will equal par at maturity.

Annuity—A series of payments made or received at regular intervals of time.

Annuity Certain—A series of payments involving a fixed number of such payments.

Annuity Due—A series of payments in which the payments are made at the beginning of each interval of time.

Annuity Factor—The present value at age x of a temporary life annuity of 1.

Annuity Immediate—A series of payments in which the payments are made at the end of each interval of time.

Annuity Mortality Table—A tabulation of probabilities of dying at each age for use with contracts where benefits are paid only if a designated person is alive.

Asset Share—The actual amount which it is forecast will have accumulated at any given time from a policy.

Attained Age—The current age at the time of calculation, i.e., the age at the time the policy was issued plus the number of years elapsed since the policy was issued.

Band Grading—Treating policies as groups according to face amounts for the purpose of calculating loading.

Base—A number which has an exponent appearing at the upper right. (See also "Exponent.")

Benefit of Survivorship—Describes the fact that payments made to surviving persons include a portion of the shares which are forfeited by those in the original group who did not survive.

Bond—A certificate of indebtedness agreeing to reimburse the purchaser and to pay periodic interest.

Bond Rate—The interest rate specified in a bond, upon which the actual periodic interest payments are based.

Book Value (of a Bond)—The value of a bond, at any particular time, according to its purchaser's accounting records.

Branching Operation—The selection by a computer of one among different sets of instructions under different circumstances.

Call Price—A lump sum of money paid to the purchaser to redeem a bond earlier than its maturity date.

Canadian Method—A prescribed method for calculating certain policies' modified net premiums and reserves, the exact rules for which are given in Section 12.5.

Cash Refund Option—A form of settlement option payments in which the insurance company pays out a series of equal payments for so long as the recipient lives; if the recipient dies before the total payments equal the proceeds of the policy, the balance necessary to equal the proceeds is all paid at once.

Cash Values—The amounts, as printed in the policy, which the insurance company guarantees to pay in cash if a person voluntarily terminates his policy.

Certain Payment—A payment which will definitely be made under any circumstances, its payment not being contingent upon any predesignated condition.

Certificate—The printed document, associated with a group insurance policy, which identifies the particular life involved and provides benefit and other information pertaining to that life.

Commissioners Method—A prescribed method for calculating certain policies' modified net premiums and reserves, the exact rules for which are given in Section 12.4.

Commissions—The amounts of money paid to the agents for selling insurance policies (almost always calculated as a percentage of the premium).

Common Multiplier—A number which is being multiplied by each of several other numbers.

Commutation Functions—Symbols representing a combination of mortality-table figures and interest-table figures.

Complementary Probabilities—Two probabilities whose total equals 1.

Compound—To add interest to the amount invested, so that this interest may earn interest.

Compound Interest—Interest which is earned upon previous interest.

Conservative (Mortality Table)—Describes rates of mortality that are higher than expected if used for life insurance calculations, or lower than expected if used for annuity calculations.

Contingencies—Events which are possible, but may or may not actually happen.

Contingent Payment—A payment which will be made only if some predesignated condition is met, such as the recipient being alive.

Continuous Functions—Refers to calculations of premiums and reserves involving both the assumptions of the death benefit payable immediately at the moment of death and of the premiums payable continuously.

Continuously (Annuity Payable)—The ultimate frequency at which payments would be made; i.e., with no interval of time between each payment. This concept is only theoretical and could not exist in practice.

Conversion Privilege—The promise that a person may change his insurance to another type, in certain prescribed situations.

Coupon—A detachable portion of a bond, which may be presented on or after a specified date to receive interest payments.

Coupon Bond—A bond wherein the promised interest is represented in the form of coupons to be detached.

Coupon Rate—The interest rate specified in a bond, upon which the actual periodic interest payments are based.

Death Benefit—The amount of the payment to be made when a designated insured person dies.

Death Claims—The amounts of money which are actually paid out by an insurance company because of deaths under their life insurance policies.

Decimal Form—A form of writing numbers in which numbers to the right of the decimal point constitute a fraction with a value of less than 1.

Decimal Places—The number of digits appearing to the right of a decimal point in a number.

Deferred Annuity—A series of payments which has its first payment postponed for one or more periods.

Deferred Life Annuity—A series of payments, each of which is made only if a designated person is alive, with the first payment postponed one or more periods.

Disability Benefits—Benefits which are payable periodically while the insured continues to be disabled. "Being disabled" is generally defined in terms of inability to work.

Disability Table—A tabulation of the probabilities of becoming disabled at each age, plus certain related figures. A second kind is a tabulation of numbers of persons who are still disabled at each age and duration of disability, plus certain related figures.

Discount (Bond Purchased at)—The amount by which the purchase price of a bond is less than its face amount.

Discounting (as used in this text)—Finding the present value at a specified rate of interest of an amount due in the future.

Dividend Credits—The values resulting from dividends having been left with the company under a dividend option; the values are available to be used (along with the cash value) under the nonforfeiture options.

Dividend Expenses—The amount which a company chooses to use in calculating dividends, as representing its present year's cost for maintaining a certain policy in force.

Dividend Interest Rate—The interest rate which a company chooses to use in calculating dividends, as representing the rate being earned on its present investments.

Dividend Options—The various ways in which a policyowner may choose to receive the dividends from his policy.

Dividend Rate of Mortality—The rate of mortality (for a given age) which a company chooses to use in calculating dividends, as representing the rate being experienced on its own insurance at the present time.

Dividends (as used in this text)—That part of the profits, or savings from operations, which is returned to the owner of a participating policy each year.

Effective Interest Rate—An annual interest rate which produces the same accumulated values as the nominal rate compounded more frequently than annually.

Endowment Insurance—Insurance which provides a benefit either if death occurs during a specified number of years or at the end of that time if the person is then alive.

Equation—A statement that two expressions are equal to each other.

Equivalent Rates—Two interest rates which produce the same accumulated value in the same period of time.

Equivalent Single Payment—One payment which can replace several other payments, because it equals the value of the other payments.

Evaluation Date—The date as of which the accumulated value or present value is being calculated.

Experience Premiums—Special annual premiums which are calculated using dividend rates of mortality and expenses, but using the tabular interest rate.

Experience-Premium Method—A method for calculating dividends, wherein a basic amount is calculated (difference between gross premium and experience premium), to which the year's contribution from interest is added.

Exponent—A number appearing at the upper right of another number, indicating how many times this other number (known as the "base") is multiplied by itself. Also called the "power" to which the base is raised.

Extended Term Insurance—A nonforfeiture option; the full amount of insurance continues in effect, but for a shorter period of time and no more premiums are payable.

Face Amount—(1) The amount which is stated on a bond, upon which the interest payments and redemption price are based. (2) The amount of the death benefit in a life insurance policy.

Factoring—Removing a common multiplier from several numbers, i.e., writing the expression as the common multiplier times a quantity.

Factors—Those numbers which, when multiplied together, equal a certain specified number.

Fifth Dividend Option—The use of the policy dividend (or part thereof) to purchase one-year term insurance.

Fixed Payment Option—A settlement option in which the company pays out a series of equal payments of a certain amount, such as $100 per year.

Fixed Period Option—A settlement option in which the company pays out a series of equal payments for a certain period of time only, such as for 10 years.

Fractional Premiums—Premiums which are paid in installments over each year, such as semiannually, quarterly, or monthly.

Full Preliminary Term Method—A method for calculating modified net premiums and reserves, as described in Section 12.2.

Grace Period—The period of time (usually 31 days) following the date a premium is due during which it may be paid without the loss of any rights.

Graduation—A mathematical process to smooth out an observed series of numbers so that the series more nearly represents the average expected results.

Gross Premium—The actual amount to be paid by the policyowner for life insurance, calculated to include the net premium plus loading.

Group Insurance—Insurance which is granted to members of a group under a master policy.

Guaranteed Insurability Benefit—Insurance which promises that the insured can purchase additional insurance at standard premium rates at specified dates in the future, without evidence of insurability.

Hospital Insurance—Insurance which pays a benefit towards daily hospital room and other hospital charges.

Illinois Standard Method—A prescribed method for calculating certain policies' modified net premiums and reserves, the exact rules for which are given in Section 12.3.

Infinitely—In a way that is endless.

Infinitesimally—In a way that is immeasurably small; virtually zero.

Infinity—A number which is infinitely (endlessly) large.

Initial Reserve—The reserve on a policy at the beginning of any given policy year (which includes the net annual premium then due).

Installment Refund Option—A settlement option in which the insurance company guarantees a series of equal payments until such time as the total paid out equals the proceeds of the policy; thereafter the payments will continue only as long as the original recipient lives.

Insurance Mortality Table—A tabulation of probabilities of dying at each age for use with insurance contracts.

Insured—The person whose death (or disability) is the subject of the insurance.

Interest—Money which is paid for the use of money.

Interest Conversion Period—The period of time between interest compoundings.

Interest Option—A settlement option under which the insurance company holds the proceeds of a policy and periodically pays out the interest thereon.

Interest Rate—The percentage by which an amount of money is multiplied to derive the amount paid for the use of that money.

Invest—To lay out money in the expectation of receiving interest or other gain therefrom.

Investment—The property or rights which are acquired in the expectation of receiving interest or other gain therefrom; or the money laid out to acquire such property or rights; or the act of so laying out money.

Lapse—Termination of an insurance policy because of nonpayment of premiums.

Life Annuity—A series of payments at regular intervals, each of which is made only if a designated person is then alive.

Life Contingencies—The probabilities of living or dying; also describes the condition that payments to be made depend upon certain persons being alive.

Life Income Option—A settlement option in which the insurance company pays out a series of equal payments for as long as the recipient lives.

Life Income Option with Period Certain—A settlement option in which the insurance company guarantees a series of equal payments for a designated period of time (such as 10 years); thereafter the payments will continue only as long as the original recipient lives.

Life Income Option with Refund—A settlement option in which the insurance company pays out a series of equal payments until such time as the total paid out equals the proceeds of the policy; thereafter the payments will continue only as long as the original recipient lives.

Loading—An amount which is added to net premiums to provide for expenses and adverse contingencies.

Major Medical Insurance—Insurance which pays a stipulated percentage (such as 80%) of hospital, surgical, and medical bills, after first deducting certain amounts, with an upper limit on benefits.

Mature (as an Endowment)—Describes the situation where the endowment amount becomes due and payable at the end of the contract period, or earlier by the use of dividends.

Mean Reserve—The average of the initial and terminal reserves of a policy in any given policy year.

Medical Expense Insurance—Insurance which pays benefits toward doctors' bills.

Modified Net Premiums—Net premiums which are other than level, generally being lower for the first year than for subsequent years.

Modified Preliminary Term Method—One of several methods for calculating modified net premiums and reserves. (Canadian, Commissioners, and Illinois Standard methods)

Modified Reserves—Reserves calculated using modified net premiums.

Morbidity—Sickness.

Mortality Rate—The probability of dying within one year after attaining a specified age.

Mortality Table—A tabulation of the probabilities of dying at each age, plus certain related figures.

National Association of Insurance Commissioners (NAIC)—An organization composed of the insurance supervisory authorities (commissioners) of each of the states.

Natural Premium—The amount a person should pay for one year of insurance, i.e., the net single premium for one year of term insurance.

Net Amount at Risk—That portion of a policy's death benefit which exceeds its terminal reserve.

Net Level Annual Premium—A net premium which stays the same each year during the premium-payment period.

Net Level Premium Reserve—The amount of liability which an insurance company establishes for a policy, calculated using net level annual premiums.

Net Premium—An amount necessary to provide insurance benefits, calculated by using the assumed rate of interest and the tabular mortality rate.

Net Single Premium—A net premium of an amount equal to the present value of death and endowment benefits.

Nominal Interest Rate—An annual interest rate which is quoted with the understanding that interest is compounded more than once a year.

Nonforfeiture Factors—Special values, similar to annual premiums, which some companies calculate and use for deriving cash values.

Nonforfeiture Values—The benefits, as printed in the policy, which the insurance company guarantees if a person stops paying premiums for his policy. These amounts may be used in a variety of options.

Nonparticipating—A type of insurance or annuity in which the policyowner does not receive any policy dividends.

Option—A choice which may be made with respect to settlement options, dividends, or nonforfeiture values.

Ordinary Life Policy—An insurance policy which has premiums payable for the person's entire lifetime, and provides a benefit whenever death occurs.

Paid-Up—Describes an insurance policy having benefits in the future but no further premium payments.

Paid-Up Additions—Additional insurance purchased by dividends, with no premiums payable on this insurance.

Par—100% of the face amount of a bond.

Participating—A type of insurance or annuity on which policy dividends are paid.

Payment Certain—A payment which is not contingent upon any predesignated condition.

Percent—Hundredths; such as "3 percent" means $\frac{3}{100}$ or .03.

Policy Charge—An amount which a company may include in the gross premium each year; this amount is the same regardless of the size of the policy. (Sometimes called "Policy Fee.")

Policyowner—The person who actually controls the policy and has all of its rights and privileges as long as it is in force (not necessarily the same person whose life is insured).

Policy Reserve—Amount which an insurance company is required by law to establish as a liability for each policy at any given time.

Premium (Bond Purchased at)—The amount by which the purchase price of a bond exceeds its face amount.

Premium Deficiency Reserve—An additional amount which an insurance company is required to have on hand, over and above the regular reserve, for any policy having a gross premium less than its net premium.

Present Value—The amount of money which must be invested on the evaluation date in order to accumulate to a specified amount at a later date.

Present Value Factor—The number by which the amount of money to be paid later is multiplied in order to derive the present value of that money on the evaluation date. (May be calculated with interest only or with benefit of survivorship.)

Probability—The likelihood of some event occurring.

Proceeds—The amount of money which the insurance company is obligated to pay for the settlement of a policy (death benefit, endowment benefit, or cash value).

Prospective Method—A method of calculating reserves by looking to the future; terminal reserve equals the present value of future benefits minus the present value of future net premiums.

Pure Endowment—An amount which is paid at the end of the endowment period only if a designated person is then alive.

Quantity—That which is included inside a pair of parentheses or brackets.

Rate of Disability—The probability of becoming disabled within one year after attaining a specified age.

Redemption Price—A lump sum of money paid to the purchaser to redeem a bond.

Reduced Paid-Up Insurance—A nonforfeiture option; the insurance continues in effect for a smaller amount with no more premiums payable.

Reducing Fractions—Dividing numerator and denominator by the same number without changing the value of the fraction.

Retroactive Rate Reduction—A refund of part of the premium paid for group insurance; similar to a policy dividend (also called an *experience refund.*)

Retrospective Method—A method for calculating reserves by using past happenings; terminal reserve equals the accumulated value of net premiums received minus the accumulated cost of insurance.

Rider—An agreement providing separate benefits and premiums which is attached to a basic insurance policy.

Select and Ultimate Mortality Table—A tabulation of basic mortality information during the "select period" and the period beyond it.

Select Mortality Table—A mortality table for the "select period."

Select Period—The period of years during which there is a significant difference in mortality rates between persons whose good health was established at the beginning of the period and other persons of the same age.

Setback—The number of years subtracted from the true age in insurance calculations.

Settlement Option Payments—Periodic payments made by an insurance company in lieu of an immediate lump-sum settlement of a policy.

Settlement Option Table—A tabulation of the various amounts which the insurance company is willing to pay as periodic payments in the settlement of a policy.

Sinking Fund—A fund which is being accumulated by periodic payments for the purpose of attaining a certain amount by a certain date.

Sinking Fund Payment—A regular periodic payment into a sinking fund.

Standard Nonforfeiture Law—A law, which is virtually uniform in all states, specifying minimum cash values.

Standard Risk—An applicant for insurance who is considered to have a normal chance of dying.

Standard Valuation Law—A law, which is virtually uniform in all states, specifying minimum standards for calculating insurance reserves.

Stored Program—A series of instructions which is stored in a computer.

Subscript—A part of a symbol, appearing at the lower right of the main part of the symbol.

Substandard—Having a higher than normal chance of dying (or becoming disabled).

Surrender Charge—An amount which is deducted from a policy's reserve to arrive at its cash value.

Tabular Cost of Insurance—The contribution which must be made by each of those insured in order to make up the full amount of the death claims payable in any year.

Tabular Cost of Insurance Based on the Net Amount at Risk—Means the same as "Tabular Cost of Insurance"; this name refers to a method of calculating it by multiplying the net amount at risk by the mortality rate.

Tabular Interest Rate—The interest rate which is used in calculating the policy's reserves.

Tabular Rate of Mortality—The rate of mortality (for a given age) shown in the mortality table which is used in calculating the policy's reserves.

Temporary Life Annuity—A series of payments, each of which is made only if a designated person is then alive, with the number of such payments limited to a specified number. Each such payment is made at the *end* of an interval of time.

Temporary Life Annuity Due—A series of payments, each of which is made only if a designated person is then alive, with the number of such payments limited to a specified number. Each such payment is made at the *beginning* of an interval of time.

Term Insurance—Insurance which provides a benefit only if death occurs during a specified period.

Terminal Reserve—The reserve on a policy at the *end* of any given policy year.

Three-Factor Contribution Method—A method for calculating policy dividends, with contributions arising from interest, mortality, and expenses considered separately.

Ultimate Mortality Table—A mortality table covering years beyond the "select period."

Whole Life Annuity—A series of payments, each of which is made only if a designated person is then alive, with the payments continuing for that person's entire lifetime. Each such payment is made at the *end* of an interval of time.

Whole Life Annuity Due—A series of payments, each of which is made only if a designated person is then alive, with the payments continuing for that person's entire lifetime. Each such payment is made at the *beginning* of an interval of time.

Whole Life Insurance—Insurance which provides a benefit whenever death occurs.

With Benefit of Survivorship—Describes the fact that payments made to surviving persons include a portion of the shares which are forfeited by those of the original group who did not survive.

Yield Rate—The interest rate which the purchaser of a bond will actually realize on his investment.

List of Equations

Number in parentheses refers to the section where the equation is first presented

(3.1) Expression for the accumulated value of money invested:

$$S = A + I$$

(3.1) Expression for the amount of interest earned in 1 period:

$$I = Ai$$

(3.1) Expression for the accumulated value at the end of 1 period:

$$S = A(1 + i)$$

(3.2) Expression for the accumulated value at the end of n periods:

$$S = A(1 + i)^n$$

(3.5) Equation for calculating the effective rate of interest corresponding to a given nominal rate (in decimal form):

$$\text{Effective Rate (decimal)} = (1 + i)^n - 1$$

(3.5) Equation for calculating the effective rate of interest corresponding to a given nominal rate (in percentage form):

$$\text{Effective Rate (\%)} = [(1 + i)^n - 1]100$$

(4.2) Expression for the present value n periods earlier:

$$A = \frac{S}{(1 + i)^n}$$

(4.2) Definition of the symbol "v":

$$v = \frac{1}{1 + i}$$

(4.2) Another expression for the present value n periods earlier:

$$A = Sv^n$$

(5.2) Expression for the symbol "$s_{\overline{n}|i}$":

$$s_{\overline{n}|i} = (1 + i)^{n-1} + (1 + i)^{n-2} + \cdot \cdot \cdot + (1 + i)^2 + (1 + i)^1 + 1$$

(5.3) Relationship between successive values of $s_{\overline{n}|i}$:

$$s_{\overline{n+1}|i} = s_{\overline{n}|i} + (1+i)^n$$

(5.4) Another expression for the relationship between successive values of $s_{\overline{n}|i}$:

$$s_{\overline{n+1}|i} = (1+i)s_{\overline{n}|i} + 1$$

(5.4) Equation for calculating values of $s_{\overline{n}|i}$ when n is larger than shown in table (25 in this case):

$$s_{\overline{n}|i} = s_{\overline{25}|i} + s_{\overline{n-25}|i}(1+i)^{25}$$

(5.5) Expression for the symbol "$\ddot{s}_{\overline{n}|i}$":

$$\ddot{s}_{\overline{n}|i} = (1+i)^n + (1+i)^{n-1} + \cdots + (1+i)^2 + (1+i)^1$$

(5.5) Relationship between accumulated values of an annuity due and an annuity immediate:

$$\ddot{s}_{\overline{n}|i} = (1+i)s_{\overline{n}|i}$$

(5.5) Another expression for the relationship between the accumulated values of an annuity due and an annuity immediate:

$$\ddot{s}_{\overline{n}|i} = s_{\overline{n+1}|i} - 1$$

(5.6) Equation for calculating sinking fund payment (made at the end of each period):

$$\begin{pmatrix}\text{Sinking Fund}\\ \text{Payment}\end{pmatrix} = \frac{\text{Accumulated Value}}{s_{\overline{n}|i}}$$

(5.6) Another way of stating the above equation:

$$\begin{pmatrix}\text{Sinking Fund}\\ \text{Payment}\end{pmatrix} = \text{Accumulated Value}\left(\frac{1}{s_{\overline{n}|i}}\right)$$

(5.6) Equation for calculating sinking fund payment (made at the beginning of each period):

$$\begin{pmatrix}\text{Sinking Fund}\\ \text{Payment}\end{pmatrix} = \frac{\text{Accumulated Value}}{\ddot{s}_{\overline{n}|i}}$$

(5.6) Another way of stating the above equation:

$$\begin{pmatrix}\text{Sinking Fund}\\ \text{Payment}\end{pmatrix} = \text{Accumulated Value}\left(\frac{1}{\ddot{s}_{\overline{n}|i}}\right)$$

(5.6) Relationship between sinking fund factor (made at the end of each period) and sinking fund factor (made at beginning of each period):

$$(1+i)\frac{1}{\ddot{s}_{\overline{n}|i}} = \frac{1}{s_{\overline{n}|i}}$$

(6.2) Expression for the symbol "$a_{\overline{n}|i}$":

$$a_{\overline{n}|i} = v^1 + v^2 + \cdots + v^{n-1} + v^n$$

(6.3) Relationship between successive values of $a_{\overline{n}|i}$:

$$a_{\overline{n+1}|i} = a_{\overline{n}|i} + v^{n+1} \quad \text{or} \quad a_{\overline{n}|i} = a_{\overline{n-1}|i} + v^n$$

(6.4) Another expression for the relationship between successive values of $a_{\overline{n}|i}$:

$$a_{\overline{n+1}|i} = v(a_{\overline{n}|i} + 1)$$

(6.4) Another way of stating the above equation:

$$a_{\overline{n+1}|i} = \frac{a_{\overline{n}|i} + 1}{1 + i}$$

(6.4) Equation for calculating values of $a_{\overline{n}|i}$ when n is larger than shown in table (25 in this case):

$$a_{\overline{n}|i} = a_{\overline{25}|i} + a_{\overline{n-25}|i}v^{25}$$

(6.5) Expression for the symbol "$\ddot{a}_{\overline{n}|i}$":

$$\ddot{a}_{\overline{n}|i} = 1 + v^1 + v^2 + \cdots + v^{n-2} + v^{n-1}$$

(6.5) Relationship between present value of an annuity due and an annuity immediate:

$$\ddot{a}_{\overline{n}|i} = (1 + i)a_{\overline{n}|i}$$

(6.5) Another expression for the relationship between the present value of an annuity due and an annuity immediate:

$$\ddot{a}_{\overline{n}|i} = a_{\overline{n-1}|i} + 1$$

(6.7) Equation for calculating amortization payment (made at the end of each period):

$$\begin{pmatrix}\text{Amortization}\\ \text{Payment}\end{pmatrix} = \frac{\text{Present Value}}{a_{\overline{n}|i}}$$

(6.7) Another way of stating the above equation:

$$\begin{pmatrix}\text{Amortization}\\ \text{Payment}\end{pmatrix} = \text{Present Value}\left(\frac{1}{a_{\overline{n}|i}}\right)$$

(6.7) Equation for calculating amortization payment (made at the beginning of each period):

$$\begin{pmatrix}\text{Amortization}\\ \text{Payment}\end{pmatrix} = \frac{\text{Present Value}}{\ddot{a}_{\overline{n}|i}}$$

(6.7) Another way of stating the above equation:

$$\begin{pmatrix}\text{Amortization}\\ \text{Payment}\end{pmatrix} = \text{Present Value}\left(\frac{1}{\ddot{a}_{\overline{n}|i}}\right)$$

(6.10) Relationship between the present value and the accumulated value of an annuity:

$$s_{\overline{n}|i} = a_{\overline{n}|i}(1+i)^n$$

(6.10) Another expression for the relationship between the present value and the accumulated value of an annuity:

$$a_{\overline{n}|i} = s_{\overline{n}|i}v^n$$

(7.4) Relationship between successive values of l_x:

$$l_{x+1} = l_x - d_x$$

(7.4) Equation for calculating values of d_x:

$$d_x = l_x q_x$$

(7.4) Equation for calculating values of q_x:

$$q_x = \frac{d_x}{l_x}$$

(7.6) Equation for calculating values of p_x:

$$p_x = \frac{l_{x+1}}{l_x}$$

(7.6) Relationship between p_x and q_x:

$$p_x + q_x = 1$$

(7.6) Equation for calculating values of ${}_np_x$:

$${}_np_x = \frac{l_{x+n}}{l_x}$$

(7.6) Equation for calculating values of ${}_nq_x$:

$${}_nq_x = \frac{l_x - l_{x+n}}{l_x}$$

(7.6) Relationship between ${}_np_x$ and ${}_nq_x$:

$${}_np_x + {}_nq_x = 1$$

(8.1) Expression for the present value n years earlier, with benefit of survivorship:

$$\begin{pmatrix}\text{Present Value of \$1}\\ \text{Due in } n \text{ Years to a}\\ \text{Life Now Age } x\text{, with}\\ \text{Benefit of Survivorship}\end{pmatrix} = \$1\left(\frac{l_{x+n}v^n}{l_x}\right)$$

(8.2) Relationship between present value of a whole life annuity due and a whole life annuity immediate:

$$\begin{pmatrix}\text{Present Value at Age } x\\ \text{of Whole Life Annuity Due}\end{pmatrix} = \begin{pmatrix}\text{Present Value at Age } x\\ \text{of Whole Life Annuity}\end{pmatrix} + 1$$

(8.2) Relationship between present value of temporary life annuity due and a temporary life annuity immediate:

$$\begin{pmatrix}\text{Present Value at Age } x\\ \text{of } n\text{-Year Life Annuity Due}\end{pmatrix} = \begin{pmatrix}\text{Present Value at Age } x\\ \text{of } (n-1)\text{-Year Life Annuity}\end{pmatrix} + 1$$

(8.2) Relationship between temporary, deferred, and whole life annuities:

$$\begin{pmatrix}\text{Present Value at Age } x\\ \text{of } n\text{-Year Temporary}\\ \text{Life Annuity}\end{pmatrix} + \begin{pmatrix}\text{Present Value at Age } x\\ \text{of Life Annuity}\\ \text{Deferred } n \text{ Years}\end{pmatrix} = \begin{pmatrix}\text{Present Value at Age } x\\ \text{of Whole Life}\\ \text{Annuity}\end{pmatrix}$$

(8.3) Expression for the accumulated value at the end of n years, with benefit of survivorship:

$$\begin{pmatrix}\text{Accumulated Value of \$1}\\ \text{at End of } n \text{ Years to a}\\ \text{Life Age } x \text{ at the Beginning,}\\ \text{with Benefit of Survivorship}\end{pmatrix} = \$1\left[\frac{l_x(1+i)^n}{l_{x+n}}\right]$$

(8.7) Definition of the commutation symbol "D_x":

$$D_x = l_x v^x$$

(8.7) Expression for the present value, n years earlier, with benefit of survivorship (using commutation functions):

$$\begin{pmatrix}\text{Present Value of \$1}\\ \text{Due in } n \text{ Years to a}\\ \text{Life Now Age } x\text{, with}\\ \text{Benefit of Survivorship}\end{pmatrix} = \$1\left(\frac{D_{x+n}}{D_x}\right)$$

(8.7) Expression for the accumulated value at the end of n years, with benefit of survivorship (using commutation functions):

$$\begin{pmatrix}\text{Accumulated Value of \$1}\\ \text{at End of } n \text{ Years to a}\\ \text{Life Age } x \text{ at the Beginning,}\\ \text{with Benefit of Survivorship}\end{pmatrix} = \$1\left(\frac{D_x}{D_{x+n}}\right)$$

(8.7) Definition of the commutation symbol "N_x":

$$N_x = (D_x + D_{x+1} + D_{x+2} + \cdots \text{ to the end of the mortality table})$$

(9.1) Expression for the net single premium for 1-year term insurance (natural premium):

$$\begin{pmatrix}\text{Net Single Premium for}\\ \text{\$1,000 Death Benefit}\\ \text{to a Life Age } x\text{, If}\\ \text{Death Occurs in 1 Year}\end{pmatrix} = \$1{,}000\left(\frac{d_x v}{l_x}\right)$$

(9.4) Expression for the net single premium for a pure endowment:

$$\begin{pmatrix}\text{Net Single Premium for}\\ \text{\$1,000 Pure Endowment to}\\ \text{a Life Age } x\text{, Due at the}\\ \text{End of } n \text{ Years}\end{pmatrix} = \$1{,}000\left(\frac{l_{x+n}v^n}{l_x}\right)$$

(9.6) Relationship between accumulated cost of insurance and net single premium:

$$\begin{pmatrix}\text{Accumulated Cost}\\ \text{of Insurance}\end{pmatrix} = \begin{pmatrix}\text{Net Single}\\ \text{Premium}\end{pmatrix}\left[\frac{l_x(1+i)^n}{l_{x+n}}\right]$$

(9.8) Definition of the commutation symbol "C_x":

$$C_x = d_x v^{x+1}$$

(9.8) Expression for the net single premium for 1-year term insurance (natural premium) (using commutation functions):

$$\begin{pmatrix}\text{Net Single Premium for}\\ \text{\$1,000 Death Benefit}\\ \text{to a Life Age } x\text{, If}\\ \text{Death Occurs in 1 Year}\end{pmatrix} = \$1{,}000\left(\frac{C_x}{D_x}\right)$$

(9.8) Definition of the commutation symbol "M_x":

$$M_x = (C_x + C_{x+1} + C_{x+2} + \cdots \text{ to the end of the mortality table})$$

(10.2) Basic principle for calculating net annual premiums:

$$\begin{pmatrix}\text{Present Value of}\\ \text{Net Annual Premiums}\end{pmatrix} = \begin{pmatrix}\text{Present Value of}\\ \text{Benefits}\end{pmatrix}$$

(10.5) Relationship between net premiums and life annuities:

$$\begin{pmatrix}\text{Net Annual}\\ \text{Premium}\end{pmatrix}\begin{pmatrix}\text{Annuity}\\ \text{Factor}\end{pmatrix} = \begin{pmatrix}\text{Net Single}\\ \text{Premium}\end{pmatrix}$$

(10.7) A simple equation that might be used to calculate gross annual premiums:

$$\text{Gross} = \text{Net} + \text{Percent of Gross}$$

(10.7) Another equation that might be used to calculate gross annual premiums:

$$\text{Gross} = \text{Net} + \text{Constant} + \text{Percent of Gross}$$

(11.2) Expression for the retrospective method of calculating terminal reserves:

$$\begin{pmatrix}\text{Terminal}\\ \text{Reserve}\end{pmatrix} = \begin{pmatrix}\text{Accumulated Value}\\ \text{of Net Premiums}\\ \text{Received}\end{pmatrix} - \begin{pmatrix}\text{Accumulated}\\ \text{Cost of}\\ \text{Insurance}\end{pmatrix}$$

(11.3) Expression for the prospective method of calculating terminal reserves:

$$\begin{pmatrix}\text{Terminal}\\ \text{Reserve}\end{pmatrix} = \begin{pmatrix}\text{Present Value}\\ \text{of Future Benefits}\end{pmatrix} - \begin{pmatrix}\text{Present Value of}\\ \text{Future Net Premiums}\end{pmatrix}$$

(11.6) Expression for the mean reserve:

$$\text{Mean Reserve} = \frac{\text{Initial Reserve} + \text{Terminal Reserve}}{2}$$

(11.6) Another expression for the mean reserve:

$$\text{Mean Reserve} = \frac{\text{Net Premium} + \text{Previous Terminal Reserve} + \text{Terminal Reserve}}{2}$$

(11.7) Definition of the net amount at risk:

$$\begin{pmatrix}\text{Net Amount}\\ \text{at Risk}\end{pmatrix} = \begin{pmatrix}\text{Amount of}\\ \text{Insurance}\end{pmatrix} - \begin{pmatrix}\text{Terminal}\\ \text{Reserve}\end{pmatrix}$$

(11.8) An equation for calculating the tabular cost of insurance:

$$\begin{pmatrix}\text{Tabular Cost}\\ \text{of Insurance}\end{pmatrix} = \begin{pmatrix}\text{Initial}\\ \text{Reserve}\end{pmatrix}(1+i) - \begin{pmatrix}\text{Terminal}\\ \text{Reserve}\end{pmatrix}$$

(11.8) A 2nd equation for calculating the tabular cost of insurance:

$$\begin{pmatrix}\text{Tabular Cost}\\ \text{of Insurance}\end{pmatrix} = \left[\begin{pmatrix}\text{Net}\\ \text{Premium}\end{pmatrix} + \begin{pmatrix}\text{Previous}\\ \text{Terminal Reserve}\end{pmatrix}\right](1+i) - \begin{pmatrix}\text{Terminal}\\ \text{Reserve}\end{pmatrix}$$

(11.8) A 3rd equation for calculating the tabular cost of insurance:

$$\begin{pmatrix}\text{Tabular Cost}\\ \text{of Insurance}\end{pmatrix} = \begin{pmatrix}\text{Net Amount}\\ \text{at Risk}\end{pmatrix} q_x$$

(11.8) A 4th equation for calculating the tabular cost of insurance:

$$\begin{pmatrix}\text{Tabular Cost}\\ \text{of Insurance}\end{pmatrix} = \left[\begin{pmatrix}\text{Amount of}\\ \text{Insurance}\end{pmatrix} - \begin{pmatrix}\text{Terminal}\\ \text{Reserve}\end{pmatrix}\right] q_x$$

(12.3) Equations for calculating the modified net premiums used in the Illinois Standard Method:

$$\begin{pmatrix}\text{Years 2–20}\\ \text{Modified}\\ \text{Net Premium}\end{pmatrix} = \begin{pmatrix}\text{Net Level}\\ \text{Premium}\end{pmatrix} + \frac{\begin{pmatrix}\text{Net Level Premium}\\ \text{for 19-Payment}\\ \text{Life, 1 Age Older}\end{pmatrix} - \begin{pmatrix}\text{1-Year}\\ \text{Term Net}\\ \text{Premium}\end{pmatrix}}{\begin{pmatrix}\text{Present Value of Life Annuity Due}\\ \text{of 1 for Premium Period, but Not}\\ \text{More Than 20 Years}\end{pmatrix}}$$

$$\begin{pmatrix}\text{1st-Year}\\ \text{Modified}\\ \text{Net Premium}\end{pmatrix} = \begin{pmatrix}\text{Years 2–20}\\ \text{Modified}\\ \text{Net Premium}\end{pmatrix} - \left[\begin{pmatrix}\text{Net Level Premium}\\ \text{for 19-Payment}\\ \text{Life, 1 Age Older}\end{pmatrix} - \begin{pmatrix}\text{1-Year}\\ \text{Term Net}\\ \text{Premium}\end{pmatrix}\right]$$

(12.4) Equations for calculating the modified net premiums used in the Commissioners Method:

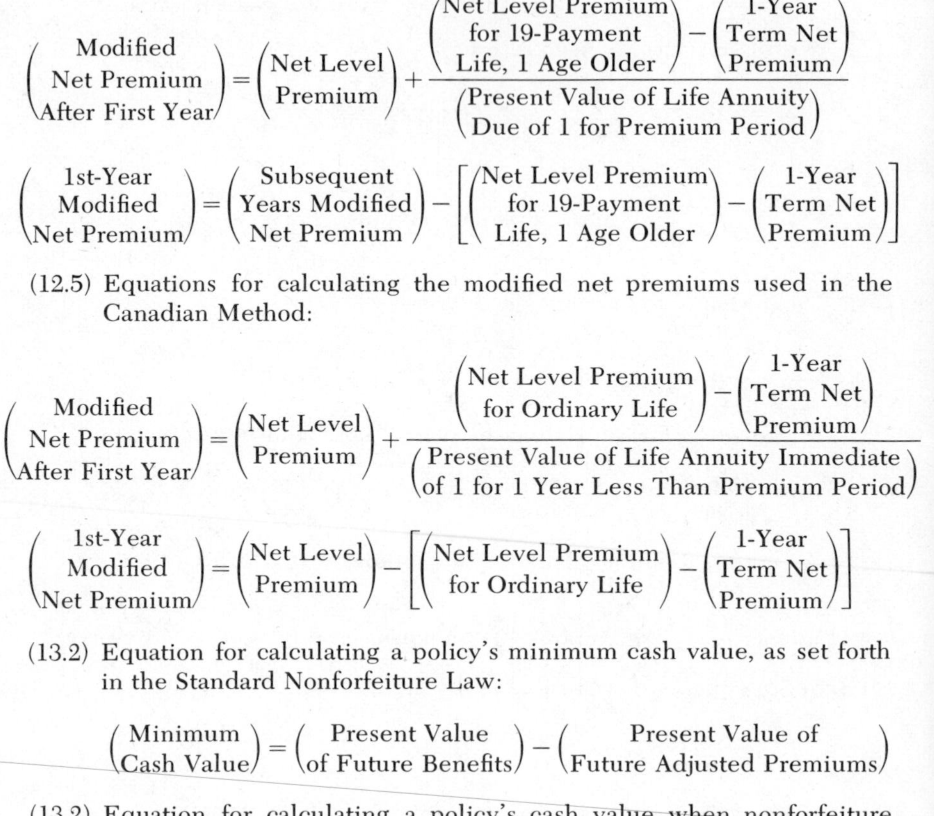

$$\begin{pmatrix}\text{Modified}\\ \text{Net Premium}\\ \text{After First Year}\end{pmatrix} = \begin{pmatrix}\text{Net Level}\\ \text{Premium}\end{pmatrix} + \frac{\begin{pmatrix}\text{Net Level Premium}\\ \text{for 19-Payment}\\ \text{Life, 1 Age Older}\end{pmatrix} - \begin{pmatrix}\text{1-Year}\\ \text{Term Net}\\ \text{Premium}\end{pmatrix}}{\begin{pmatrix}\text{Present Value of Life Annuity}\\ \text{Due of 1 for Premium Period}\end{pmatrix}}$$

$$\begin{pmatrix}\text{1st-Year}\\ \text{Modified}\\ \text{Net Premium}\end{pmatrix} = \begin{pmatrix}\text{Subsequent}\\ \text{Years Modified}\\ \text{Net Premium}\end{pmatrix} - \left[\begin{pmatrix}\text{Net Level Premium}\\ \text{for 19-Payment}\\ \text{Life, 1 Age Older}\end{pmatrix} - \begin{pmatrix}\text{1-Year}\\ \text{Term Net}\\ \text{Premium}\end{pmatrix}\right]$$

(12.5) Equations for calculating the modified net premiums used in the Canadian Method:

$$\begin{pmatrix}\text{Modified}\\ \text{Net Premium}\\ \text{After First Year}\end{pmatrix} = \begin{pmatrix}\text{Net Level}\\ \text{Premium}\end{pmatrix} + \frac{\begin{pmatrix}\text{Net Level Premium}\\ \text{for Ordinary Life}\end{pmatrix} - \begin{pmatrix}\text{1-Year}\\ \text{Term Net}\\ \text{Premium}\end{pmatrix}}{\begin{pmatrix}\text{Present Value of Life Annuity Immediate}\\ \text{of 1 for 1 Year Less Than Premium Period}\end{pmatrix}}$$

$$\begin{pmatrix}\text{1st-Year}\\ \text{Modified}\\ \text{Net Premium}\end{pmatrix} = \begin{pmatrix}\text{Net Level}\\ \text{Premium}\end{pmatrix} - \left[\begin{pmatrix}\text{Net Level Premium}\\ \text{for Ordinary Life}\end{pmatrix} - \begin{pmatrix}\text{1-Year}\\ \text{Term Net}\\ \text{Premium}\end{pmatrix}\right]$$

(13.2) Equation for calculating a policy's minimum cash value, as set forth in the Standard Nonforfeiture Law:

$$\begin{pmatrix}\text{Minimum}\\ \text{Cash Value}\end{pmatrix} = \begin{pmatrix}\text{Present Value}\\ \text{of Future Benefits}\end{pmatrix} - \begin{pmatrix}\text{Present Value of}\\ \text{Future Adjusted Premiums}\end{pmatrix}$$

(13.2) Equation for calculating a policy's cash value when nonforfeiture factors are used:

$$\begin{pmatrix}\text{Cash}\\ \text{Value}\end{pmatrix} = \begin{pmatrix}\text{Present Value}\\ \text{of Future Benefits}\end{pmatrix} - \begin{pmatrix}\text{Present Value of}\\ \text{Future Nonforfeiture Factors}\end{pmatrix}$$

(13.3) Equation for calculating the amount of reduced paid-up insurance which is available:

$$\begin{pmatrix}\text{Amount of}\\ \text{Reduced}\\ \text{Paid-Up}\end{pmatrix} = \frac{\text{Total Value}}{\begin{pmatrix}\text{Net Single Premium}\\ \text{for \$1 of Insurance}\end{pmatrix}}$$

(13.5) The smallest amount of dividend credit needed in order to declare a policy to be fully paid up:

$$\begin{pmatrix}\text{Value of}\\ \text{Dividend Credits}\end{pmatrix} = \begin{pmatrix}\text{Net Single}\\ \text{Premium}\end{pmatrix} - \begin{pmatrix}\text{Cash}\\ \text{Value}\end{pmatrix}$$

(14.2) In the 3-factor contribution method, the contribution towards the dividend from the area of interest:

$$\begin{pmatrix}\text{Contribution}\\ \text{from Interest}\end{pmatrix} = \begin{pmatrix}\text{Initial}\\ \text{Reserve}\end{pmatrix}\left[\begin{pmatrix}\text{Dividend}\\ \text{Interest}\\ \text{Rate}\end{pmatrix} - \begin{pmatrix}\text{Tabular}\\ \text{Interest}\\ \text{Rate}\end{pmatrix}\right]$$

(14.3) In the 3-factor contribution method, the contribution toward the dividend from the area of mortality:

$$\begin{pmatrix}\text{Contribution}\\ \text{from Mortality}\end{pmatrix} = \begin{pmatrix}\text{Net Amount}\\ \text{at Risk}\end{pmatrix}\left[\begin{pmatrix}\text{Tabular}\\ \text{Rate of}\\ \text{Mortality}\end{pmatrix} - \begin{pmatrix}\text{Dividend}\\ \text{Rate of}\\ \text{Mortality}\end{pmatrix}\right]$$

(14.4) In the three-factor contribution method, the contribution toward the dividend from the area of expenses:

$$\begin{pmatrix}\text{Contribution}\\ \text{from Expenses}\end{pmatrix} = \left(\text{Loading}\right) - \begin{pmatrix}\text{Dividend}\\ \text{Expenses}\end{pmatrix}$$

(14.6) Equation for calculating the amount of paid-up additions which a dividend will purchase:

$$\begin{pmatrix}\text{Amount of Paid-Up}\\ \text{Additions}\end{pmatrix} = \frac{\text{Dividend}}{\begin{pmatrix}\text{Net Single Premium}\\ \text{for \$1 of Insurance}\end{pmatrix}}$$

TABLE I

2%

n	(1) Accumulated Value of 1 $(1+i)^n$	(2) Present Value of 1 v^n or $\frac{1}{(1+i)^n}$	(3) Accumulated Value of 1 per Period $s_{\overline{n}\rvert i}$	(4) Present Value of 1 per Period $a_{\overline{n}\rvert i}$	(5) Payment per Period Which Has Accumulated Value of 1 (Sinking Fund Payment) $\frac{1}{s_{\overline{n}\rvert i}}$	(6) Payment per Period Which Has a Present Value of 1 (Amortization Payment) $\frac{1}{a_{\overline{n}\rvert i}}$
1	1.020000	.980392	1.000000	0.980392	1.000000	1.020000
2	1.040400	.961169	2.020000	1.941561	.495050	.515050
3	1.061208	.942322	3.060400	2.883883	.326755	.346755
4	1.082432	.923845	4.121608	3.807729	.242624	.262624
5	1.104081	.905731	5.204040	4.713460	.192158	.212158
6	1.126162	.887971	6.308121	5.601431	.158526	.178526
7	1.148686	.870560	7.434283	6.471901	.134512	.154512
8	1.171659	.853490	8.582969	7.325481	.116510	.136510
9	1.195093	.836755	9.754628	8.162237	.102515	.122515
10	1.218994	.820348	10.949721	8.982585	.091327	.111327
11	1.243374	.804263	12.168715	9.786848	.082178	.102178
12	1.268242	.788493	13.412090	10.575341	.074560	.094560
13	1.293607	.773033	14.680332	11.348374	.068118	.088118
14	1.319479	.757875	15.973938	12.106249	.062602	.082602
15	1.345868	.743015	17.293417	12.849264	.057825	.077825
16	1.372786	.728446	18.639285	13.577709	.053650	.073650
17	1.400241	.714163	20.012071	14.291872	.049970	.069970
18	1.428246	.700159	21.412312	14.992031	.046702	.066702
19	1.456811	.686431	22.840559	15.678462	.043782	.063782
20	1.485947	.672971	24.297370	16.351433	.041157	.061157
21	1.515666	.659776	25.783317	17.011209	.038785	.058785
22	1.545980	.646839	27.298984	17.658048	.036631	.056631
23	1.576899	.634156	28.844963	18.292204	.034668	.054668
24	1.608437	.621721	30.421862	18.913926	.032871	.052871
25	1.640606	.609531	32.030300	19.523456	.031220	.051220

p	2	4	6	12	∞
$s^{(p)}_{\overline{1}\rvert i}$	1.0049752	1.0074686	1.0083012	1.0091339	1.0099670

TABLE I – (Continued)

$2\frac{1}{2}\%$

	(1) Accumulated Value of 1	(2) Present Value of 1	(3) Accumulated Value of 1 per Period	(4) Present Value of 1 per Period	(5) Payment per Period Which Has Accumulated Value of 1 (Sinking Fund Payment)	(6) Payment per Period Which Has a Present Value of 1 (Amortization Payment)
n	$(1+i)^n$	v^n or $\frac{1}{(1+i)^n}$	$s_{\overline{n}\rvert i}$	$a_{\overline{n}\rvert i}$	$\frac{1}{s_{\overline{n}\rvert i}}$	$\frac{1}{a_{\overline{n}\rvert i}}$
1	1.025000	.975610	1.000000	0.975610	1.000000	1.025000
2	1.050625	.951814	2.025000	1.927424	.493827	.518827
3	1.076891	.928599	3.075625	2.856024	.325137	.350137
4	1.103813	.905951	4.152516	3.761974	.240818	.265818
5	1.131408	.883854	5.256329	4.645828	.190247	.215247
6	1.159693	.862297	6.387737	5.508125	.156550	.181550
7	1.188686	.841265	7.547430	6.349391	.132495	.157495
8	1.218403	.820747	8.736116	7.170137	.114467	.139467
9	1.248863	.800728	9.954519	7.970866	.100457	.125457
10	1.280084	.781198	11.203382	8.752064	.089259	.114259
11	1.312087	.762145	12.483466	9.514209	.080106	.105106
12	1.344889	.743556	13.795553	10.257765	.072487	.097487
13	1.378511	.725420	15.140442	10.983185	.066048	.091048
14	1.412974	.707727	16.518953	11.690912	.060537	.085537
15	1.448298	.690466	17.931927	12.381378	.055766	.080766
16	1.484506	.673625	19.380225	13.055003	.051599	.076599
17	1.521618	.657195	20.864730	13.712198	.047928	.072928
18	1.559659	.641166	22.386349	14.353364	.044670	.069670
19	1.598650	.625528	23.946007	14.978891	.041761	.066761
20	1.638616	.610271	25.544658	15.589162	.039147	.064147
21	1.679582	.595386	27.183274	16.184549	.036787	.061787
22	1.721571	.580865	28.862856	16.765413	.034647	.059647
23	1.764611	.566697	30.584427	17.332110	.032696	.057696
24	1.808726	.552875	32.349038	17.884986	.030913	.055913
25	1.853944	.539391	34.157764	18.424376	.029276	.054276

p	2	4	6	12	∞
$s^{(p)}_{\overline{1}\rvert i}$	1.0062114	1.0093268	1.0103666	1.0114072	1.0124486

TABLE I – (Continued)

3%

	(1)	(2)	(3)	(4)	(5)	(6)
	Accumulated Value of 1	Present Value of 1	Accumulated Value of 1 per Period	Present Value of 1 per Period	Payment per Period Which Has Accumulated Value of 1 (Sinking Fund Payment)	Payment per Period Which Has a Present Value of 1 (Amortization Payment)
n	$(1+i)^n$	v^n or $\frac{1}{(1+i)^n}$	$s_{\overline{n}\mid i}$	$a_{\overline{n}\mid i}$	$\frac{1}{s_{\overline{n}\mid i}}$	$\frac{1}{a_{\overline{n}\mid i}}$
1	1.030000	.970874	1.000000	0.970874	1.000000	1.030000
2	1.060900	.942596	2.030000	1.913470	.492611	.522611
3	1.092727	.915142	3.090900	2.828611	.323530	.353530
4	1.125509	.888487	4.183627	3.717098	.239027	.269027
5	1.159274	.862609	5.309136	4.579707	.188355	.218355
6	1.194052	.837484	6.468410	5.417191	.154598	.184598
7	1.229874	.813092	7.662462	6.230283	.130506	.160506
8	1.266770	.789409	8.892336	7.019692	.112456	.142456
9	1.304773	.766417	10.159106	7.786109	.098434	.128434
10	1.343916	.744094	11.463879	8.530203	.087231	.117231
11	1.384234	.722421	12.807796	9.252624	.078077	.108077
12	1.425761	.701380	14.192030	9.954004	.070462	.100462
13	1.468534	.680951	15.617790	10.634955	.064030	.094030
14	1.512590	.661118	17.086324	11.296073	.058526	.088526
15	1.557967	.641862	18.598914	11.937935	.053767	.083767
16	1.604706	.623167	20.156881	12.561102	.049611	.079611
17	1.652848	.605016	21.761588	13.166118	.045953	.075953
18	1.702433	.587395	23.414435	13.753513	.042709	.072709
19	1.753506	.570286	25.116868	14.323799	.039814	.069814
20	1.806111	.553676	26.870374	14.877475	.037216	.067216
21	1.860295	.537549	28.676486	15.415024	.034872	.064872
22	1.916103	.521892	30.536780	15.936917	.032747	.062747
23	1.973587	.506692	32.452884	16.443608	.030814	.060814
24	2.032794	.491934	34.426470	16.935542	.029047	.059047
25	2.093778	.477606	36.459264	17.413148	.027428	.057428

p	2	4	6	12	∞
$s^{(p)}_{\overline{1}\mid i}$	1.0074446	1.0111807	1.0124282	1.0136766	1.0149261

TABLE I – (Continued)

4%

	(1)	(2)	(3)	(4)	(5)	(6)
	Accumulated Value of 1	*Present Value of 1*	*Accumulated Value of 1 per Period*	*Present Value of 1 per Period*	*Payment per Period Which Has Accumulated Value of 1 (Sinking Fund Payment)*	*Payment per Period Which Has a Present Value of 1 (Amortization Payment)*
n	$(1+i)^n$	v^n or $\frac{1}{(1+i)^n}$	$s_{\overline{n}\vert i}$	$a_{\overline{n}\vert i}$	$\frac{1}{s_{\overline{n}\vert i}}$	$\frac{1}{a_{\overline{n}\vert i}}$
1	1.040000	.961538	1.000000	0.961538	1.000000	1.040000
2	1.081600	.924556	2.040000	1.886095	.490196	.530196
3	1.124864	.888996	3.121600	2.775091	.320349	.360349
4	1.169859	.854804	4.246464	3.629895	.235490	.275490
5	1.216653	.821927	5.416323	4.451822	.184627	.224627
6	1.265319	.790315	6.632976	5.242137	.150762	.190762
7	1.315932	.759918	7.898294	6.002055	.126610	.166610
8	1.368569	.730690	9.214226	6.732745	.108528	.148528
9	1.423312	.702587	10.582795	7.435332	.094493	.134493
10	1.480244	.675564	12.006107	8.110896	.083291	.123291
11	1.539454	.649581	13.486351	8.760477	.074149	.114149
12	1.601032	.624597	15.025806	9.385074	.066552	.106552
13	1.665074	.600574	16.626838	9.985648	.060144	.100144
14	1.731676	.577475	18.291911	10.563123	.054669	.094669
15	1.800944	.555264	20.023588	11.118387	.049941	.089941
16	1.872981	.533908	21.824531	11.652296	.045820	.085820
17	1.947900	.513373	23.697512	12.165669	.042199	.082199
18	2.025817	.493628	25.645413	12.659297	.038993	.078993
19	2.106849	.474642	27.671229	13.133939	.036139	.076139
20	2.191123	.456387	29.778079	13.590326	.033582	.073582
21	2.278768	.438834	31.969202	14.029160	.031280	.071280
22	2.369919	.421955	34.247970	14.451115	.029199	.069199
23	2.464716	.405726	36.617889	14.856842	.027309	.067309
24	2.563304	.390121	39.082604	15.246963	.025587	.065587
25	2.665836	.375117	41.645908	15.622080	.024012	.064012

p	2	4	6	12	∞
$s^{(p)}_{\overline{1}\vert i}$	1.0099020	1.0148774	1.0165396	1.0182035	1.0198693

TABLE I—(Concluded)

5%

	(1)	(2)	(3)	(4)	(5)	(6)
	Accumulated Value of 1	*Present Value of 1*	*Accumulated Value of 1 per Period*	*Present Value of 1 per Period*	*Payment per Period Which Has Accumulated Value of 1 (Sinking Fund Payment)*	*Payment per Period Which Has a Present Value of 1 (Amortization Payment)*
n	$(1+i)^n$	v^n or $\frac{1}{(1+i)^n}$	$s_{\overline{n}\vert i}$	$a_{\overline{n}\vert i}$	$\frac{1}{s_{\overline{n}\vert i}}$	$\frac{1}{a_{\overline{n}\vert i}}$
1	1.050000	.952381	1.000000	0.952381	1.000000	1.050000
2	1.102500	.907029	2.050000	1.859410	.487805	.537805
3	1.157625	.863838	3.152500	2.723248	.317209	.367209
4	1.215506	.822702	4.310125	3.545950	.232012	.282012
5	1.276282	.783526	5.525631	4.329477	.180975	.230975
6	1.340096	.746215	6.801913	5.075692	.147017	.197017
7	1.407100	.710681	8.142008	5.786373	.122820	.172820
8	1.477455	.676839	9.549109	6.463213	.104722	.154722
9	1.551328	.644609	11.026564	7.107822	.090690	.140690
10	1.628895	.613913	12.577892	7.721735	.079505	.129505
11	1.710339	.584679	14.206787	8.306414	.070389	.120389
12	1.795856	.556837	15.917126	8.863252	.062825	.112825
13	1.885649	.530321	17.712983	9.393573	.056456	.106456
14	1.979932	.505068	19.598632	9.898641	.051024	.101024
15	2.078928	.481017	21.578564	10.379658	.046342	.096342
16	2.182875	.458112	23.657492	10.837770	.042270	.092270
17	2.292018	.436297	25.840366	11.274066	.038699	.088699
18	2.406619	.415521	28.132385	11.689587	.035546	.085546
19	2.526950	.395734	30.539004	12.085321	.032745	.082745
20	2.653298	.376889	33.065954	12.462210	.030243	.080243
21	2.785963	.358942	35.719252	12.821153	.027996	.077996
22	2.925261	.341850	38.505214	13.163003	.025971	.075971
23	3.071524	.325571	41.430475	13.488574	.024137	.074137
24	3.225100	.310068	44.501999	13.798642	.022471	.072471
25	3.386355	.295303	47.727099	14.093945	.020952	.070952

p	2	4	6	12	∞
$s^{(p)}_{\overline{1}\vert i}$	1.0123475	1.0185594	1.0206357	1.0227148	1.0247967

TABLE II

Annuity Table for 1949 – $2\frac{1}{2}\%$ Interest (male)

Age x	l_x	d_x	q_x	D_x	N_x
0	10 104 755	40 823	.004040	10 104 755	340 256 770
1	10 063 932	15 901	.001580	9 818 470	330 152 015
2	10 048 031	8 913	.000887	9 563 861	320 333 545
3	10 039 118	7 178	.000715	9 322 319	310 769 684
4	10 031 940	6 290	.000627	9 088 442	301 447 365
5	10 025 650	5 675	.000566	8 861 214	292 358 923
6	10 019 975	5 271	.000526	8 640 193	283 497 709
7	10 014 704	5 007	.000500	8 425 022	274 857 516
8	10 009 697	4 875	.000487	8 215 424	266 432 494
9	10 004 822	4 822	.000482	8 011 145	258 217 070
10	10 000 000	4 830	.000483	7 811 984	250 205 925
11	9 995 170	4 918	.000492	7 617 767	242 393 941
12	9 990 252	5 015	.000502	7 428 311	234 776 174
13	9 985 237	5 112	.000512	7 243 494	227 347 863
14	9 980 125	5 230	.000524	7 063 206	220 104 369
15	9 974 895	5 357	.000537	6 887 321	213 041 163
16	9 969 538	5 493	.000551	6 715 729	206 153 842
17	9 964 045	5 650	.000567	6 548 321	199 438 113
18	9 958 395	5 816	.000584	6 384 983	192 889 792
19	9 952 579	6 001	.000603	6 225 614	186 504 809
20	9 946 578	6 207	.000624	6 070 108	180 279 195
21	9 940 371	6 441	.000648	5 918 361	174 209 087
22	9 933 930	6 695	.000674	5 770 269	168 290 726
23	9 927 235	6 969	.000702	5 625 737	162 520 457
24	9 920 266	7 272	.000733	5 484 671	156 894 720
25	9 912 994	7 613	.000768	5 346 976	151 410 049
26	9 905 381	7 984	.000806	5 212 555	146 063 073
27	9 897 397	8 403	.000849	5 081 321	140 850 518
28	9 888 994	8 861	.000896	4 953 177	135 769 197
29	9 880 133	9 356	.000947	4 828 038	130 816 020
30	9 870 777	9 910	.001004	4 705 821	125 987 982
31	9 860 867	10 522	.001067	4 586 435	121 282 161
32	9 850 345	11 190	.001136	4 469 796	116 695 726
33	9 839 155	11 935	.001213	4 355 823	112 225 930
34	9 827 220	12 746	.001297	4 244 429	107 870 107
35	9 814 474	13 652	.001391	4 135 535	103 625 678
36	9 800 822	14 642	.001494	4 029 056	99 490 143
37	9 786 180	15 726	.001607	3 924 914	95 461 087
38	9 770 454	16 932	.001733	3 823 031	91 536 173
39	9 753 522	18 259	.001872	3 723 323	87 713 142
40	9 735 263	19 714	.002025	3 625 710	83 989 819
41	9 715 549	21 569	.002220	3 530 115	80 364 109
42	9 693 980	24 051	.002481	3 436 369	76 833 994
43	9 669 929	27 114	.002804	3 344 237	73 397 625
44	9 642 815	30 732	.003187	3 253 522	70 053 388
45	9 612 083	34 844	.003625	3 164 052	66 799 866
46	9 577 239	39 420	.004116	3 075 690	63 635 814
47	9 537 819	44 418	.004657	2 988 322	60 560 124
48	9 493 401	49 802	.005246	2 901 859	57 571 802
49	9 443 599	55 528	.005880	2 816 230	54 669 943
50	9 388 071	61 558	.006557	2 731 386	51 853 713
51	9 326 513	67 869	.007277	2 647 294	49 122 327
52	9 258 644	74 421	.008038	2 563 931	46 475 033
53	9 184 223	81 189	.008840	2 481 290	43 911 102
54	9 103 034	88 136	.009682	2 399 371	41 429 812

(Continued on next page)

TABLE II – (Continued)

Annuity Table for 1949 – $2\frac{1}{2}$% Interest (male)

Age x	l_x	d_x	q_x	D_x	N_x
55	9 014 898	95 242	.010565	2 318 186	39 030 441
56	8 919 656	102 496	.011491	2 237 750	36 712 255
57	8 817 160	109 862	.012460	2 158 084	34 474 505
58	8 707 298	117 340	.013476	2 079 214	32 316 421
59	8 589 958	124 915	.014542	2 001 165	30 237 207
60	8 465 043	132 580	.015662	1 923 965	28 236 042
61	8 332 463	140 560	.016869	1 847 641	26 312 077
62	8 191 903	149 084	.018199	1 772 169	24 464 436
63	8 042 819	158 170	.019666	1 697 480	22 692 267
64	7 884 649	167 809	.021283	1 623 510	20 994 787
65	7 716 840	177 997	.023066	1 550 202	19 371 277
66	7 538 843	188 697	.025030	1 477 507	17 821 075
67	7 350 146	199 873	.027193	1 405 390	16 343 568
68	7 150 273	211 484	.029577	1 333 828	14 938 178
69	6 938 789	223 443	.032202	1 262 807	13 604 350
70	6 715 346	235 655	.035092	1 192 334	12 341 543
71	6 479 691	247 991	.038272	1 122 432	11 149 209
72	6 231 700	260 304	.041771	1 053 145	10 026 777
73	5 971 396	272 415	.045620	984 541	8 973 632
74	5 698 981	284 106	.049852	916 708	7 989 091
75	5 414 875	295 116	.054501	849 765	7 072 383
76	5 119 759	305 184	.059609	783 855	6 222 618
77	4 814 575	313 987	.065216	719 151	5 438 763
78	4 500 588	321 198	.071368	655 855	4 719 612
79	4 179 390	326 465	.078113	594 193	4 063 757
80	3 852 925	329 437	.085503	534 418	3 469 564
81	3 523 488	329 774	.093593	476 804	2 935 146
82	3 193 714	327 174	.102443	421 637	2 458 342
83	2 866 540	321 376	.112113	369 213	2 036 705
84	2 545 164	312 213	.122669	319 824	1 667 492
85	2 232 951	299 613	.134178	273 748	1 347 668
86	1 933 338	283 638	.146709	231 236	1 073 920
87	1 649 700	264 501	.160333	192 499	842 684
88	1 385 199	242 582	.175124	157 693	650 185
89	1 142 617	218 412	.191151	126 905	492 492
90	924 205	192 683	.208485	100 143	365 587
91	731 522	166 196	.227192	77 331	265 444
92	565 326	139 823	.247332	58 305	188 113
93	425 503	114 443	.268960	42 814	129 808
94	311 060	90 866	.292118	30 535	86 994
95	220 194	69 765	.316834	21 088	56 459
96	150 429	51 616	.343122	14 055	35 371
97	98 813	36 657	.370973	9 007	21 316
98	62 156	24 884	.400352	5 528	12 309
99	37 272	16 072	.431199	3 234	6 781
100	21 200	9 824	.463415	1 795	3 547
101	11 376	5 652	.496870	939	1 752
102	5 724	3 042	.531389	461	813
103	2 682	1 520	.566757	211	352
104	1 160	700	.602714	89	141
105	462	295	.638956	35	52
106	167	113	.675143	12	17
107	54	38	.710898	4	5
108	16	12	.745822	1	1
109	4	4	1.000000	0	0

Note: l_x, d_x, D_x, and N_x values adjusted by authors to display only whole numbers.

TABLE III

1958 C.S.O. Table (male)

Age x	l_x	d_x	q_x	Age x	l_x	d_x	q_x
0	10 000 000	70 800	.00708	50	8 762 306	72 902	.00832
1	9 929 200	17 475	.00176	51	8 689 404	79 160	.00911
2	9 911 725	15 066	.00152	52	8 610 244	85 758	.00996
3	9 896 659	14 449	.00146	53	8 524 486	92 832	.01089
4	9 882 210	13 835	.00140	54	8 431 654	100 337	.01190
5	9 868 375	13 322	.00135	55	8 331 317	108 307	.01300
6	9 855 053	12 812	.00130	56	8 223 010	116 849	.01421
7	9 842 241	12 401	.00126	57	8 106 161	125 970	.01554
8	9 829 840	12 091	.00123	58	7 980 191	135 663	.01700
9	9 817 749	11 879	.00121	59	7 844 528	145 830	.01859
10	9 805 870	11 865	.00121	60	7 698 698	156 592	.02034
11	9 794 005	12 047	.00123	61	7 542 106	167 736	.02224
12	9 781 958	12 325	.00126	62	7 374 370	179 271	.02431
13	9 769 633	12 896	.00132	63	7 195 099	191 174	.02657
14	9 756 737	13 562	.00139	64	7 003 925	203 394	.02904
15	9 743 175	14 225	.00146	65	6 800 531	215 917	.03175
16	9 728 950	14 983	.00154	66	6 584 614	228 749	.03474
17	9 713 967	15 737	.00162	67	6 355 865	241 777	.03804
18	9 698 230	16 390	.00169	68	6 114 088	254 835	.04168
19	9 681 840	16 846	.00174	69	5 859 253	267 241	.04561
20	9 664 994	17 300	.00179	70	5 592 012	278 426	.04979
21	9 647 694	17 655	.00183	71	5 313 586	287 731	.05415
22	9 630 039	17 912	.00186	72	5 025 855	294 766	.05865
23	9 612 127	18 167	.00189	73	4 731 089	299 289	.06326
24	9 593 960	18 324	.00191	74	4 431 800	301 894	.06812
25	9 575 636	18 481	.00193	75	4 129 906	303 011	.07337
26	9 557 155	18 732	.00196	76	3 826 895	303 014	.07918
27	9 538 423	18 981	.00199	77	3 523 881	301 997	.08570
28	9 519 442	19 324	.00203	78	3 221 884	299 829	.09306
29	9 500 118	19 760	.00208	79	2 922 055	295 683	.10119
30	9 480 358	20 193	.00213	80	2 626 372	288 848	.10998
31	9 460 165	20 718	.00219	81	2 337 524	278 983	.11935
32	9 439 447	21 239	.00225	82	2 058 541	265 902	.12917
33	9 418 208	21 850	.00232	83	1 792 639	249 858	.13938
34	9 396 358	22 551	.00240	84	1 542 781	231 433	.15001
35	9 373 807	23 528	.00251	85	1 311 348	211 311	.16114
36	9 350 279	24 685	.00264	86	1 100 037	190 108	.17282
37	9 325 594	26 112	.00280	87	909 929	168 455	.18513
38	9 299 482	27 991	.00301	88	741 474	146 997	.19825
39	9 271 491	30 132	.00325	89	594 477	126 303	.21246
40	9 241 359	32 622	.00353	90	468 174	106 809	.22814
41	9 208 737	35 362	.00384	91	361 365	88 813	.24577
42	9 173 375	38 253	.00417	92	272 552	72 480	.26593
43	9 135 122	41 382	.00453	93	200 072	57 881	.28930
44	9 093 740	44 741	.00492	94	142 191	45 026	.31666
45	9 048 999	48 412	.00535	95	97 165	34 128	.35124
46	9 000 587	52 473	.00583	96	63 037	25 250	.40056
47	8 948 114	56 910	.00636	97	37 787	18 456	.48842
48	8 891 204	61 794	.00695	98	19 331	12 916	.66815
49	8 829 410	67 104	.00760	99	6 415	6 415	1.00000

TABLE IV

1958 C.S.O. Table – 3% Interest (male)

Age x	D_x	N_x	C_x	M_x
0	10 000 000	288 963 016	68 738	1 583 602
1	9 640 000	278 963 016	16 472	1 514 864
2	9 342 751	269 323 016	13 788	1 498 392
3	9 056 845	259 980 265	12 838	1 484 604
4	8 780 216	250 923 420	11 934	1 471 766
5	8 512 547	242 143 204	11 157	1 459 832
6	8 253 452	233 630 657	10 417	1 448 675
7	8 002 643	225 377 205	9 789	1 438 258
8	7 759 766	217 374 562	9 267	1 428 469
9	7 524 487	209 614 796	8 839	1 419 202
10	7 296 488	202 090 309	8 572	1 410 363
11	7 075 398	194 793 821	8 450	1 401 791
12	6 860 869	187 718 423	8 393	1 393 341
13	6 652 645	180 857 554	8 526	1 384 948
14	6 450 353	174 204 909	8 705	1 376 422
15	6 253 773	167 754 556	8 865	1 367 717
16	6 062 760	161 500 783	9 065	1 358 852
17	5 877 110	155 438 023	9 244	1 349 787
18	5 696 688	149 560 913	9 347	1 340 543
19	5 521 418	143 864 225	9 327	1 331 196
20	5 351 273	138 342 807	9 300	1 321 869
21	5 186 111	132 991 534	9 214	1 312 569
22	5 025 845	127 805 423	9 076	1 303 355
23	4 870 385	122 779 578	8 937	1 294 279
24	4 719 593	117 909 193	8 752	1 285 342
25	4 573 377	113 189 600	8 570	1 276 590
26	4 431 602	108 616 223	8 433	1 268 020
27	4 294 094	104 184 621	8 296	1 259 587
28	4 160 727	99 890 527	8 200	1 251 291
29	4 031 341	95 729 800	8 141	1 243 091
30	3 905 782	91 698 459	8 077	1 234 950
31	3 783 944	87 792 677	8 046	1 226 873
32	3 665 687	84 008 733	8 008	1 218 827
33	3 550 912	80 343 046	7 998	1 210 819
34	3 439 489	76 792 134	8 014	1 202 821
35	3 331 295	73 352 645	8 118	1 194 807
36	3 226 149	70 021 350	8 269	1 186 689
37	3 123 915	66 795 201	8 492	1 178 420
38	3 024 435	63 671 286	8 838	1 169 928
39	2 927 506	60 646 851	9 237	1 161 090
40	2 833 002	57 719 345	9 709	1 151 853
41	2 740 778	54 886 343	10 218	1 142 144
42	2 650 731	52 145 565	10 732	1 131 926
43	2 562 794	49 494 834	11 271	1 121 194
44	2 476 878	46 932 040	11 831	1 109 923
45	2 392 905	44 455 162	12 429	1 098 092
46	2 310 779	42 062 257	13 079	1 085 663
47	2 230 396	39 751 478	13 772	1 072 584
48	2 151 661	37 521 082	14 519	1 058 812
49	2 074 472	35 369 421	15 307	1 044 293

(Continued on next page)

TABLE IV – (Continued)

1958 C.S.O. Table – 3% Interest (male)

Age x	D_x	N_x	C_x	M_x
50	1 998 744	33 294 949	16 145	1 028 986
51	1 924 383	31 296 205	17 020	1 012 841
52	1 851 313	29 371 822	17 902	995 821
53	1 779 489	27 520 509	18 814	977 919
54	1 708 845	25 741 020	19 743	959 105
55	1 639 330	24 032 175	20 691	939 362
56	1 570 892	22 392 845	21 672	918 671
57	1 503 465	20 821 953	22 683	896 999
58	1 436 992	19 318 488	23 717	874 316
59	1 371 420	17 881 496	24 752	850 599
60	1 306 724	16 510 076	25 805	825 847
61	1 242 859	15 203 352	26 836	800 042
62	1 179 823	13 960 493	27 846	773 206
63	1 117 613	12 780 670	28 830	745 360
64	1 056 231	11 663 057	29 780	716 530
65	995 688	10 606 826	30 692	686 750
66	935 995	9 611 138	31 569	656 058
67	877 164	8 675 143	32 395	624 489
68	819 220	7 797 979	33 151	592 094
69	762 208	6 978 759	33 752	558 943
70	706 256	6 216 551	34 140	525 191
71	651 546	5 510 295	34 254	491 051
72	598 315	4 858 749	34 069	456 797
73	546 819	4 260 434	33 584	422 728
74	497 308	3 713 615	32 890	389 144
75	449 933	3 216 307	32 050	356 254
76	404 779	2 766 374	31 117	324 204
77	361 872	2 361 595	30 109	293 087
78	321 223	1 999 723	29 022	262 978
79	282 844	1 678 500	27 787	233 956
80	246 819	1 395 656	26 354	206 169
81	213 275	1 148 837	24 713	179 815
82	182 351	935 562	22 868	155 102
83	154 171	753 211	20 863	132 234
84	128 818	599 040	18 761	111 371
85	106 305	470 222	16 631	92 610
86	86 578	363 917	14 527	75 979
87	69 529	277 339	12 497	61 452
88	55 007	207 810	10 588	48 955
89	42 818	152 803	8 832	38 367
90	32 738	109 985	7 251	29 535
91	24 533	77 247	5 854	22 284
92	17 965	52 714	4 638	16 430
93	12 803	34 749	3 596	11 792
94	8 834	21 946	2 716	8 196
95	5 861	13 112	1 999	5 480
96	3 692	7 251	1 436	3 481
97	2 148	3 559	1 019	2 045
98	1 067	1 411	692	1 026
99	344	344	334	334

Note: Values adjusted by authors to display only whole numbers.

Answers to Exercises*

*(Note: In many cases answers will vary slightly, depending upon rounding used in the calculation.)

Following Section 1.3

1 $\frac{17}{12}$ **2** $\frac{23}{24}$ **3** $\frac{13}{10}$

4 $\frac{2}{3}$ **5** $\frac{1}{12}$ **6** $\frac{3A + 5B}{15}$

7 $\frac{17}{8}$ **8** $\frac{12}{5(A + B)}$ **9** $\frac{3}{16}$

10 $\frac{2}{5}$ **11** $\frac{2}{9}$ **12** $\frac{3}{4}$

13 $\frac{7}{25}$ **14** $\frac{B + 10}{2}$

Following Section 1.5

1 76.652 **2** 1.880004 **3** .14286

4 (*a*) 4837.5; (*b*) .841; (*c*) 327490; (*d*) .0421; (*e*) 72.842; (*f*) .038214; (*g*) 4.2956; (*h*) .0007148

5 .48265; .95373; .38496; .71826; .48; .95; .38; .72

6 (*a*) \$103.79; (*b*) \$1,030.00; (*c*) 34,344; (*d*) \$1,204.76; (*e*) $3(Y - 10YZ + 4Z)$

Following Section 1.6

1 398.02 **2** 11.40434 **3** 1025.35876 **4** 127,995.34

5 4900 **6** 10.24404 **7** .6085325 **8** 1006.6984

9 180.0349 **10** .0004392

Following Section 2.3

1 9 **2** 3 **3** 3 **4** 12

5 30 **6** 10 **7** 3 **8** 10

9 3	**10** 7	**11** 1	**12** 2
13 7	**14** 5^9	**15** 5^{14}	**16** 5^{40}
17 5^5	**18** 5	**19** $(1.04)^{11}$	**20** R^{29}
21 v^9	**22** $\left(\frac{1}{1+i}\right)^{18}$	**23** $\left(\frac{a+b}{c+d}\right)^3$	

24 $25(1.03)[1 + (1.03) + (1.03)^2]$

25 $7(1.02)^2[1 + 2(1.02)^2 + 3(1.02)^4]$

26 $\frac{100}{1.04}\left[2 + \frac{1}{1.04} + \frac{3}{(1.04)^2} + \frac{1}{(1.04)^3}\right]$

Following Section 3.3

3 \$3,311.44 **4** \$9,869.49 **5** 3.555673 **6** 2.427261

Following Section 3.5

1 \$10.00 **2** 232 **3** \$5,193.06 **4** \$2,020.00
5 \$609.50 **6** \$2,677.14 **7** 5.0625% **8** 4.0604%
9 5% **10** Between 5% and 6%

Following Section 4.3

3 \$1,463.42 **4** \$1,171.80 **5** \$610.27 **6** \$9,872.56
7 \$2,468.14 + \$2,373.21 + \$2,281.94 + \$2,194.17 = \$9,317.46
8 .591899 and .526788 **9** .411987

Following Section 5.4

3 \$8,622.22 **4** \$1,045.91 **5** \$2,429.74
6 112.7969, rounded to 4 decimal places **7** 8.394 and 5.637
8 \$54.00 **9** \$1,915.61 **10** \$1,156.68

Following Section 5.6

3 \$1,116.87 **4** \$2,759.32 **5** \$1,963.75 **6** \$161.71
7 \$39.42 **8** \$99.37 **9** \$403.50 **10** \$24.12

Following Section 6.4

2 \$528.16 **3** \$4,178.28 **4** \$892.65
7 5.971 and 4.766
8 \$873.92 **9** \$391.96 **10** \$2,735.55

Following Section 6.6

1 3.723248 **3** \$583.11 **4** \$1,265.30 **5** \$482.31
6 \$1,089.86 and \$2,157.86 **7** \$62.25
8 \$64.74 **9** \$641.28

Following Section 6.8

1 $25.38 2 $24.88 3 $1,849.36
4 $263.97 5 $226.14 6 $1,707.24
7 $1,023.23 8 $4,812.89 10 $373.54

Review Exercises End of Chapter 6

1 $640.04 2 $390.60 3 $429.15
4 $1,371.89 5 $792.23 6 $1,790.90
7 $1,469.88 8 21.412313 and 24.297370 9 5.417191 and 7.019692
10 $150.09 11 $4,905.43 12 $2,327.27
13 $235.49 15 12.6162% 16 $190.27
17 $1,327.88 18 $2,313.15 19 $406.88
20 $700.21 21 $2,091.59 22 $127.07 and $112.90
23 $729.40 24 $668.92

Following Section 7.2

1 $\frac{1}{6}$ 2 $\frac{1}{36}$ 3 .0134 4 .00079952
5 .4961 6 $\frac{2}{1000}$, or .002 7 $\frac{998}{1000}$, or .998 8 .18033

Following Section 7.5

1 .015662 2 $\frac{2034}{100,000}$ 3 797 4 .89881
5 .00196 6 993,737 7 33,869 8 2,092
9 948,911 10 .07317, rounded to 5 decimal places

11

Age x	d_x	q_x
20	723	.00780
21	722	.00786
22	721	.00791

Following Section 7.7

1 .9982 2 .9363 3 .9243 4 .9443
5 7,255 6 .2827 7 2,060 8 Approximately 78
9 .9243 10 .0013 11 .0587 12 .9981
13 .9976 14 .0203 15 .9858 16 .00012

Following Section 8.2

1 $\$250\left(\frac{l_{35}v^{25}}{l_{10}}\right)$

2 $\$50\left(\frac{l_{65}+l_{66}v+l_{67}v^2+l_{68}v^3}{l_{65}}\right)$

3 $\$750\left(\frac{l_{42}v^{22}+l_{43}v^{23}+l_{44}v^{24}}{l_{20}}\right)$

4 $\$1{,}000\left(\frac{l_{97}v + l_{98}v^2 + l_{99}v^3}{l_{96}}\right)$

5 \$17.93 6 \$68.02 7 \$31.40 8 \$2.91

9 \$165.67 10 \$153.06

Following Section 8.6

1 $\$1{,}000\left[\frac{l_{20}(1+i)^{45}}{l_{65}}\right]$

2 $\$25\left[\frac{l_{21}(1+i)^4 + l_{22}(1+i)^3 + l_{23}(1+i)^2 + l_{24}(1+i)}{l_{25}}\right]$

3 \$130.01

4 \$2,501.46; \$2,513.96; \$2,522.29; \$2,526.46

5 \$2,551.46; \$2,538.96; \$2,530.63; \$2,526.46

6 \$435.83

7 \$38.81 per \$1,000 of proceeds

8 \$2,690.52

Following Section 8.7

1 $\$1{,}000\left(\frac{D_{62}}{D_{24}}\right) = \$323.11$

2 $\$500\left(\frac{D_{21}}{D_{63}}\right) = \$1{,}743.28$

3

With Benefit of Survivorship	*Interest Only*
.773434	.781198
.678086	.690466
.591746	.610271
.510828	.539391

4 \$168.99

5 $\$1\left(\frac{N_{23}}{D_{23}}\right) = \$28.89$; $\$1\left(\frac{N_{24}}{D_{23}}\right) = \$27.89$; $\$1\left(\frac{N_{55}}{D_{23}}\right) = \$6.94$

6 $\$100\left(\frac{N_{46} - N_{56}}{D_{36}}\right) = \$668.23$

7 \$37,586.07 8 \$8,776.54

9 \$273.06 11 \$512.25

12 The present value at age 20 of a deferred whole life annuity of \$100 per year, first payment at age 69
The present value at age 20 of a deferred temporary life annuity of \$100 per year, first payment at age 69, last payment at age 78

Following Section 9.7

1 $\$4{,}000\left(\frac{d_{25}v}{l_{25}}\right) = \$7.50$

2 $\$1{,}000\left(\frac{d_{45}v + d_{46}v^2 + d_{47}v^3}{l_{45}}\right) = \$16.42$

3 $\$10{,}000\left(\frac{d_{97}v + d_{98}v^2 + d_{99}v^3}{l_{97}}\right) = \$9{,}517.47$

4 $\$1{,}000\left(\frac{l_{65}v^{15}}{l_{50}}\right) = \$498.16$

5 $\$5{,}000\left(\frac{d_{20}v + d_{21}v^2 + d_{22}v^3 + l_{23}v^3}{l_{20}}\right) = \$4{,}576.46$

6 \$25.78 and \$4,550.68

8 $\$1{,}000\left[\frac{d_{19}(1+i)^2 + d_{20}(1+i) + d_{21}}{l_{22}}\right] = \$5.54$

9 \$283.33

10 \$4,576.85

Following Section 9.8

1 $\$10{,}000\left(\frac{C_{10}}{D_{10}}\right) = \$11.75$

2 $\$10{,}000\left(\frac{M_{10} - M_{40}}{D_{10}}\right) = \$354.29$

3 $\$1{,}000\left(\frac{M_{65}}{D_{65}}\right) = \$689.72$

4 $\$2{,}000\left(\frac{D_{30}}{D_5}\right) = \$917.65$

5 $\$5{,}000\left(\frac{M_{40} - M_{70} + D_{70}}{D_{40}}\right) = \$2{,}352.48$

6 $\$10{,}000\left(\frac{M_{18} - M_{30}}{D_{30}}\right) = \$270.35$

7 $\$1{,}000(1.015)\left(\frac{M_{15} - M_{65}}{D_{15}}\right) = \$110.52$

8 *a*) Net single premium at age 43 for \$1,000 1-year term insurance
b) Net single premium at age 43 for \$1,000 4-year term insurance
c) Net single premium at age 43 for \$1,000 4-year term insurance
d) Net single premium at age 62 for \$5,000 whole life insurance
e) Net single premium at age 25 for \$15,000 25-year endowment insurance (endowment-at-age-50 insurance)
f) Net single premium at age 25 for \$1,500 40-year pure endowment (pure endowment due at age 65)
g) Net single premium at age 0 for \$1,500 40-year term insurance, with insurance payable at the moment of death

Following Section 10.5

1 *a*) $\binom{\text{Net Annual}}{\text{Premium}}(l_{75}) = \$1{,}000(d_{75}v)$; \$71.23

b) $\binom{\text{Net Annual}}{\text{Premium}}(l_{69} + l_{70}v + l_{71}v^2) = \$1{,}000(d_{69}v + d_{70}v^2 + d_{71}v^3)$; \$48.18

c) $\binom{\text{Net Annual}}{\text{Premium}}(l_{97} + l_{98}v + l_{99}v^2) = \$1{,}000(d_{97}v + d_{98}v^2 + d_{99}v^3)$; \$574.49

d) $\binom{\text{Net Annual}}{\text{Premium}}(l_{97} + l_{98}v) = \$1{,}000(d_{97}v + d_{98}v^2 + d_{99}v^3)$; \$635.91

e) $\binom{\text{Net Annual}}{\text{Premium}}(l_{10} + l_{11}v + l_{12}v^2) = \$1{,}000(d_{10}v + d_{11}v^2 + d_{12}v^3 + l_{13}v^3)$; \$314.52

f) $\binom{\text{Net Annual}}{\text{Premium}}(l_{25} + l_{26}v) = \$1{,}000(d_{25}v + d_{26}v^2 + d_{27}v^3 + d_{28}v^4 + l_{29}v^4)$; \$451.40

3 \$75.05 4 7.914 5 \$412.37

Following Section 10.6

1 *a)* $\$1{,}000\left(\frac{M_{25} - M_{45}}{N_{25} - N_{45}}\right) = \$2.60$

b) $\$1{,}000\left(\frac{M_{65} - M_{66}}{N_{65} - N_{66}}\right)$, or $\$1{,}000\left(\frac{C_{65}}{D_{65}}\right) = \$30.82$

c) $\$1{,}000\left(\frac{M_{40} - M_{65}}{N_{40} - N_{65}}\right) = \$9.87$

d) $\$1{,}000\left(\frac{M_0}{N_0}\right) = \$5.48$

e) $\$1{,}000\left(\frac{M_{21}}{N_{21} - N_{51}}\right) = \$12.91$

f) $\$1{,}000\left(\frac{M_{30}}{N_{30} - N_{70}}\right) = \$14.45$

g) $\$1{,}000\left(\frac{M_{28} - M_{53} + D_{53}}{N_{28} - N_{53}}\right) = \$28.37$

h) $\$1{,}000\left(\frac{M_{15} - M_{45} + D_{45}}{N_{15} - N_{35}}\right) = \$28.20$

i) $\$1{,}000\left(\frac{M_{22} - M_{70} + D_{70}}{N_{22} - N_{52}}\right) = \$15.08$

2 \$148.45 3 \$11.49

4 *a)* Net annual premium for a \$1,000 20-payment 30-year endowment insurance policy issued at age 5
b) Net annual premium for a \$1,000 20-payment life policy issued at age 60
c) Net annual premium for a \$1,000 5-payment 10-year term insurance policy issued at age 14
d) Net annual premium for a \$5,000 40-year endowment insurance policy (endowment-at-age-65) issued at age 25, with insurance payable at the moment of death

Following Section 10.8

1 \$15.06 2 \$158.60 3 \$26.17 4 \$398.55
5 \$647.60 6 \$800.50 7 \$27.56 8 \$75.92

Following Section 11.3

2 \$144.22

3 \$450.97

4 *a*) Retrospective:

$$\$23.563\left[\frac{l_{60}(1+i)^2 + l_{61}(1+i)}{l_{62}}\right] - \$1{,}000\left[\frac{d_{60}(1+i) + d_{61}}{l_{62}}\right]$$

Prospective:

$$\$1{,}000\left(\frac{d_{62}v + d_{63}v^2 + d_{64}v^3}{l_{62}}\right) - \$23.563\left(\frac{l_{62} + l_{63}v + l_{64}v^2}{l_{62}}\right)$$

Value = \$6.30

b) Retrospective:

$$\$479.992\left[\frac{l_{96}(1+i)^2 + l_{97}(1+i)}{l_{98}}\right] - \$1{,}000\left[\frac{d_{96}(1+i) + d_{97}}{l_{98}}\right]$$

Prospective:

$$\$1{,}000\left(\frac{d_{98}v + d_{99}v^2}{l_{98}}\right) - \$479.992\left(\frac{l_{98} + l_{99}v}{l_{98}}\right)$$

Value = \$326.83

c) Retrospective:

$$\$595.950\left[\frac{l_{96}(1+i)^2 + l_{97}(1+i)}{l_{98}}\right] - \$1{,}000\left[\frac{d_{96}(1+i) + d_{97}}{l_{98}}\right]$$

Prospective:

$$\$1{,}000\left(\frac{d_{98}v + d_{99}v^2}{l_{98}}\right)$$

Value = \$961.46

d) Retrospective:

$$\$232.896\left[\frac{l_{30}(1+i)^2 + l_{31}(1+i)}{l_{32}}\right] - \$1{,}000\left[\frac{d_{30}(1+i) + d_{31}}{l_{32}}\right]$$

Prospective:

$$\$1{,}000\left(\frac{d_{32}v + d_{33}v^2 + l_{34}v^2}{l_{32}}\right) - \$232.896\left(\frac{l_{32} + l_{33}v}{l_{32}}\right)$$

Value = \$484.16

e) Retrospective:

$$\$226.086\left[\frac{l_{25}(1+i)^2 + l_{26}(1+i)}{l_{27}}\right] - \$1{,}000\left[\frac{d_{25}(1+i) + d_{26}}{l_{27}}\right]$$

Prospective:

$$\$1{,}000\left(\frac{d_{27}v + d_{28}v^2 + d_{29}v^3 + l_{30}v^3}{l_{27}}\right) - \$226.086\left(\frac{l_{27} + l_{28}v}{l_{27}}\right)$$

Value = \$470.16

Following Section 11.4

1 *a*) Retrospective:

$$\$6.308\left(\frac{N_{40} - N_{50}}{D_{50}}\right) - \$1{,}000\left(\frac{M_{40} - M_{50}}{D_{50}}\right)$$

Prospective:

$$\$1{,}000\left(\frac{M_{50} - M_{55}}{D_{50}}\right) - \$6.308\left(\frac{N_{50} - N_{55}}{D_{50}}\right)$$

Value = \$15.61

b) Retrospective:

$$\$11.278\left(\frac{N_{25} - N_{65}}{D_{65}}\right) - \$1{,}000\left(\frac{M_{25} - M_{65}}{D_{65}}\right)$$

Prospective:

$$\$1{,}000\left(\frac{M_{65}}{D_{65}}\right) - \$11.278\left(\frac{N_{65}}{D_{65}}\right)$$

Value = \$569.58

c) Retrospective:

$$\$21.145\left(\frac{N_{30} - N_{35}}{D_{35}}\right) - \$1{,}000\left(\frac{M_{30} - M_{35}}{D_{35}}\right)$$

Prospective:

$$\$1{,}000\left(\frac{M_{35}}{D_{35}}\right) - \$21.145\left(\frac{N_{35} - N_{50}}{D_{35}}\right)$$

Value = \$104.40

d) Retrospective:

$$\$37.266\left(\frac{N_0 - N_8}{D_8}\right) - \$1{,}000\left(\frac{M_0 - M_8}{D_8}\right)$$

Prospective:

$$\$1{,}000\left(\frac{M_8 - M_{20} + D_{20}}{D_8}\right) - \$37.266\left(\frac{N_8 - N_{20}}{D_8}\right)$$

Value = \$323.81

2 \$57.37 3 \$236.32 4 \$133.53; \$400.59

Following Section 11.11

1 \$1,107.65 2 \$3,197.35 3 \$773.53 4 \$8,708.70

5 \$398.17 6 \$9.33 7 \$23.43

8 $\$2.15\left(\frac{l_{63}+l_{64}v}{l_{63}}\right) = \$4.18$

9 \$5.32, \$5.18, \$5.18, \$5.23, \$5.74

10 $\text{Net Annual Premium} = \frac{\$265.75(1.015)}{25.209 - \frac{1}{2}} = \$10.917$

$\text{5th Terminal Reserve} = \$300.74(1.015) - \$10.917(24.008 - \tfrac{1}{2}) = \$48.61$

Following Section 12.6

1 \$17.14 2 \$22.57

3 First Year = \$19.48
Years 2–20 = \$43.30
Subsequent = \$41.70

4 First Year = \$320.80
Subsequent = \$588.27

5 First Year = \$204.31
Subsequent = \$422.43

6 \$22.22; \$257.07; \$202.29

Following Section 13.5

1 \$4,871.16 2 \$394.33 per \$1,000 3 \$173.39 4 \$13.67

5 \$316.19 6 \$94.16 7 \$95.66 8 \$741

9 \$35,838 10 \$5,645 insurance for 22 years and 220 days

11 \$10,000 term insurance for 5 years, plus \$7,761 pure endowment at end of 5 years

12 No

Following Section 14.7

1 \$1.97 + \$3.21 + \$3.66 = \$8.84 2 \$4.74 + \$.86 + (−\$5.12) = \$.48

3 \$6.38 + \$1.28 = \$7.66 4 \$58

5 \$47 6 \$13

7 \$52 8 \$8.94

9 \$1,574.80 10 \$2.34

Index

This book has been set Linofilm in 10 and 9 point Caledonia, leaded 2 points. Chapter numbers are in 48 point Helvetica Medium, and chapter titles are in 24 point (small) Helvetica Medium. The size of the type page is 27 by 45½ picas.